LAND OF
PLENTY

By the same author

DESIGN THIS DAY

LAND OF
PLENTY

A SUMMARY OF POSSIBILITIES

WALTER DORWIN TEAGUE

HARCOURT, BRACE AND COMPANY, NEW YORK

COPYRIGHT, 1947, BY

WALTER DORWIN TEAGUE

first edition

PRINTED IN THE UNITED STATES OF AMERICA

CONTENTS

v

TO BEGIN

THIS book is not primarily a treatise on either economics or politics. It is an effort to convey some idea of what we can make of life in this country if we have sense enough to use the scientific, technological, and productive resources now at our command.

Any such painting of so vast a canvas must of course be sketchy: it is a matter of hints and glimpses and suggestions; it cannot be a fully developed picture. But it will serve its purpose if it conveys some of the wonder and enthusiasm I myself have felt as I have explored the many fields of creative activity into which my professional work as an industrial designer has carried me. Such stupendous opportunities for the betterment of human living have never been presented to any people at any time: and it makes one shiver to think that we may not make the most of them.

And of course we may not. The fact that possibilities exist, are even crowding upon us for realization, is no guarantee that they actually will be translated into conditions of living. Their realization depends on many factors other than their imminence.

It is a sardonic paradox that this dawn of utmost felicity is also the time of ultimate peril. I am not referring now to either the opportunities or the dangers suddenly created by the release of atomic energy, although both accent the urgency of the hour. The full practical utilization of atomic energy still lies a little way in the future, and we have at hand many more ready and manageable means of lifting the race to new levels of well-being. These can become, fortunately, preparatory steps leading up to the utterly revolutionary beneficences with which the atomic age will confront us; and if we cannot accommodate ourselves to these present releases, it is not much use speculating as to what we can do in vastly more spacious vistas. As to the possibility that civilization and ultimately the earth may be destroyed by atomic fission, it is not to be discounted; but again I feel there are more immediate and more insidious dangers threatening us, and if we are too stupid to deal with these less novel problems in human relations we might as well resign ourselves to being blown to hell in one clean, scientific sweep rather than to sink gradually into universal misery.

It is true that no matter how wise we may be in arranging our own affairs, we cannot travel very far unless the rest of the world advances along the same road. The peace and prosperity of the world cannot be partitioned by national frontiers. But, also, peace and prosperity are not spontaneous growths that will spring up evenly everywhere at once, as Spring comes to a countryside. They must be nurtured somewhere, at a source from which they can spread over the earth. Only a strong and united people loving peace and able to create great wealth can be that source, and only we can be that people. The world needs our unity, our conviction, our good-will and our wealth creation more than it needs anything else at this time: the salvation of the world depends on us.

But it seems to me the scope and splendor of internationalism have dazzled many people into forgetting that our own garden is our first responsibility: with our eyes on great, shining objectives we take headers over boulders at our feet. We undertake, at once, to unite the world without having achieved unity ourselves, and write a world constitution without having clearly established our own principles or reconciled in our own minds the differences which split world thought to its epistemological roots. It seems to me essential to prove our capacity for leadership toward world order by creating a reasonable degree of domestic order, and toward world prosperity by demonstrating a high degree of domestic efficiency in wealth creation.

So it is not enough to talk about scientific and technological possibilities for the betterment of living: whether they are ever to be anything more tangible than alluring dreams will be decided by other factors, and among these our psychological attitudes are most influential. Psychological attitudes are translated into social forms and political action, and these determine the

climate in which human welfare expands and advances, or withers
and contracts.

That is why I must begin with the conditions and attitudes
that exist at the dawn of peace, as I see them, and end with
decisions I think must be made if we are to enter our promising
land.

I warn the reader now, at the start, that I believe our hope
lies in the individual, here and elsewhere—millions of him, everywhere: in his confidence, his courage, his freedom to choose and
act, his will to progress. In the worldwide struggle now going on
between the concept of individual liberty and the concept of enforced organization—the same battle that was partially won for
liberty here and in some parts of Europe in the Eighteenth Century and must I suppose be fought all over again periodically as
each revolutionary cycle completes its round and arrives back at
its starting point—in this struggle I am all for the individual and
against the epidemic reaction of these times. Anyone who doesn't
agree with me, but believes that the individual for the general
good should be fitted into molds and harnessed to formulas, will
be irritated by my argument and probably will not be convinced
by it: reactionary inclination is deep-seated, the desire to place
the responsibility for one's life and decisions in other and stronger
hands has thousands of years of racial habit to feed its roots.
The concept of personal freedom and personal responsibility is
still new and imperfectly assimilated after a mere couple of centuries. It is an ideal hard to hold firmly as a rule of life.

But there never was a time when it was more important that the
energies of individual men should be stimulated and released, and
their activities channeled into a mighty stream of common effort.
If this can be done with a reasonable percentage of success
throughout the world, we now have the means to make this earth
a far better dwelling place for human beings than it ever has
been before. And that possibility is what this book is about.

PART ONE

OPPORTUNITY

CHAPTER I

THE OPENING DOOR

LET's suppose a group of people have spent their lives exploring a widening but dusky corridor filled with obstacles they must make their way through or over, with fear and doubt slinking along at no comfortable distance and with only intermittent spells of watery sunlight to hearten them. Let's suppose they come at last to a doorway opening on the most alluring prospect imaginable—a garden luxuriant with flowers and fruit, its millions of leaves sparkling and dancing in the wind and sun.

You'd say they would rush out with a yelp of delight and make the most of it, wouldn't you? But, the human mind being what it is, there is no assurance that they would do anything of the kind.

The outlook would be strange to them, and some might shrewdly suspect that it was a mirage or a trap. Others might develop sudden loyalties to the dear old familiar corridor, and with typical inconsistency at the same time decide that any place that damned corridor would lead to couldn't be much good anyhow. There would be those who would want to form the group into a marching column, so that it could advance into the park in orderly fashion and under strict regulation, making jolly well sure that no one took riotous advantage of the abundant opportunities. And some very fast talkers would whip out, with astounding facility, blueprints for building a conservatory over the whole scene with a central power plant maintaining a constant temperature and all the devices of an inspired system of horticulture thoroughly installed. There would also be the cautious ones who would refuse to go off half-cocked without exploring carefully the alternatives to the right and to the left, and in the resulting confusion the whole group might get themselves hopelessly lost again in the gloomy mazes they might have escaped.

There is no certainty that they would follow these courses—or any others—but it would not be out of character if they did. It is fair to hope that there would be enough sane and hardy souls to insist on seizing the beckoning opportunities and letting even the dissenters benefit in spite of themselves.

A nation is merely a great many erratic men and women, an unoriginal truth there would be no point in repeating if economists and sociologists didn't persist in talking about nations as if they were not collections of individuals but homogeneous masses of dough. A nation reacts in exactly the same way as the preponderant individuals in it, with a time-lag while they coalesce but with an intensity stepped up by their mutual stimulation. Whatever heroism or stupidity we can expect of individuals under stress we can also expect of a nation, with a reservation that the action of a nation will be on an exaggerated scale emotionally and morally, and less rational than its more cool-headed citizens could wish.

There is a point in these observations, because this nation of ours is experiencing the crisis of the corridor dwellers at the magic portal. From the beginning of our racial career we have been trying, in our fumbling but persistent way, to work out a design in which the masses of men could live comfortably and happily. Here in the United States we have accomplished more than has ever been done elsewhere, but the total achievement even here has fallen far short of reasonable expectations. And the immediate past has been particularly gloomy: we have been passing through a generation of bewilderments and frustrations, with a frightful war at its beginning and another at its end. It has been a time when defeatism claimed many and others turned to desperate remedies. Now, if we look in the right direction, we can see daylight ahead. Now the segment of humanity in this country has arrived in sight of a possible felicity greater than we ever dreamed of realizing so soon and probably much greater than we deserve. This doesn't mean that any Utopian millennium is around the corner, with want and misery banished altogether, but it does

mean that we have the means to project ourselves abruptly a
long way up the expanding spiral that is ours to climb. The opportunity for swift advancement is greater than was ever afforded any
other nation.

The question is whether we make the most of it, or muff the
chance; and it is a question peremptorily posed to us by the
winning of the war. In fact, it is a corollary of winning the war,
for if we fail in this the war will have yielded no victory.

And it is not only our own welfare that is being laid on the
line: the welfare of the whole world will depend on what we
make of our immediate future. It would seem that Providence, or
fate, or a concatenation of circumstances—you can choose the
cause according to your point of view—has appointed us for the
salvation of the world in this crisis. We and no other people are
equipped for leadership. All the requisites of great strength—the
strength of health and abundant vitality—have been or are being
conferred on us: we are required to supply only the discretion and
common sense to use our strength for the permanent good of
ourselves and our fellows. Under these circumstances there may
not be any great credit coming to us if we succeed in doing a
good job, but there will be abysmal ignominy if we don't. And
failure is well within the range of possibility.

2

Against all logic and without any relation to our deserts, we
are in the way of benefiting enormously from the most frightful
war in history. This is no argument for war. It is merely an
example of destiny's frequently irrational allocations of consequences. The world burns up, we emerge with the possibility of
being far better off than before. And it isn't justice—on the contrary. A collection of lucky breaks—geography, for which we certainly can take no credit, being the principal item and the canny
wisdom of our forefathers another—has made our position unique
among the nations which have been at war. So may be our social
and economic circumstances when the war is finally finished and
done with, as it is not yet.

Whatever values accrue from war are the product of the united effort it inspires. War unfortunately seems to be the only emotional stimulus strong enough to arouse a whole people and polarize its activities voluntarily in one direction. Normally we are at sixes and sevens, and the Richard Roes spend a large part of their time frustrating the John Does and vice versa, while none of us tries any harder than personal ambition, usually deliberate, compels us. But in war most of us are swept up by an emotion bigger than ourselves. As a nation we pool our strength and put forth an effort that is prodigious, almost incredible, if measured by peacetime standards. We get things done swiftly that would take twenty times as long at the jog-trot of peace, if they would ever get done at all. No doubt the release of atavistic savage energies normally suppressed but not outgrown contributes a great deal to our fury of achievement. And this pouring of primitive adrenalin into our national bloodstream may be a very good thing. It may augment our national vitality decisively at the moment that we gain a new social consciousness: as we prove to ourselves that voluntary co-operation is not only possible among men— temporarily at least and to a large degree—but enormously effective.

Whether any permanent good accrues from war depends on the residue of the emotional storm left with us after it subsides, and the net product of the physical effort remaining for use when the fight is over. One or both may be greatly valuable, or they may be negative quantities.

The experience of united effort may leave a defeated people crushed in spirit and psychologically deformed, and it may leave a victorious people nervously and morally exhausted, ready to give its less noble inclinations a relaxing field day; or it may act as an emotional catharsis, from which a people emerges serene, clearer in vision, and more certain of its future. On the material side, war may leave a people in devastation and want, or it may place powerful agencies of well-being in a victor's hands. It appears that in our case both the psychological and physical effects may be fabulously valuable, if we keep our heads.

Our condition is in striking contrast to that of all other nations. The Axis enemies, Germany and Japan, are continuing problems, and in no position to be of any help to civilization as they climb back to it up the long ladder from semisavagery and ruin. Italy, freed from the Fascists and their imperial obsession, may be expected to revert to the more amiable dreaming which is better suited to her temperament but is alien to the mood of the modern world.

Of all the surviving victims of the Axis, the vitality of the great French people will carry them forward more rapidly than the others, but it is hardly conceivable that the French can do more for a long time than get on with their repairs and reconstruction. They have done much for the world in many creative fields but throughout modern times they have shown a minimum of practical political skill and sagacity and there is no indication that they will be able now to lead the world to a solution of the problems that face it.

We can hope China will achieve union and strength, but at present she is no more than a nation of immense potentials and equivalent incapacities.

The Latin American Republics are rising powers and they have been stimulated by the war, but meagerly as compared with us and they have a long way to go before they arrive at the stage of material development and political maturity at which we begin our postwar career.

If the loose federation of the British Commonwealth of Nations continues to act together, its peoples will have great power for their own and the world's good, but most of their countries are relatively undeveloped by our standards and in scattered combination they do not have our compact resources and massive strength.

Britain herself is a small nation and in this war she has made a titanic effort for which the world owes her eternal gratitude: but it has been an exhausting drain on her resources and her vitality. She was long a leader in establishing the rights of the individual and in industrial development, but in her present state of fatigue her people appear inclined, understandably but regrettably, to seek the illusory, minimal blessings of "security" rather than undertake the further effort of energizing an expanding economy of abundance. This decision may be amended, since courage is by no means exhausted in the British people, but hardly in time to show us the way to build a society both free and prosperous on an industrial basis. Instead she moves to shift the balance between the individual and the State in the ancient and forlorn hope that a few men can better direct the intimate affairs of all. If that is the solution we too must accept, we can find more experienced guides to collectivism than Britain—Russia, for instance.

Russia is huge and potentially rich and she has demonstrated the gigantic power of her people when moved wholeheartedly to a common effort. Her vitality has suffered no depletion from the war. Instead she emerges with her spirit refreshed and triumphant, even more than a little arrogant in the manner of autocratic conquerors since the world began. But Russia has only begun to work out the problems of her industrial development—it must be remembered that in this war her people's courage was implemented to a decisive extent by supplies from Great Britain and from us.

And before the war she had confined her people in what is probably the most airtight system of total controls ever devised. The National Socialist order in Germany was more vicious, but certainly it was not more complete, or more firmly administered. The Russian order has no truck with individual right, personal liberty, or even the equality which is its ostensible long-range objective, and it imposes much more drastic restrictions on free discussion and individually initiated action than those from which the democratic peoples of the West escaped in the Eighteenth Century. It is a system very effective in the swift conversion of a backward society from an agrarian to an industrial basis (although this process is still far from complete in Russia) and it is even more efficient in the preparation for war and the waging of war, as we have seen. But it is not a system conducive to independent creative industrial development and civilian abundance. "A directed society," as Walter Lippmann was driven to conclude, "must be bellicose and poor. If it is not both bellicose and poor, it cannot be directed." And the companion truth is equally inescapable, that "a prosperous and peaceable society must be free. If it is not free, it cannot be prosperous and peaceable." *

The Russians must accomplish their emancipation as individuals before they can hope to be productive on the democratic scale. They may very well do this in time as a sequel to their triumphant determination of their own fate as a nation, and if so we gladly admit that we shall have only the advantage of an earlier start. But that advantage is enormous.

So Russia stands little more chance than China of leading our world in the development of a free industrial society. This does not mean that Russia certainly will not lead the world. But, if so, it will not be toward freedom, abundance, and tranquillity. It will mean that we have abandoned our own ambitions and ideals and accepted the Russian concept of absolute state supremacy, a directed economy and rigid social controls, since this is the only direction in which Russia is now qualified to exercise leadership. And with her system we inevitably will have accepted her privations. It is not likely that we will make this choice, unless we already are suffering privations to the point of utter discouragement and a conviction that nothing could be worse.

3

All these other great nations involved in this war have borne its brunt on their own soil, but not the United States. Our strength may well have been decisive in the conflict, but we come out of the war relatively unscratched. We bear few psychological or physical scars—as a matter of fact, the amount of actual material sacrifice detectable on our home front can safely be put in

* *The Good Society*, Little, Brown, 1937, page xii. One of the most important books of these times. It should be reread frequently, especially by Mr. Lippmann. We see a fresh demonstration of its thesis in the postwar course of the Soviet Union. Powerful, triumphant, facing no threat more tangible than the "imperialist ambitions" of the United States, we see Marshal Stalin whipping up the militaristic fervor of his people, calling for fresh sacrifices to meet encircling dangers, and tightening the discipline of his huge armed forces as we democratize ours. At the same time we read of queues lining up in Moscow to gaze hungrily at goods offered at a 40% reduction, so that men's ready-made suits cost only $240 each and an overcoat can be had for $320! (N. Y. *Herald Tribune*, July 3, 1946.) ·

the eye that looks for it. Instead we are enormously enhanced in potential wealth and in power, with equipment for the betterment of human living and the betterment of human beings such as no nation ever possessed before. Tremendous new knowledge, skills, manpower, resources, tools—all are ours in abundance. We alone of all the nations of the world stand at the frontier of an epoch of unimaginable advancement, with all the facilities at hand to make it a shining reality and no material handicaps that seriously impair our chances of success.

This does not mean that the war has not charged us a fearful price, and may not still raise the ante to disastrous heights.

Some dozen millions of our picked young men and women have been diverted from productive activities at a critical time in their careers, and thousands of them have died and thousands more have suffered bitterly and may be incapacitated for the rest of their lives. To them and their families this is unrelieved tragedy and it is a heavy sacrifice for the nation as a whole. But it is nothing like the terrible draining away of their best blood that our principal allies and enemies have suffered. It is not enough to impair even temporarily the vitality of the American people. In fact it is much less than the normal loss through civilian accidents in a period equal to the war's duration,* which is not a standard of comparison to be proud of, God knows, but does indicate that the expenditure will not be ruinous. And there are compensations in the betterment of great numbers of the young men who come back safe and sound, as we shall see.

The war also has posed for us a series of immediate and difficult problems, so critical that a mistake in solving any one of them can negative much of our advantage. They are formidable hazards set up between us and our future state of well-being.

There is our utterly fantastic debt, certain to break the back

---

* The National Safety Council announced in September, 1945, that Army and Navy casualties since the beginning of the war had totaled 251,000 killed and 819,000 wounded, missing or prisoners. More than half the wounded had returned to duty. Civilian accidents from December 7, 1941, to June 1, 1945, resulted in 334,000 deaths and 34,000,000 injuries! In 1944 alone, civilian accidents caused 340,000 disabilities such as the loss of a finger, arm, eye, total blindness or crippling, while 7,400,000 other accidents caused disability beyond the day of the accident.

of any weaker nation and quite able to break ours. Only production permanently expanded far beyond anything we have
known in peacetime will enable us to manage it, and even then
the problem of balancing the budget and keeping the national
credit unimpaired, without either dangerous inflation or deflation,
calls for wisdom and courage of a very rare order.

Allied to the credit problem and impinging on every one of
us personally is our exhaustive tax drainage, syphoning through
the national treasury a flow of economic lifeblood much greater
than the civilian economy can spare if it is to function independently and consume its own production. Ways must be found to
adjust taxes to peacetime practicability without making the maintenance of national credit impossibly difficult.

Our enormous war-grown bureaucracy has been a diversion of
energy from productive activities which we cannot stand permanently as a nation of free men any more than we can continue
to pay over to it a half or a third of our earnings. This elephan-
tiasis must be reduced, and with it its wartime concentration of
authority over our personal affairs and its ownership of a fifth of
our productive plant and a quarter of our land. There is no doubt
that we are still as a whole loyal to our native standards of individual freedom, but to get them out of hock again and put them
back in working order calls for rugged and difficult operations.
We have made a vigorous start in that direction and the danger is
not in our intention: it is that we may fail to recognize and
extirpate some of the more plausible statist habits and expedients
with which the depression and the war have given us an easy
familiarity, and so preserve conditions in which an individualist
system cannot work. Certainly we cannot proceed as a nation
half collectivist and half individualist: that inevitably becomes an
unworkable one horse, one rabbit formula.

Even while these bridges are being crossed, we enter into the
peacetime years with a volume of production immensely greater
than the best ever attained before the war, and if the passages
are successfully negotiated we shall be in a position to push it
steadily upward to undreamed-of levels of well-being. If we don't
succeed in doing this, and getting on with it reassuringly from
scratch, it won't make much difference what we decide about

anything else: our hands will be forced on these imminent practical issues and so on a list of more basic ones, and we may find ourselves slipping willy-nilly down the drain to statism as several other nations have done in the past three decades. In that case the war, after introducing us to entrancing prospects of advancement, will have cost us practically everything we value most.

But it is clear that these penalties are only tentatively assessed, posted as forfeits in a game we may win or lose. All the other combatant nations face these hazards or others special to themselves, besides their appalling labors of reconstruction, and they do not have the fabulous stack of blue chips we hold. Actually all that is required of us in this most crucial period is cool judgment, discretion, firm loyalty to our native principles, and ability to distinguish between them and specious expedients. A great deal to ask, of course, and perhaps too much; but at least we have all the material advantages on our side.

4

In addition, we have very great subjective advantages. Our political health and social sanity may not be perfect, but they are in better state than those of any other combatant. Our traditional loyalty is given to a set of political and social principles younger, more flexible and more fertile than any of the hoary throwbacks now hypnotizing so many of the world's peoples. These native principles of ours have an earthy rationalism which does not inhibit either our sense of humor or our sense of proportion. They do not encourage the kind of ecstatic fanaticism that hurls men under juggernaut's wheels or into sacrificial flames, all for the common good: we have watched that kind of spectacle, as it occurred again and again during the past thirty years, in horrified amazement. We may detect the first twitching muscles and glazed eyes of a seizure in some quarters here, but as a people we are by no means converted to any of the rituals by which heaven is to be brought to earth in one spasm of blood and fire.

It is especially necessary that we keep our wits about us, because we still find ourselves in warfare as critical as the struggle just ended: for us the fight for survival has merely shifted from a military to an ideological plane. This is such a blessed relief that we may underestimate the importance of the continuing conflict. As a matter of fact, if we lose the ideological argument we shall suffer exactly the same consequences that loss of the military war would have brought down on our heads, the only difference being that we shall then do the harm to ourselves instead of having it done to us by others. As between sadism and masochism, there is not much to choose.

With the world today full of Holy Rollers shrieking creeds, formulas, absolutes, plans for perfect societies, we need to remember that the American system is none of these things. It is in fact founded on the rejection of any such telescoping of destiny. Our only doctrine is the simple one that since individuals make up the race, and individuals labor and triumph and contribute any human good there is in the world, then whatever is set up in the way of governments and economic systems, whatever is evolved in the way of societies, should be directed to the difficult objective of securing to the individual the right to choose his way of life, try his ideas, make his own mistakes and successes and assume the consequences of his acts—with scrupulous regard for the right of all other individuals to follow the same course.

If this concept of individualism implied a hermit-crab kind of segregation, with each of us living in a ready-made, private shell, we should not have to worry about programs or institutions. Life would be simple and cellular. But we have adopted an individualist structure of society precisely because we believe it the best way to release the maximum amount of ingenuity and energy for the co-operative building of a world in which everybody can enjoy peace, happiness, and plenty. In this undertaking we cannot afford to dispense with the help of any member of society. Our individualism calls for a voluntary co-ordination of effort as complete as it can be made, a more inclusive and authentic union, in fact, than is required by any other social philosophy. When men are free to think and act for themselves they must arrive at agreement if they are not to waste their efforts in confusion.

It is for the sake of this unity that we have a Bill of Rights. Without the inviolability of our persons, the right of dissent, criticism, and full and unhampered discussion under all the conditions which such discussion requires, agreement cannot be conscious and dynamic, and the essential authority from which all formal institutions derive their legitimacy cannot exist. The winds of thought and talk must blow with unrestricted vigor if the single current into which they finally converge is to have effective power.

Thus ours is an evolving process and not at all a static order. The American Revolution, as the acute Peter Drucker has perceived,* "reasserted the imperfection of man," and accepted this obvious fact as the basis of its procedure. It undertook to arrange for the improvement of man by the method of fluid experiment, conducted with as much intelligence and honesty as we can bring to the task. It placed guards against snap judgments and against arbitrary conclusions by majorities as well as by minorities, and it provided for its own progressive adaptation to changing circumstances.

Our system thus aims to be a completely rational design placing no reliance on any emotional appeal, and it leaves us somewhat at a loss when we must oppose the frenetic fervors of the collectivists with mere reasonableness. Our system is lacking in voodoo characteristics. Against compact and passionate ideologies we can offer only a flexible technique; and a technique, at that, which admits its own imperfections.

We have given these principles of ours, new as they are, a longer life in continuous, practical application than any others now being tried, which would not be important if they had not been, during the same period, more successful than any others in accomplishing what political principles are supposed to accomplish. While other nations have tried this and that, we have gone steadily forward along our own chosen path until today we are incomparably, by a wide margin, the richest and best served nation in the world, enjoying the widest measure of personal liberty, the greatest abundance and the highest standard of living; with now the prospect of a far more opulent future opening before us.

Not even the most evangelical supporters of neater and tighter systems deny these facts. What they do deny is that there is enough or any life in the old dog yet. They stress certain indis-

* The Future of Industrial Man, John Day, 1942, page 223.

putable facts of which we friends of our system should be much more acutely conscious than anybody else:

Our abundance, while greater than any other nation has known, is merely relative and falls far short of adequacy, our high standard of living is much lower than it could and should be and is tragically uneven. We have built an enormous industrial mechanism obviously capable of supplying the material needs of all our people—but to date it has not done so; it has not functioned continuously and dependably even at an inadequate level. With such a mechanism as the supply source of our civilization, we should have equalized the social status, expanded the personal freedom, broadened the opportunities of all our people—but we have not done do: we have allowed a large and important part of the population to become an essential factor in and dependent on an industrial complex in which it feels it has no autonomy. We have allowed millions of our citizens, and not only industrial workers, to be excluded from the basic privileges of the individualist system—independence in shaping one's own career, a voice in the control of the processes on which one's fortunes depend, a social position having both dignity and responsibility.

There is no denying a serious time-lag in keeping our economic, social, and political development abreast of industrial development and in harmony with it, so that all benefits and privileges may be equitably shared by all. From this lapse the enemies of free societies obtain their ammunition, while it makes inroads on our own confidence: it is argued that there are quicker roads to felicity than our habitual trial and error method. We are urged to resign our characteristic skepticism, perform an act of faith in the acceptance of one or another comprehensive dogma, and fit ourselves into rigid and predetermined social, economic, and political patterns. The various dogmas differ in ritual but they all boil down to putting our fate into a few well-chosen hands.

5

This alternative, in whatever form it is offered to us—and in any form it should scare us into instant action—proposes to take independence and responsibility away from all who have them now, bar them from all who don't yet have them, and lodge them exclusively in the State. This has been the essence of all the statist orders that have dominated mankind from the beginning of time, and it is the essence of all the statist plans descending from Hegel through Marx and Engels to Lenin, Stalin, Hitler, Laski, and Sir William Beveridge.

In the theoretical stage of all these orders, ancient and modern, the State has a remarkably Old Testament character: a gaseous omniscience brooding omnipotently over the affairs of men, their good its only concern. But in practice the State diminishes to a small group of limited and overworked little persons who, to list characteristics of current examples, are apt to be neurotic, selfish, stubborn, handicapped, ruthless, visionary, hag-ridden, cruel, venal, insatiable, overcunning, or stupid. In short, governing coteries possess exactly the same defects as other human beings, with their inadequacies enormously magnified by the power they wield.

So the proposal is to take all control over the productive mechanisms of society—with which goes control over the labor and consumption and hence the lives and fortunes of every one of us—away from the great mass of individuals who may augment and check each other, and deposit it with a few equally fallible individuals who are thereby subjected to such intolerable strains on their intellects and moral stamina as the private citizen never knows.

This is not merely a proposal: it is a plan which has been put into effect over large areas of the earth's surface, with results we can observe. We have seen all control of wealth allocated to government, all the management-specialist group become appointees in a political bureaucracy, all workers become voiceless automatons in mechanical treadmills. We have also seen these societies quickly transform themselves into armed camps, directing their energies to war, since such a system can only be administered on a military basis and war can be the only justification for its privations. And we have been subjected to pressures from within and without to move in the same direction.

It may seem incredible that such appalling reaction could make headway against the superior achievements that our free society, with all its imperfections, already has to its credit. It would be incredible if man were really a rational animal. But the race is only beginning to be influenced by reason, and the primitive urge to surrender still rules by far the greater part of it.

Taking the race and its history as a whole, tough-minded realists are still a novel sport. General rejection of superstitions, acceptance of the captaincy of one's soul and one's own life, willingness to make one's own decisions and take the consequences, compose a pattern of behavior so rare that when de Tocqueville encountered it as a fully developed characteristic of the people of the young United States, he had to invent the name it now bears.* Faced with the "barbarous French term" of "individualism," his first English translator apologetically retained it because it had no equivalent in the English language.

This attribute, so new that there was no word for it until a hundred years ago, has flourished here and in Britain and her graduate colonies; and in the northwestern fringes of the European continent it has been periodically in the ascendancy, in a seesaw contest with a succession of old and new cults in the statist tradition. For a few generations the concept dominated enlightened thinking everywhere, and there have been pubescent stirrings and isolated instances of maturity even beyond the Rhine. But only in a few most progressive nations has the supreme dignity of the individual been established as the first principle of life, to which political and social institutions are expected to conform. Elsewhere it has been definitely atypical. Elsewhere the habit of submission and conformity, overlaid but not eradicated even in us, has never been broken. From this dark well in the primitive substratum of our natures, the forces of reaction draw their strength—paradoxically, from the innate timorousness of the human animal and the loneliness of his heart.

There exists in the depths of every one of us a longing for protection, an eagerness to entrust our fate to a wiser power, a yearning to lose ourselves in an entity big enough to swallow us whole and relieve us of our burdensome identity. At various stages in our racial past, this lure of parental arms has been extended by

* Democracy in America, Knopf, 1945, Vol. II, p. 98.

primitive systems of taboo and magic, by priestly hierarchies, by the seigneur and the divinely appointed king, as now by more up-to-date plans for making the individual an ant-like automaton in a directed society. While surrender never has been a way to peace and plenty in the past or present, it is still a refuge that appeals powerfully to tired, discouraged men—as well as to those who expect to be on the receiving end of the submission. The impulse may be repressed in the courageous, but in weaker brothers this self-obliterative longing may grow so strong that it will seek gratification at no matter what cost: the exaltation of complete sacrifice makes any agony bearable.

There are always men, too, who are ready to meet this demand by arranging satisfactory rites of immolation: they feed the same craving in themselves by the subjugation and absorption of others. They are most effective when they are most sincere and believe utterly in the Moloch-paradise they have dreamed up, on the other side of the flames. It makes them tragically convincing leaders, saviors, and masters of destiny, and if their audience is properly conditioned by suffering they all go ecstatically to hell together. It takes both kinds, the high priests and the sacrificial multitude, to make a totalitarian society, and both kinds are always present in all peoples.

Human tendencies being opposed so unequally, and we being careless guardians of our own standards, it was inevitable that the new ideal of freedom would have to fight for survival against the ancient fear of life. Since we in the United States have not succeeded in evolving free institutions—social, economic, and political—perfectly adapted to the industrial basis of modern civilization, it has not been done. And the world has been in turmoil for thirty years as a result. Wars, revolutions, inflationary and deflationary cycles have destroyed millions of lives and the stored-up energy of generations of labor. The sheer human misery of these times is beyond all comprehension. The old terror and despair have risen in a vast conflagration and we have seen more and more peoples throwing themselves into the fire as more and more psychotic leaders egg them on.

6

Here in the United States we have had our share of these eager messiahs, and a short time ago we had a great many tired, discouraged people. Too many of us succumbed to the world-tide rolling in from the East. There are those who still see it as inescapable, a portent, "the wave of the future," a "sign of the times." * Reaction has been greeted by too many with fatalistic acceptance.

But the amount of discouragement visible in the American scene has distinctly lessened since 1940, and after a brief experience in the direction of a wartime economy, even some of those who were quite ready to take on the job of reorganizing our lives are not so sure that they'd like it as a permanent assignment; while the people remember those well-meant and necessary ministrations with extreme distaste. Our confidence in ourselves, our principles and our future has noticeably revived, and our political shrewdness is active: nothing we have observed in the rest of the world leads us to suppose that another type of regime would be more desirable than our own. Conscious of our magnificent demonstration of potency in the late world-wide test, we are strengthened in our preference for relying on the energies and good sense of the many rather than on the will and benevolence of the few, and we are in a mood to continue our search for greater well-being through diversity rather than conformity. This is one of the most salutary benefits of the war, and it seems to be uniquely ours.

But as an island of freedom in a world rapidly committing itself to one form or another of statism, we are in no position to be complacent. Victory in the military war has had little effect on the ideological struggle, except to sharpen and intensify its issues. Victory has come equally to the partisans of statism and the partisans of individual freedom, since the alignment of the two ideological camps did not coincide with the military line-up in the

* "In some respects both the Prussians and the Russians have perceived the signs of the times rather than we." Henry Wallace.

later decisive stages of the war. The issue will not be decided even if we should involve ourselves in, and win, any still more catastrophic wars in the future when the issue might be clearly drawn. If we let it come to that unthinkable pass, we shall deserve whatever happens to us.

We have been lucky to come through this generation of war without, as yet, losing our grip on our national objectives, probably because we have thoroughly hated the whole business of war. But war as a habit is the enemy of freedom, a breeder of despair and submission. Freedom may create the power which wins wars, but free institutions are not efficient in the military exercise of that power. There the statist nations have us at such a disadvantage that we must put our principles in escrow in order to meet them on an even level of military effectiveness. Given wars enough, any free system must succumb: it cannot survive in a permanently mobilized State.

Freedom is a way of peace and it must be proven in peaceful ways. Its aim is the insurance of dignity and an abundant life for all men, and this is an aim that can be achieved only by a unified society devoted to the arts of peace.

Thus we bear a terrifying responsibility. We owe it to ourselves and the rest of the world to develop a state of social and economic health which shall be sound, abundant and continuous, such as no other nation has the capacity to attain under any other system. Our responsibility, in short, is for our own surpassing and permanent prosperity. It is only in this pragmatic manner that the world-wide ideological conflict can be resolved.

Here we come to a climacteric. Beyond it we can no longer tolerate the wastes of productive energy, the inequalities of opportunity, the exclusion of large sectors of the population from benefit of a system that we profess to be universally applicable. We may have managed to survive this kind of defective performance in the past, but then we did not face serious challenge. Now, in the eyes of a hostile world, we shall have to make good on our professions. We shall have to make our system work at maximum efficiency as a creator of abundance.

This can't be accomplished by any such simple and illusory recourses as State "guarantees" of "social security" and "full employment." Even full employment at high wages will not in itself do what needs must be done. Our system can only be made to function at its full, dependable capacity by uniting all our people in common loyalties and common privileges, so that all their energies are exerted to common ends instead of being dissipated in domestic feuds. This is an immensely difficult undertaking, and a great deal besides our own welfare depends on it.

The cleavages we have to mend did not originate in anybody's evil designs, as partisans of the right and the left both heatedly insist; and they are not the workings of irresistible historic necessity, as Marxian metaphysics contends. The causes are not so simple—they can't be removed by electing, defeating, suppressing, interning, or hanging any persons, groups, or classes; or by relieving everybody of rights which some do not now possess. The causes are to be found in mental and physical inertia retarding adaptation, preserving forms and methods beyond their usefulness, delaying the adoption of new ways of dealing with unfolding circumstances. And the responsibility is general: it is the sort of thing that happens to any people whose original inspirations grow faint with time and usage. It can be set right only by a general awakening to a fresh and dynamic conception of the principle of individual freedom, and a new determination to make it work for everybody without exception. The war may well have snapped us out of our lethargy to such a revitalization and if so an era of renewed evolutionary progress is beginning.

If, on the other hand, we return to the time-marking of 1914 to 1940, with the economic subnormality of a dozen years before the second war and the succession of erratic improvisations characteristic of that time, this will be a clear indication that we still are failing to make our system work as it should. It may only prove that we aren't very bright, but it will appear to prove that the way of freedom is not a practicable way to well-being. The evidence will be in everybody's empty pockets and on everybody's underfurnished dinner table, and this kind of evidence outweighs a lot of dialectics no matter how logical and a lot of past performance no matter how impressive. It will not eradicate the dream of freedom but it will push far into the future any hope of its fulfillment. It will also dash the hope of world peace.

It is true of course that we cannot be prosperous very long apart from the rest of the world and a general rise must follow ours or it cannot be maintained. But the cycle must start with us or it will not be started at all. We must find the way to abundance and to peace, which are inseparable. And if we, with everything in our favor and a long experience in evolving free institutions, cannot regulate our own affairs for the welfare of our own people, we can't expect to lead the rest of the world into any golden age of tranquillity and happiness. A people that can't solve its own problems will not be invited to deal with other people's destinies. It will not matter how altruistic our aims may be or how clever our international planning: we simply will not have the proven capacity and serene assurance for leadership. If we do not have it, it will not exist in the camp of freedom. There is no other free nation in a position to supply it. Some of our allies know this well and beg us above everything else to set our house in order.

This physician must heal himself before he will have other patients. The doctors of opposing schools are all set to force their bitter medicines down our throats. If they take over, the state of the world's health will be acutely and chronically miserable for a very long time, and a desperate world armed with atomic bombs may easily bring its career to an end.

CHAPTER II

WE MAKE AND BREAK OUR WORLD

THE PROSPERITY we have to achieve can be nothing superficial or transient: it will be a state of fundamental well-being, compounded of the good living, satisfaction and enlarging opportunities of the greatest possible number of people. It will be rooted deeply in the processes by which the needs of the people are served, and it must flower in their ampler existence.

It will be necessary frequently to apply a yardstick of dollars to this state of well-being, and the factors that contribute to it. But in doing this it is not necessary to confuse the metric system with the substance it measures. We are dropping a lead weight and a line into a deep flowing stream. Money it is true is something more than that: a convenience whereby we can convert our kinetic energy, symbolically, into units of static energy so that it can be handled, preserved, exchanged, and reconverted into kinetic energy at will. Dollars are thus essential tools, but that can be admitted without confusing the symbols with the wealth they represent.

Wealth is productive energy in action. Wealth is ingenuity and energy acting on material things to create new forms of material things for which people are willing to exchange the products of their own ingenuity and energy. Wealth, in short, is production. And the amount of our production, with equivalent consumption, determines our degree of well-being. Adam Smith perceived this truth many years ago, and in the interval since it has almost but not quite passed into the consciousness of the race.

If we should make a graph of production for consumer use in the industrialized nations during the past century and a half, and another of human welfare in the same lands and times, one would fit neatly over the other and the two would synchronize. Welfare and happiness rise with prosperity, decline with hard times; and prosperity and hard times are merely other names for high and low production-consumption.

This is because ours is an artificial world, built by us between ourselves and the world of nature. Instead of worrying along with whatever environment fate decreed for us, adapting ourselves to its inhospitable conditions as other animals do, we have insisted on making it over according to our own ideas of what it ought to be. We have been working at this environmental reconstruction for a great many hundreds of generations and it has become our principal racial preoccupation.

We have divorced ourselves so completely from the world of nature that we use almost nothing directly and unchanged as nature supplies it. All the elements of our shelter, food, clothing reach us at the end of a long and artful sequence of extraction or cultivation, processing, fabrication, and distribution, with nature receding more and more remotely as the original supplier of certain raw materials, unusable in their natural state. This vital sequence is dependent on systems of communication, transportation and exchange which also are wholly artificial.

We have insulated ourselves so completely that unless our artificial world is supplied and maintained we shall perish, and unless it is continually enlarged and improved we are miserable. Other animals are satisfied with the necessities of life, and in general they manage to survive. But not man: we want cream with our apricots. Ortega y Gasset has said it: man is "the animal which considers necessary only the objectively superfluous." * The biological necessities we take for granted as a mere starting point.

If there had been any limit to our ambitions, we probably would have attained them long ago and arrived at a static compromise with our environment. In that case we might now be going monotonously through the routine of some communal society of status, like the ants and the bees. But we have the divine gift of perpetual dissatisfaction. As soon as any condition of exist-

* Toward a Philosophy of History, Norton, 1941, p. 100.

ence is firmly established, we classify it with the taken-for-granted necessities and set our sights on still unattained superfluities. Ours is a mobile and elusive goal, our needs are infinitely expansible and we are insatiable.

An anti-materialist would have every right to remind us, derisively, that no amount of marble halls and velvet carpets—or bathtubs and electric ranges—will guarantee us happiness. But we should answer that that is not the point. What we really are seeking is independence of the natural conditions of life, and the freedom of action which that independence gives us. This urge may be subconscious or at most inarticulate, but it is the motivating force of all our racial strivings. We instinctively seek a state in which we can devote ourselves without distraction to the exercise of our peculiarly human—or are they divine?—faculties of thought and fabrication. It is only in this state that we feel we are really living. Sometimes we call it, simply but all-embracingly, freedom.

We ought to have, all of us, all those things that make up environmental felicity as we conceive it today—the luxuries of yesterday, necessities now; those things that place us above and outside the natural conditions of life. If some people with every privilege remain loafers and parasites, this is merely evidence that their capacity for enjoyment is limited to a very meager range, and that the human stock is still highly imperfect. If some men have accomplished tremendous things against every sort of physical handicap, this merely proves the strength of the creative impulse in exceptional cases. But we should not have to depend on abilities great enough to function in spite of obstacles. For the truly creative, a state of health, comfort and well-being is conducive to maximum productivity. As these conditions of life become more and more generally shared, productivity also becomes more and more common, if not always on the scale of outstanding genius. This is as it should be: genius is important, but the average of the racial stock is more so—it is, after all, the soil in which genius is rooted, and the soil it fertilizes.

There is no material reason why all these conditions cannot be provided for all people. More and more people are expecting them as a matter of course, at the price of diligence and decency and a reasonable degree of prudence, and those who have them are steadily adding new requirements. It is like pouring sand on a conical pile—the peak rises, the base widens.

But the base widens too slowly, and the peak is slender. Only a minor part of our American population and only a minute fraction of the world's population have obtained the minimum privileges of decent housing, adequate education, sanitation and balanced diets, dental and medical care. We have never provided enough of them to go around, or enough of other goods to balance them in exchange. With all the swift proliferation of technology, production has never caught up with need. And, so far as we can see, it never will, because need races ahead into new realms as supply advances. Production pursues need up an ascending and expanding spiral, and the sad day when one will overtake the other is so far distant it doesn't matter.*

Any other prospect would be terrifying, because it would mean that we were due to arrive at that ultimate freedom from want which is synonymous with the death of initiative, the end of the generation of fresh energy. On that plane of static balance the evolutionary cycle of the human race will have been completed, and nothing worth hoping for will lie beyond except the relief from boredom which extinction will bring. Let's say it will come with the end of the world, and not worry about it. For the present, our interest is fixed on the practically limitless job of climbing that is still to be done.

2

In recent times we have found means of speeding up our ascent enormously, by the cross-breeding of science and mechanics. During the latter half of the Eighteenth Century, abstract knowledge of nature and nature's laws began to be applied through deliber-

* This is not intended to imply the inevitability of progress—I am no optimistic determinist. Animal life has frequently improved its position in relation to its environment, but it has also frequently failed to do so, to the point of extinction. Man is in no way exempt from this contingency. We progress as a result of intelligent endeavors, not because any irresistible necessity compels us.

ate mechanical invention to the subjugation of nature and the production of goods. And this reduction of abstract knowledge to practice greatly facilitated the acquisition of further abstract knowledge, as it enabled us to supplement our very limited five senses with increasingly subtle instruments of perception. Thus since about 1770 our portion of the human race has registered the most substantial gains in our environmental warfare ever made since our first hairy ancestor picked up a stick to lengthen his arm.

It is no coincidence that the Industrial Revolution occurred simultaneously with a Political Revolution. The same regions, the same men experiencing the same mental ferment gave birth to both. And they are now both threatened by the same forces of reaction. The truth is that they are interdependent, neither could have nor can exist without the other, and both will succumb if either does.

Both revolutions hit their stride in the latter half of the Eighteenth Century. In aiming at the emancipation of the individual, the Political Revolution might have created an anarchic society except for one indispensable reservation: the requirement that each man scrupulously respect every other man's right to follow an equally independent but responsible course. This reservation is a formidable one. It calls for degrees of restraint, mutual consideration, co-operative action and even-handed fairness which nothing in the past history or present imperfection of mankind would indicate as practicable. Needless to say the ideal has been far from fully attained, but the speed and extent of the advance in its direction for a long time was truly astonishing. It was enough to release immense floods of human energy, vitalized by the courage, ambition, ingenuity which freedom generates in the minds and spirits of men.

This outpouring of energy, made up of big and little streams from multitudinous sources, has supplied the productive and expansive power of the Industrial Revolution. It has been effective throughout Western Europe and America, wherever men have been illuminated in any degree by the sense of freedom. But it has accomplished most here in the United States, where the ideal of individual freedom has been most nearly approached. Here we have built a system which is quite capable, if its capacities are utilized by a unified society, of providing a state of environmental well-being for the whole population.

But no matter how powerful the impulses carrying it forward, a society not wholly united in its loyalties is bound to be economically and psychologically unstable. Its progress will not be continuous. Divided in its interests, it becomes as suspicious and weather-wise as a flock of crows. Let it detect a state of unbalance in the structure of production, consumption, and credit—which must expand in equilibrium if the system as a whole is to prosper— and it moves swiftly to protect itself not as a whole but as a mob of scrambling units. Losing confidence in certain values, it seeks to convert them in panicky haste into others it hopes will be more permanent.

This sort of thing happened spectacularly in Germany in 1922, when the people were seized with total distrust of their own money, and tried all at once to get rid of it in exchange for goods —any goods, at any price. It happened here in 1929 when people suddenly concluded that the values of securities and commodities were inflated—as they were—and hastened to exchange them for money—almost any amount of money, regardless of loss.

We slide down the spiral with disastrous swiftness, once the confidence and energy which push us upward are withdrawn. This should not happen in a free and rational society. It does not happen, of course, in a society where production is entirely controlled by the State, goods are strictly rationed to all consumers, and the value of money is fixed not by free exchange, which does not exist, but by governmental fiat. In these societies, cyclic depressions are avoided by accepting a continuous depression and a total loss of freedom of choice and action. Equally fallacious is the present tendency in this country to rely on safeguards and insurances established by law: these are necessary recourses so long as depressions are certain to occur, but they are palliatives and not preventives. They in fact are legislative acknowledgements of economic insecurity.

The only way in which depressions can be minimized in a free society is by reducing their cause, which is to be found in internal divisions generating a lack of confidence in the soundness of the system itself. Completely united loyalties and common objectives should enable men to maintain unshaken confidence in the future stability of their sources of livelihood, the same confidence a farmer of good land feels in the fertility of his own acres. Even then, a free society of abundance will never move at the economic dead level of a completely controlled society, where the only certainty is that of continued scarcity. In a free society there will be fluctuations as balances are adjusted, and these must be discounted as the farmer who farms in the free air accepts the possibility of an occasional late frost or inadequate rainfall. But in a society that is not only free but unified, it should be possible to keep these fluctuations within the upper levels of abundance instead of letting them range all the way from prosperity to acute privation and general misery. There is no inherent reason why this cannot be done: with suspicions and uncertainties allayed and mutual trust established between all elements of society, it should be possible to detect signs of disequilibrium and restore a balance before panic fear has a chance to rise and do its destructive work.

In fact, until recent years the people of this country have had a large measure of such confidence in the basic soundness of their system, in spite of the schism in our industrial structure and serious faults in our political organization. They have been subject to fits of nervous alarm, with good cause, but they have had an underlying faith that the system would be equal to any strains put upon it. The unparalleled advances in well-being made between depressions have given a reasonable basis for this belief.

Therefore until recently our slumps, although too frequent and too acute, have been temporary and self-corrective. A new state of balance has been reached in a short time even though this has been accomplished by chucking overboard great and precious values representing years of work. The descent is halted when liquidation is completed, confidence revives, and the climb upward is resumed. Always in the past it has carried us quickly past the point at which the descent began. We may have slid two steps backwards, but we have then gone three steps forward—often much more. In fact, we doubled our output every twenty years.

3

It had worked out this way before 1929, but events in America did not follow this pattern after 1929. We did not succeed in climbing back to the production level of 1929 until 1940, and then only when large war orders were added to the output of civilian goods and services. Our national income in 1929 was 83.3 billion dollars. If the rate of expansion of the twenties had been maintained through the thirties, our income in 1939 should have been at least 110 billions, probably more. Instead, it was only 70.8 billions and we had ten million unemployed. The total loss of potential income during the decade has been estimated at as much as 400 billion dollars.*

A depression that lasts eleven years, and deprives us of such enormous potential wealth, and then is relieved only by the abnormal acceleration required by a major war, is something more than a mere interval of readjustment. It had the effect, quite naturally, of shaking many individuals' basic confidence in our future. The more nervous and less courageous were in a state to be persuaded that there is something hopelessly wrong with our system itself, something calling for drastic revision of its fundamentals.

It is this shaken confidence which has made us vulnerable to the forces of reaction: the ancient fear of life has risen from the depths of our animal natures, here as elsewhere. And it has been stimulated by the fact that apparently we were less successful than other less liberal nations in dealing with the immediate problems of depression.

Our collapse beginning in 1929 was part of the world-wide débacle of that year. The political world structure created after the first World War was inherently unstable. In it any number of bitter national antagonisms were given constitutional implementation, and it was not dominated by any strong, stabilizing

* Dr. Alvin H. Hansen, speaking at New York University, May 5, 1943. Address published in America After the War, New York University. The figures on national income are from Markets After the War, Bureau of Foreign and Domestic Commerce, Department of Commerce, 1943.

influence such as Great Britain had exercised during the century between 1815 and 1914. Jerry-built political frameworks were superimposed on the uncompleted and unassimilated Industrial Revolution. In several nations the industrial system came under state control and was used to further selfish nationalist ends at the expense of other peoples. Currency inflation in bankrupt nations was severe and recurrent. Hatreds, resentments, jealousies, burning injustices bore fruit in an evil crop of barriers to healthy intercourse and the exchange of goods, and in widespread privations and grievous frustrations. Maladjustments between production, consumption, and credit accumulated until the crash came in 1929.

We suffered because of the political ill-health of Europe, but we actually did not share its acute phases. We were politically stable in 1929, we were not ridden by the dark passions of Europe, our national destiny was in no way frustrated and our productive resources were greater than ever. Prices of goods and securities were inflated, but otherwise our national economy was sound: "Our Federal budget was balanced; taxes were not excessive and the portion of our national income absorbed by National, State and Municipal budgets was not large." * We had maladjustments of our own; especially, the need for eliminating class divisions from our industrial system, which was growing more urgent precisely as the workers shared more liberally in the system's benefits without acquiring equivalent rights, responsibilities, and loyalties within its hierarchy. Infections in both the body politic and the economic mechanism demanded drastic treatment. These disabilities were serious, but appeared to be in no way irremediable: there seemed to be no reason why our evolutionary progress should not be resumed after we had got rid of the hang-over of an inflationary debauch, and no reason why the adjustments necessary to insure genuine stability should not be brought that much nearer and that much easier of accomplishment.

Yet all the rest of the principal industrial nations, with the exception of France, pulled themselves out of the slump much faster than we did.

* Robert Hunter, *Revolution*, Harper, 1937, p. 107.

4

The downward slide throughout the world hit bottom in 1932, and in that same year Great Britain and Germany (the latter had sunk lower than we) began a swift recovery. Great Britain passed its 1929 level in 1934 and continued to rise rapidly from then on, wiping out avoidable unemployment and advancing to unparalleled prosperity before the war. The world as a whole passed its 1929 level in 1935, and Germany did it in 1936. France never passed its 1929 level before its fall, the United States not until war preparations pushed us over in 1940.

The fact that other nations recovered so sharply does not mean that they had solved the problems that troubled us. It merely proves that they had taken certain practical steps which had the effect of accelerating production and restoring former levels of prosperity. In Germany and Japan this was done by beginning large-scale preparations for war, and this abnormal activity had the same effect on their economies that serious preparation for war had on ours seven years later. Great Britain took what seemed— and in a peaceful world would have been—the wiser course of allowing liquidation to complete its work swiftly, at the same time removing barriers to trade and handicaps on industry so that production could revive along normal lines: which put her at a great disadvantage when she had to fight fully-armed Germany in 1939.

In France, the depression brought to a crisis the bitter distrust and antagonism that had long existed between her ancient agrarian society and her new and undigested industrialism. France thus suffered from a double division. Even in prosperous times her industrial class, both management and workers, lived as a huge alien group among her land-based peasantry and bourgeoisie who considered themselves, and in the historical sense were, the only true France. This disunity contributed to parliamentary chaos, and years of exacerbation left France deeply divided, stalemated, sullen, and hating with the emotional intensity that in other manifestations is one of the finest traits of the French character. France went somberly into the war, her energies so completely spent on internal antagonisms that she looked on an external enemy with apathy.

In America, under Mr. Hoover, we all enthusiastically made the mistake—which Britain did not make—of attempting to prevent the liquidation by which an equilibrium of values could be restored. These efforts to maintain prices by government support and an artificially created scarcity, expanded under Mr. Roosevelt, had the natural effect of aggravating the disease they were meant to cure. And while we suffered from nothing like the schism that divided France, we managed after 1933 to create a somewhat similar antagonism between our national policy and the industrial system which must create and sustain any prosperity we enjoy. This was not so easy to do, since we had effected our transfer to an industrial economy much more completely than France had succeeded in doing.

We brought about our division by adopting as the basis of national policy the assumption that our industrial-economic vitality had exhausted itself and accomplished all that could be expected of it as a creator of abundance. Henceforth, it would be maintained in *status quo* by artificial respiration applied by government. Ours was officially diagnosed as a "mature economy," and, neglecting all the adjustments that cried out to be made in order that the system could function again on its own immense energy, national policy was shaped to this extraordinary assumption of permanent invalidism.

5

There was nothing new about this theory of a "mature economy" * except the name—it has cropped up in every period of retrogression, both here and elsewhere. One of the most convinc-

* For an authoritative statement of the "mature economy" theory see *Fiscal Policy and Business Cycles*, by Alvin Hansen, Norton, 1941. For a total demolition of the theory as an interpretation of the economic status of the United States, see *Capital Expansion, Employment and Economic Stability*, by Moulton, Edwards, Magee, and Lewis, Brookings Institution, 1940, especially Chapter XI.

ing all-is-finished statements ever recorded was made by Carroll D. Wright, Commissioner of Labor in 1886, a year of world-wide depression.* Mr. Wright made a thorough study of the situation and in his report he reviewed the state of the world in detail. On the basis of an impressive array of facts he concluded that the railroads, canals, tunnels, river and harbor improvements had all been completed, telegraph and cable lines had been laid down, the merchant marine largely made over from wood to iron. Little remained to be done. And the "circle of producing nations has been so enlarged as to make the means of production far in excess of the needs of consumption." He conceded "that the discovery of new processes of manufacture will undoubtedly continue, and this will act as an ameliorating influence, but it will not leave room for a marked extension, such as has been witnessed during the last fifty years, or afford a remunerative employment of the vast amount of capital which has been created during that period. . . . There may be room for further intensive, but not extensive, development of industry in the present area of civilization."

Mr. Wright may not have been aware that three years previously Thomas A. Edison had installed a few dynamos in a small building in Pearl Street, New York, and opened the world's first plant for the production and sale of electric current. He could not know that during 1887 this irrepressible Edison person—who had neglected to read the report of the Commissioner of Labor— would perfect a motor-driven machine for reproducing sounds recorded as tiny grooves on a wax cylinder, and would begin work on a method whereby pictures of a moving object taken at very brief intervals could be shown again at the same brief intervals and so create the appearance of movement. The next year after that, a young Rochester bookkeeper named George Eastman, who thought that practically anybody would enjoy taking photographs if it could be made easy enough, would begin manufacturing a simple box camera to which he would give the queer name of "Kodak," and in the following year he would produce a flexible sensitized film for use in this camera instead of glass plates. Edi-

* Report of the Commissioner of Labor, 1886, Chapter III, pp. 254-263.

son would hear of it, obtain fifty feet of the film, and before 1889 had advanced into winter would have made the first strip of motion picture film.

Exactly ten years after Mr. Wright had spoken, an Italian scientist named Marconi would patent in England a method of transmitting messages by means of electrical impulses discharged through the air without the aid of wires. Also in 1896 a French scientist named Becquerel would observe that photographic plates were blackened by some sort of radiations emanating from the mineral uranium, and the Curies in Paris begin a series of investigations which would result in the isolation of radium. The new science of electronics would thus be hitting its stride, but not until 1907 would Lee de Forest devise the first of the electron tubes which are rapidly becoming the greatest of all practical tools.

In the same memorable year of 1896 Henry Ford would build his first automobile in his back yard in Detroit, and after seven years more Orville and Wilbur Wright (no relation to Carroll) would make man's first flights in a heavier-than-air machine at Kittyhawk. In 1906 Dr. Leo Hendrik Baekland would begin compressing a resinoid compound into a hard, smooth substance which he would call Bakelite and think might be useful. There also would be any number of chemists, physicists, metallurgists, engineers, and electricians working away at one interesting problem after another, without having been weighted in the statistics of Carroll D. Wright, Commissioner of Labor in 1886.

The President in 1886 was a bluff realist who was not converted to Mr. Wright's thesis and if he had been would not have considered it the duty of the federal government to undertake the management of a febrile economy. He believed and said, with a bluntness which sounds positively brutal in these soft-spoken times, that if the people couldn't run their own private businesses, they needn't expect the government to do it for them. The fact that he might be defeated for re-election two years later—as he was—did not appear to influence his thinking. So Mr. Cleveland kept his hands off, and the country promptly entered upon a forty-year period of stupendous although occasionally interrupted expansion; a period which saw the rise from scratch of electric utilities and the whole power industry, the development of the internal combustion engine, the automobile, aviation, the oil industry, movies, radio, electronics, and plastics; not to mention the rebuilding of our highway system, the growth of huge new cities, and great progress in chemistry, medicine, dietetics, and household comforts. All of which was accompanied by a doubling and redoubling of wages and a very substantial rise in the standard of living of the great majority of our people.

But it seems that no lesson is permanently learned. When depression recurred in 1929, Mr. Wright's conclusions were advanced again, on much the same grounds, by Lord Keynes in England and a vociferous group of economists headed by Dr. Alvin Hansen in the United States. Dr. Hansen became after 1933 the most influential economist in government councils, and the theory of a "mature economy" became, for the time being and almost inadvertently, the law of the land.

6

We elected in 1932, at the low point of the depression, a President of a social type extremely rare in America: an agrarian aristocrat, patrician in background and training, cosmopolitan in upbringing and sympathies, who had had practically no experience in or intimate contact with either commerce or industry. It is a type much more common in England than in America, although even there it is a vanishing species. At its best, as in Mr. Roosevelt, it is moved by strong humanitarian instincts and a deep sense of responsibility for the welfare of those less fortunate. And, also at its best as in Mr. Roosevelt, its qualifications fit it admirably to deal with the complications of critical international affairs and the major strategy of a global war, a fact which was to be of incalculable value to the United States and the world as a whole.

Personally, Mr. Roosevelt had most unusual endowments: a warm and expansive temperament, great charm, infectious high spirits, political skill amounting to genius, superb powers of leadership, great courage and supreme self-confidence. He brought to the Presidency exactly what the nation needed to lift its spirits after the capable but fatigued and depressed Mr. Hoover. It might have been supposed that with his luminous genius to mold our thought and action this country would have surged upward to prosperity much more rapidly than England did under less inspiring leadership.

But it happened that Mr. Roosevelt possessed another characteristic frequently although not universally present in this patrician type: his lifelong insulation from the processes by which men of his capacity usually make a living had predisposed him to a suspicious attitude toward "trade" and toward men engaged in it. He had an aristocratic distaste for commercial activities and a perhaps compensatory antagonism toward the mechanisms of commerce, which may have been mainly subconscious and therefore ineradicable.

This attitude of mind prepared Mr. Roosevelt to become a convert to the "mature economy" theory. It was easy for him to accept the "mature economists'" well-reasoned arguments, complete with statistical charts, that the economic structure with which he had so little sympathy had outlived its usefulness and in future must be largely supplanted by government.

At the time of his inauguration in 1933, in a book called *Looking Forward*,* Mr. Roosevelt revealed the innate bent of his mind and defined his economic and social principles. These principles were to guide the acts and expressions of his administration in the economic sphere at least up to his last year, and there is reason to doubt whether they had really altered even then and had not been merely overlaid by his vast and heroic preoccupations with the war and peace.

In *Looking Forward* Mr. Roosevelt accounted for the depression on the conventional "mature economy" grounds of no more public lands and the decline in the population growth with a resultant excess of savings over investment opportunities—inability to "afford a remunerative employment for the vast amount of capital which has been created," in Mr. Wright's words—and he found its immediate cause in overexpansion on the part of indus-

* John Day, 1933.

try and the accumulation of unneeded surpluses of goods, thus mistaking price inflation for overproduction. He made merry with the "Alice-in-Wonderland" idea that there is an interdependent sequence of production, employment, and consumption, and thought it absurd to suppose that a large output of goods "was all to be bought and paid for if everybody was employed and earning good wages. . . . 'No,' shouted Jabberwock. 'The more we produce, the more we can buy.'" This he said is "contrary to the teachings of history."

He argued that "our industrial plant is built." "Our physical economic plant will not expand in the future at the same rate at which it has been expanded in the past. We may build more factories but the fact remains that we have enough to supply all our domestic needs, and more, if they are used. With these factories we can now make more shoes, more textiles, more steel, more radios, more automobiles, more of almost everything than we can use." The enterpriser in future is a menace: "A mere builder of more industrial plants, a creator of more railroad systems, an organizer of more corporations, is as likely to be a danger as a help."

These things being true, he charted a new course for the country. "Our task now is not discovery of natural resources or necessarily of producing more goods. It is the soberer, less dramatic business of *administering resources and plants already in hand,* of seeking to establish foreign markets for our *surplus production,* of meeting the problem of *under-consumption,* or of *adjusting production to consumption,* of *distributing* wealth and products more equitably, of *adapting existing economic organization* to the service of the people."

The italics are mine, and they reveal the complete orientation of the President's thought away from expansion and toward the distribution of existing or more limited production. Henceforth we are to live on our hump. The "problem of under-consumption" is to be met by "adjusting production to consumption": the thought of already existing surpluses is dominant. We are to pour no more sand on the conical pile: we are to flatten it out.

This time it was not the Commissioner of Labor speaking, but the President. Thus pessimism as to the country's economic future became the official attitude of our government for the first time in its history, the motivation of a ten years' program of official utterances and acts.

As late as June, 1943, the best the President could promise our returning servicemen was not a wealth of opportunity in a healthy and advancing nation but various forms of government assistance, and the grim assurance of payments to the unemployed. When, on December 28, 1943, Mr. Roosevelt reviewed his prewar administration, listing twenty-eight achievements in which he took pride, he again revealed the unchanging direction of his thought: eight of the items in the list were corrective of symptomatic evils, eighteen were ameliorative measures, and only two could be considered as intended to stimulate normal economic expansion; and even in these two instances—the Reciprocal Trade Agreements and the promotion of private home building through the Federal Housing Administration—it is clear that other motives were involved and perhaps dominant. Nowhere in this statement is there any note of exultation in recovered economic health, expanding productivity or multiplied opportunity, or any recognition even of their desirability; and future historians may make significant psychological deductions from the President's identification of his administration with a physician ministering to a patient first critically ill of the depression and then grievously injured by the war.

7

All of the acts in Mr. Roosevelt's list are creditable in intent. Some of them were directly dictated by the emergency, others were in the direction of "social gains" that all thoughtful people agree are admirable and too long delayed. There is no question of the desirability of provisions for the superannuated, legalized collective bargaining, unemployment insurance, and proper policing and safeguarding of banking and the handling of investments. Mr. Roosevelt used his powers of leadership to lift the United States toward the level of other progressive nations by measures too long neglected under a prevalent addiction to *laissez faire*, and for this he deserves and receives great credit.

But, since no one wants to lose his standing as a humanitarian, a coldly critical examination of the actual mechanisms adopted for accomplishing these objectives hasn't yet been made, nor the ultimate workings of these mechanisms assayed. It is obvious that they are full of grave and perhaps in some cases self-defeating faults. And we do have a restless feeling that remedies and safeguards should be taken in our stride, with our main interest centered on constructive activities which will reduce the need for them.

It is very necessary to correct abuses and provide for the unfortunate, but it is even more necessary to put tools in the hands of the strong. The first requisite in any free economy is to release the self-supporting energies of millions of independent citizens who certainly do not look on themselves as permanent pensioners on public bounty. This can only be done, in our economy, through the removal of obstacles to and the stimulation of industrial expansion, which in turn will stimulate all other forms of productive activity.

It is a most unfortunate fact that not a single move was made in all this time to heal the division in industry so as to bring all its factions together in a common loyalty, a sharing of benefits and responsibilities, and a common confidence in their united strength. During this trying period, a sense of interdependence actually grew and spread among the enlightened of all groups, who see clearly that no class or section can prosper unless prosperity is shared by all. Capital has been in a mood of humility, the thought of intelligent elements of labor has been far in advance of labor's favorite political leaders, and there has been soul-searching and something like intellectual ferment in the management-specialist group. This has been evident in the studies of labor economists, in the utterances of certain capitalists and in the quiet but intense, nation-wide activities of such management-specialist organizations as the National Planning Association and the Committee for Economic Development. Wise and creative leadership in the political sphere, sincerely devoted to our national doctrine of individual liberty, might have combined these liberal trends and brought about an organization of industry devised for unity, stability, maximum productivity, and the increasing well-being of the entire society. This is a rational and feasible objective: it is only attainable if the basic provision of completely free action in a free society is continued and extended to every member of society.

It is a sad fact that we have had no such leadership from any political source in this country. Even when official emphasis shifted from pessimism to an equally unhealthy optimism, the effect was deeply disquieting. There is no reassurance in seeing the Committee for Economic Development's goal of full employment after the war picked up, exaggerated and made into a political slogan by office-holders who have been most openly skeptical of the American system's future potentialities and most eager to enlarge the powers of the State within it. "Sixty million jobs" are not all we want: as Robert Hunter pointed out several years ago,* one of the most effective ways ever found to put everybody to work was to take stones out of the fields and pile them into huge pyramids. And there was no unemployment among the Negro slaves of the South. Work should do more than keep the worker busy and alive: it should give scope to his energy and ingenuity in contributing to his own and the general betterment, and reward his efforts to do so; it should enhance his dignity, enrich his life, and benefit society. The collection of political accidents known as government cannot make work of this quality: if they are wise and well intentioned they can foster conditions in which men can create that kind of work for themselves. Otherwise such work will not exist.

Many of the measures in Mr. Roosevelt's list of achievements were so framed as to have exactly the opposite effect. They created wide areas of devastation around whatever legitimate targets they were aimed at, the effect on industry being much the same as if you weeded a garden with hundred-pound bombs. Under a punitive barrage industry could not perform its function as mass employer and supporter of all remunerative activities. Unable to expand, management-specialists concentrated on internal efficiency and substantially raised industry's man-hour output, which is admirable since it means more goods at less cost. In a healthy economy, more goods at less cost means a higher standard of

* *Revolution*, previously cited.

living, but to realize its benefits we need more employment and without expansion there can be no increased employment.

Between 1929 and 1940 our economy thus accomplished some *intensive* development, in increase of man-hour output, but no *extensive* development whatever. The level of production remained below that of 1929, the capital assets of all corporations in 1937 were almost 23 billion dollars less than they had been in 1929, and in 1939 there were still ten million idle workers. The national debt had been swollen by an uninterrupted series of deficits, taxes were high and rising, class divisions were accentuated. The depression remained with us for eleven years—seven years longer than in Great Britain and six years longer than in the world as a whole. At the end we still had with us that "third of the population" who were "ill fed, ill housed, and ill clothed," whose dire unfilled needs confront any supposition that our economy is "mature," our production adequate or our expansion completed.

Certainly the application of "mature economy" techniques during eight years did not give us an increasingly abundant life, or advance us toward it, or provide any satisfactory substitute. And even though the "mature economy" theory had no basis in fact,* its official adoption and the measures and attitudes inspired by it had exactly the same effect as if it had been true. It is of course possible to put a man to bed, tell him he's incurable, and dose him with this and that until he really is very ill indeed. In eleven years, defeatism can become a habit strong enough to impair a man's or a nation's will to progress. The discouraged will turn receptively toward other systems and other ways of life.

* The "mature economy" argument is by no means dead. It is again orchestrated sonorously by Mr. Lewis Mumford in his *City Development*, Harcourt, Brace, 1945. See his chapter, "The Social Foundations of Postwar Building," in which, however, he makes an extraordinary admission: "Individuality and initiative, to this end, [the prevention of premature fossilization!] must be divorced from *their historic connection with private capitalism; they must be fostered, as counterpoises, precisely at the moment that collectivism triumphs.*"

CHAPTER III

AN INVALID RECOVERS

BUT WE are concerned now with the postwar future and not the prewar past. Our interest in the latter is purely diagnostic— it is extremely important for us to know whether our economy is really mature, to the point of senility, or whether it is still adolescent and potentially virile. If it is stimulated, efficiently policed, and adjusted to existing conditions instead of being hampered and repressed, does it still have within it the energy to project us forward in an expanding future? We evolved it over a period of a century and a half, and, admittedly imperfect as any uncompleted human institution must be, it carried us much further in that time than any other people managed to travel. Might it be that, after all, its characteristics are those best suited to our temperament and needs?

Fortunately we needn't rely on the dialectics of economists for the answer. We have had a pragmatic demonstration.

We have lived seven years beyond 1939, mighty things have happened in that time, we have made an enormous expansion, and our invalid has strode the hills like a Paul Bunyan among economies. From a total output of 88.6 billion dollars in 1939, we rose to an output of 187 billion dollars in 1943. From 44.2 millions employed and 10.4 millions * unemployed in 1939, we rose to 63 millions employed in 1943 and we had a serious manpower short-

* Department of Commerce, *Survey of Current Business*, March and April, 1943. "Total output of goods and services" differs from "net national income," in that items of depreciation, depletion, other business reserves, and business taxes are deducted from the former to arrive at the latter. This explains the difference between these figures on output and the figures on national income given on page 36.

49

age to deal with. Production and employment maintained approximately these levels through 1944 and 1945. Wages were high, the work week was long, not enough of anything—munitions, food, commodities—were produced.

The "mature economists"—at least some of them—were dumbfounded. Dr. Hansen spoke with awe of "the discovery we have made in recent years, viz., the perfectly prodigious capacity of the American economy to produce a large variety of goods and services. I think it is no exaggeration to say that there was no one in 1940 who was able to see what a perfectly enormous increase in real income and output of goods and services our American economy was capable of achieving." * Plenty of people were capable of seeing just that, but we did not begrudge Mr. Hansen the self-defensive consolation of thinking otherwise. We could afford to be generous in the glow of reassurance we were enjoying, just as we can welcome Mr. Wallace's late conversion to an economy of plenty after his career in the enthusiastic promotion of an economy of scarcity.

"Capacity to produce" depends on men and tools, but men make tools and tools are inert without men to organize, direct, and operate them. Men and their moods are the decisive factors. The "perfectly enormous increase in real income and output of goods and services" in the brief years of 1940 to 1943 was the work of men—management, technologists, workers—the same men who had marked time for ten years previously; grousing bitterly and impotently if they were management and going somberly into WPA or some other alphabetical agency in heavy percentages if they were labor. The technologists generally had managed to keep busy with their own enterprises, as, fortunately, they usually do.

Almost overnight, the air cleared for these men, their mood changed. Once more they had a common and compelling incentive summoning all their great reserves of energy for a mighty and united creative effort. Their historic confidence in their own powers came flooding back, their labor, money, and resources were all staked in one gigantic venture. In a crisis the people became the State again, and not its wards.

* Address at New York University, May 5, 1943, previously quoted.

It has been the people's will that has been done, not the will of any group of leaders. Carrying the government with it, the nation abruptly switched from a "mature economy" policy of backing consumption to an *expanding* economy policy of backing production. There suddenly *had* to be a vastly increased output of supplies and munitions—so great an output that the most we could do was none too much. This was no occasion for pump-priming, for stimulants to keep a little life in an ailing body; this crisis called for enormous vitality, which couldn't be improvised—it had to be there, ready and waiting on demand. It *was* there, and we've seen how much there was and what it could accomplish in a short time. Whatever was the matter with our economy, it wasn't lack of latent energy to expand.

Yes, it was war that inspired us, and during the war years 85 billions of our annual production were in goods for war and twelve millions of our employed were in the armed services. It is much easier to produce for a single consumer, the military machine, which specifies the goods and quantities it needs, than to maintain an equivalent production of civilian goods to satisfy the needs and wants of millions of individuals. But there has been no calamitous unemployment during the reconversion period, and by mid-1946 Mr. Wallace's goal of 60 million jobs had been passed without the help of any of his devices. According to the Census Bureau, July of 1946 saw twelve million more people employed in civilian production than in 1940, and at much higher wage rates. And filling us with restored confidence that we can maintain these levels is the fact that we had what it took to deal with the most momentous crisis in our history, deal with it magnificently, and then go on without pause to take up the slack in our domestic schedule. We have never been more conscious of our strength, or of the opportunities to apply it. We may be torn by revived dissension, more dangerously acute because it was temporarily suppressed during the war, but there has never been a time when more men were keenly aware of the problems that face us, or the tremendous issues that hang on them. Along with climactic discord, we are experiencing a notable access of both understanding and determination.

2

We are realizing, too, with faint surprise after what we had been told, that we accomplished all we have done without any fundamental change in our historic economy. It has proven extraordinarily flexible and resourceful in adapting itself to the peculiar demands of total war, and it has remained throughout a co-operative and not a directed enterprise. We have done the job as a free association of independent men, who pooled their efforts because they saw their own good in the common good, and each made his willing contribution to the whole. No such ideal is ever realized in perfection—we are still a long way from Paradise or even Utopia. But we have convinced ourselves all over again that our welfare lies in reliance on the energies and preponderant judgment of multitudinous individuals rather than on the energy and judgments of a haphazardly selected or self-appointed few.

Our activities during the past four years have had an extraordinary and increasingly democratic character. Leadership in the sphere of international affairs has been competent. The command of our military services and their fighting ability were superb. But the organization of the national effort behind the fighting services, on which success depended, was the work of innumerable amateurs in office and out. These individuals, when called into government to make up the deficiencies of an organization geared to regulate paternalistically a moribund economy and ill-equipped to lead an expanding economy, with few exceptions retained their amateur standing. They preserved their fixed habit of thinking in terms of production rather than dole, they felt no messianic call or inherent ability to regulate the lives of others, and they regarded their governmental activities distinctly as an interlude and not a career. The vastly greater number who did their part in private life—in research, management, and the huge forces of labor—fitted themselves voluntarily into appropriate niches and pulled their weight with a surprising degree of unanimity.

To channel such diverse contributions toward a specific objective required a degree of organization we had never needed before and could not endure in normal times, but these expedients too were democratically evolved and voluntarily accepted without giving any blank check on our future liberties. In our own way we regimented ourselves, yes. But the carrying of one recalcitrant elderly gentleman out of his office by two shamefaced young soldiers could cause a national furor: this is a long way from the single party, the suppression of dissent, the Gestapo or GPU, the concentration camps, the secret trials and the purges to which even Mr. Harold Laski admits that the planned society has so far inevitably resorted in practice.*

Our experiences with the necessary regimentation of total war have convinced many of us of several truths. The most important is that the minds of individuals, no matter how capable and admirably motivated, are unequal to the task of intimately regulating a complex modern society or a vaguely understood modern economy; while if the regulating minds are something less than superlatively competent and 100 per cent pure in motive—as whose aren't?—their efforts at rulemaking are apt to be exceedingly exasperating. We have decided that even if regulation could be wise and benevolent we still wouldn't like it as a permanent practice: we prefer to work out our salvation by our own efforts rather than have it handed to us on the most modernistic of chrome-plated platters.

This is nothing less than a revival of allegiance to the trial-and-error method originally adopted as the technique of our democracy. Other nations have shown us the consequences of accepting foregone conclusions and dogmatic revelations as to the ultimate structure of society: the majority of us here are convinced all over again that it is better to advance experimentally, accepting a certain proportion of mistakes and casualties and taking more time about it, rather than to run the risk of committing ourselves to one all-embracing and irrevocable error. We prefer a fluid society and proliferating economy to a society of status and an economy of formula. The course we choose has faults and entails casualties—

* See *Reflections on the Revolution of Our Times*, Viking, 1943, Chapters II and III, in which Mr. Laski traces the evolution of a society committed to an ultimate formula, as exemplified in Soviet Russia and Fascist Germany. Mr. Laski's logic for once is convincing.

the unavoidable concomitants of life and growth—but we prefer it to rigor mortis. Even our industrial strife has a vigorous candor about it, as if we were determined to reach a settlement at last. Fear of life has declined, and there has been a noticeable stiffening of resistance to the wave of reaction from the East.

We are not, however, suffering from any optimistic illusions. It is perfectly clear that permanently doubling our prewar production-consumption, which is the modest task we have set ourselves, is nothing to be taken lightly. The difficulties we are already encountering—principally from the factional division within industry —and others that will turn up as time passes, are enough to keep us a sober and earnest people for many a day. But, besides the all-important bracer of renewed confidence in our native principles and in the vigor and adaptability of our system, we find ourselves with a bankroll of present, tangible assets greater than we ever imagined could be assembled by any nation. Looked at with the eyes of 1939, our existing resources are positively dazzling—debt and taxes notwithstanding.

It will be worth while to check over this list of war-born values, not in any gloating spirit, but simply to bolster our will to act as energetically for our preferred kind of good in peace as we have done in war.

3

Of the millions of young men who are coming back safe and sound from the war, a great majority are better for the experience. They are stronger and sounder physically and we must shame-facedly admit that a very great many have acquired better dietary habits and better habits of personal hygiene and have had better dental and medical care than they would have been blessed with if they had stayed peacefully at home.

The armed services saw to it, with swift efficiency, that there were no illiterates in their forces. It is a shameful thing that in this country there are many young men who have not had even the rudiments of an education: the number of college graduates only slightly exceeds the number of total illiterates in the nation. In schools that were models of pedagogic method, the services

gave great numbers of these untaught young men in a few weeks
the equivalent of years of early training. Thus educational as well
as physical deficiencies have been made up, at least partially, in
hundreds of thousands of cases.

This has been a technological war, and the amount of sound
technical instruction of many kinds that has been given to soldiers and sailors is astonishing. Somewhere the exact number of
trade schools conducted by the armed services may be recorded,
but without digging into the files it is enough to know that the
Army alone had more than 900 of them, many with huge enroll-
ments, certain ones graduating up to 40,000 trained men a year.
The services' training methods were direct, practical, and intensive, alert in discovering aptitudes and capitalizing abilities. Using
advanced methods of visual training, they turned out everything
from refrigeration experts to sheet metal draftsmen, and to show
for our war effort we have a half-million or so experienced young
air pilots, hundreds of thousands of air and sea navigators, airplane and automotive mechanics, radio and other electrical technicians, machinists, adepts in many fields of engineering and construction and the hundreds of crafts which an army like ours found
essential. It is a supply of skills for peacetime work in quantities
such as our educational system and civilian employment would
never have produced.

Even if these young men do not follow the trades and professions they learned in the services, they have had the tonic benefit
that the acquiring of any skillful art confers. They also have had
the bracing experience of orderly teamwork and mutual dependence in crises, they have acquired a knowledge of other men and
a degree of self-reliance and initiative that, again, they probably
would not have gained in their home-town jobs and pastimes.

In all this wealth of salutary by-products for the rank and file,
this war and our army were a new kind of war and army, and
while we could make an impressive catalog of deleterious influences also, the balance would still be heavily on the beneficial
side. Our peacetime educational system could be as effective, and
in the future may be, but the fact is that, in the past, it hasn't
been. The services are returning to us a much more competent
generation than we loaned to them.

Admitting the competence, there has been a certain amount of worry about the effect of the war on the characters of these young men—whether they may not have become permanently addicted to violence. For instance, Mr. Leo Cherne quotes * as seriously symptomatic some rather broad and gruesome humor composed by a G.I. frankly horrified by his training for hand-to-hand combat. But this has implications exactly opposite to those Mr. Cherne fears. There is not the slightest evidence in experience to indicate that familiarity with bloodshed and suffering in war inspires any love for them in after life, except in a few psychopaths of whom Hitler was the perfect type. I have known intimately the veterans of three wars preceding this, and I can attest that they included less than their share of bums, criminals, and sadists; that they have been on the whole more sedate, circumspect, considerate, and realistic than the average of their communities.

Modern war has many nervous and moral casualties, of course, and these constitute a rehabilitation problem not insoluble by psychiatry. But those of healthy minds who come back to us are a virile crowd of young adults, sobered and matured beyond their years and with a calm that may very well put the rest of us at a considerable disadvantage. We find that they are extraordinarily able to take care of themselves, generally quite clear as to their objectives, and disconcertingly firm in their determinations. We can trust their citizenship as much as their technical proficiency.

On the home front also we went to trade schools in crowds. Our industrial expansion, with its increase of industrial employment from less than 27 millions in 1940 to more than 33 millions in 1943,† called for millions of new technicians in hundreds of crafts. We turned them out, with speedy efficiency, through new and improved methods of instruction.

Executive skill and experience were expanded in the same proportion, and scope was provided for thousands of new managers, specialists, superintendents, foremen. Many a man has had the opportunity to enlarge his managerial capacity more in four years

---

* *The Rest of Your Life*, Doubleday, Doran, 1944, pp. 20-22.

† Increases in industrial employment of course bring proportionate increases of employment in construction, transportation, mining, services, etc.

than he might have been able to do in thirty under prewar pressures.

I know of one division of a great corporation which consisted of forty men in 1941. By midyear of 1943 these forty men had built up around them a smoothly running organization of 30,000 men and women functioning in enormous new buildings equipped with especially designed machinery, and maintaining an amazing level of production. As one walked through the quiet, orderly plant, past acres of engineers, draftsmen, accountants in air-conditioned and sound-conditioned halls, through elaborate testing laboratories, into rooms a thousand feet long where the intricate processes of airplane building went forward as if by some innate vitality of their own with surprising lack of noise and not a trace of confusion, one had a feeling of awe at the accomplishment of so much in so little time. Here is an experience in creative organization few men have ever had before in the history of the world, and it was not limited to the original forty but was shared by all their lieutenants as they were recruited. It has come to thousands of others in the past few years: the plant I describe was one of hundreds, and there were many more of both smaller and larger size briskly humming where there was nothing in 1940.

While individuals have gone to school, so have the corporate bodies which employ them. An industrial corporation can be more hidebound than any individual, since it has no escape into private life. Usually it has been formed to turn out a specific product or group of products, and its operations have been channeled in a more or less fixed routine. The individuals of the working staff are conditioned to this routine, just as the plant and equipment are designed for it. So a corporation may be a progressive leader in its field and still move forward in a very narrow groove.

But in the war effort, most of our industrial corporations found themselves doing work they never did before, and this work in many cases required rearrangement and re-equipment of their plants and the learning of wholly new routines. Modern ordnance and munitions are mostly high precision instruments, calling for more skill and finesse than most consumer production requires. So we saw large sections of industry promoted to a higher class, and scrambling—successfully, but with healthy effort—to keep up.

A manufacturer of cheap clocks and watches made bomb fuzes to tolerances of ten-thousandths of an inch, a manufacturer of business machines made tiny electrical gyroscopes for controlling the flight of planes, and attained an inhuman electrical and mechanical exactitude in each one of them. Our old corporations discarded the habits of a lifetime and the defeatism of the depression. They found they could learn a whole repertoire of new tricks, and they loved it. Their operations suddenly took on an interest approaching excitement, and their success fired them with a sense of mastery they have been eager to demonstrate to somebody besides the government.

Nothing could be healthier: if we are going to continue to have an economy of citizen enterprise *—and there is now no doubt that we are—we certainly want one of spirit, self-confidence, initiative. In the postwar era this new courage will carry our corporate bodies across many a frontier. Very few of them will ever get back into their old grooves. They are putting their newly acquired skills to work, undertaking all sorts of operations they never tried before, and their productive range will be expanded and diversified to an extent we can't even calculate until years of peace have given them a chance to show us what they learned.

4

In addition to the training of individuals, and the shifting and sharpening of corporate techniques, we have been mining away like mad at the unknown. In normal times some form of research is carried on by most manufacturers, and in the larger companies the research programs often reached grand proportions and were directed toward far-flung shadowy objectives.† War intensified this effort along with the productive effort. In all the old laboratories and many new ones, bigger crowds of chemists, metallur-

---

* The common term "private enterprise" is a misnomer. No enterprise today can be private. The basic distinction to be drawn in these times is between enterprise initiated and managed by citizens and enterprise initiated and directed by the State.

† See Chapter VII.

gists, physicists have been working feverishly to solve the mysteries of matter which have cramped our style in the past. Since we learned how to break up molecules and rearrange their atoms as we want them to be, we have run up a stupendous record of achievement. Powers that never were tamed have been brought to heel, old materials have been improved and many new syntheses created, and we emerge from the war with a firmer grip on the neck of nature.

Where the research men leave off, the engineers begin, and they have been perfecting new machines and devising new techniques to put the new knowledge to work. What we are now able to do with synthetic materials made from coal, wood, cotton, air, resins, oils and such suddenly tractable stuffs will be a revelation, and will amount to a technological revolution.

The work in private industry has been supplemented by the huge co-operative research program under the Office of Scientific Research and Development. This organization gathered in many of the most capable scientists in the country under the leadership of Dr. Vannevar Bush, and provided them with funds which amounted to billions of dollars. The broad scope of the work of OSRD has been overshadowed in the public mind by the revelation of the Manhattan Project responsible for the atomic bomb. This mastery of atomic energy ranks as the greatest practical scientific achievement in the history of man, and is all the more impressive because of the deliberate intention with which it was undertaken, its immense scale, its voluntary and astonishingly efficient co-ordination of the nation's academic and industrial resources, and its swift and orderly progress to complete success. Emphasis has been laid chiefly on the frightful destructive menace of the atomic bomb, and this is not to be underestimated. But we should counterbalance this fear with a realization that it has unlocked stores of power which, when they have been harnessed to useful work, will lift us to a creative plane that by all past standards is definitely superhuman.* Its implications for the future of the race are more revolutionary than we have yet had time to grasp.

But we should not lose sight of the many less spectacular but

* See Chapter V.

immediately applicable accomplishments of the research conducted by OSRD. It carried on specific research programs in more
than 200 industrial organizations and many more than 100 academic institutions. At such centers of research as Massachusetts
and California Institutes of Technology and Columbia University,
as much of the staff and facilities as were adaptable to the purpose were taken over for the duration. In a few instances OSRD
went out on its own and created entirely new physical facilities,
manned by large numbers of scientists and engineers, for the purpose of carrying on specific lines of research.

The work of course was aimed directly at the winning of
the war and much of it had to do with the improvement of
weapons and the perfection of new armament, fire control and
explosives. In this way hundreds of unpublicized weapons and
secret modifications of military equipment were devised, less spectacular than the atom bomb but potent in accelerating victory.
The professors proved to be extraordinarily lethal.

But there is almost no knowledge which is wholly destructive
and can't be put to good use. Even purely military achievements
have certain peacetime implications, and in addition there have
been great accomplishments which will be as directly and substantially useful in peace as in war. Their broad coverage includes
the fields of high-altitude aviation, jet propulsion, the gas turbine
engine, rocket development, chemistry and electrical engineering,
medicine and surgery, insect control, electronics, metallurgy, optics
and basic physics. Through more than 300 research projects the
medical group of OSRD dug into a long list of problems from
the mass production of penicillin to the development of substances to repel sharks and jelly fish. Among the largest projects
have been studies in aviation medicine, and in the use of blood
plasma and whole blood transfusions; plastic surgery, including
new methods of plastic facial reconstruction; and tropical diseases,
including the development of effective plague vaccines.

In a matter of months we covered an amount of ground in
research that would have taken us many years to cover at the
tempo of peace. All this deliberately acquired knowledge will
remain to save and ameliorate lives long after we have finished
applying it to the destruction of lives.

5

Men may be masters of their crafts and crammed with knowledge, but they are helpless without tools. Knowledge, skilled manpower and plant—these are the factors that determine capacity to produce in an industrial society. The war called for much greater production than we had ever achieved, and the "arsenal of democracy" had to be expanded on a gargantuan scale. We entered the war with an industrial plant valued at about 30 billion dollars. After the middle of 1940, when we first began to settle down to our job in earnest, we added about 20 billion dollars' worth of new plant and machinery, and 17.6 billions of this money went into manufacturing industries alone. This is a swift expansion unprecedented in our history or the history of any nation, and it is the one material item bought for the war which will remain to serve our peacetime needs with almost equal effectiveness.

This is something like a two-thirds increase in our productive equipment. We may be able to understand what that means if we realize that it is about the same as acquiring twenty new industries, each one equal to the nation's entire prewar automobile industry, which had a plant valued at one billion dollars in 1938. It took thirteen years before the war—from 1926 to 1938, inclusive —to tot up 20 billion dollars of capital expenditures for manufacturing plant and equipment, and most of that was replacement and not expansion.* Such rapid growth has had an explosive effect on our society, jostling the whole nation. We haven't yet had time to take stock of what it has done for better or worse to the face of the country, and it may take a long time to adjust ourselves comfortably to the new conditions it created.

Large sections of the Middle West and the South were industrialized, and, as the Department of Commerce said, the Pacific Coast squeezed a half century of industrial development into a scant two or three years. The working population surged about the country and alighted in new places like swarming bees. War-

* *Survey of Current Business*, Department of Commerce, March, 1941.

time production of aluminum, seven times the prewar output, and magnesium, ninety times the prewar output, amounted to great new industries in themselves. New synthetic rubber and electronic industries each approximated the prewar automobile industry in size, and the automobile manufacturers, who never built more than 4.5 million cars in one year, delivered armament at a rate equal to the building of 20 million automobiles a year. The machine tool manufacturers, who supply the means of production, turned out 350,000 units in 1942 and almost as many in 1943 and 1944, as against a yearly average of 26,000 units from 1930 to 1939. Surprisingly enough, they were still working to capacity in 1946. Our once dormant or nonexistent shipyards built 20 million tons of merchant ships a year—equal to a *Normandie* every two and a half days. We have multiplied our power plant, too, and have twice as much power from various sources available to work for us now that the war is over as when it began. We've hoisted ourselves into a new industrial era without realizing it.

This expansion had to be much swifter and greater than could ever be achieved by the process of normal growth. An economy expands normally through a co-ordinated advance along the whole front of production, employment and consumption, and while this advance may be rapid, as it was in the long pull from 1900 to 1929, it must be orderly and no one of the three factors can outrun the others very far without a pause for realignment. But the war had an urgency which could not wait for normal processes to work. To accomplish such swift expansion, the nation's money had to be syphoned through a central agency—the government. Of 20 billion dollars invested in new plant and equipment, more than 15 billions were supplied from public funds, while four to five billions were supplied from citizens' investment funds. The time factor compelled this procedure, and the people approved and put up the money—all of it, actually, coming from citizens' pockets. But the money was dispensed by government agencies and the result was that the government acquired title to at least one-fifth of our enlarged industrial plant.*

Practically all this government financed plant was leased to and

* "One-Fifth of a Nation—Government Owned," *Business Week*, June 19, 1943.

operated by citizen-owned corporations which undertook the responsibility of production, supplied managerial and technical skill, and in turn acquired a stimulating educational experience and an access of vision. Government did not itself take over industrial management except in a few brief emergencies. Government agencies collected the funds and wrote the orders, but citizen industry supplied organization, knowledge, skills, energy, workers—and results. Also government initiative was directed solely to the production of war supplies, and was not responsible for a dollar's worth of consumer goods except for a few such necessary by-products as passenger car tires.

This is very far from meaning that the country after due deliberation decided that it desired to make "wealth creation a function of government," in Mr. Adolf Berle's words.* It was a program which could be and was terminated with the war, and the advance toward state capitalism will be canceled. To accomplish this change in direction without affecting the momentum which the economy had acquired was supposed to call for great skill, wisdom, and understanding of the forces involved, but it has been done reasonably well without any noticeable display of genius. The "mature economists" did not believe it could be done at all: they insisted that the nation's funds must continue to flow through the public treasury, and the dire predictions of postwar unemployment that issued periodically from various government bureaus and from individual "mature economists" (eight millions was the usual figure) had a kind of macabre hopefulness about them. One detected a longing to see the patient safely back in bed, where he could be done good to. It is obvious that we had here a situation which very easily, with or without a "considered choice" on the part of the country, might have left government permanently dominant in fields "now supposed to be private." †

But the pessimistic viewpoint was not generally shared in the circles most intimately concerned with the problem. It is safe to say that there was not a single group of men engaged in war

* Testifying before the Temporary National Economic Committee, May 16, 1939.

† The quoted phrases are again from Mr. Berle's testimony.

production—in research, management, or labor—where able minds were not working toward a solution more in line with our habits. The same minds which accomplished the spectacular feat of converting this country in a few months into the most complete and prodigious military arsenal the world has ever seen have since been planning, each in its own sector, the permanent utilization of our enlarged capacity to produce. And that process is now well under way. By midyear of 1946 there was nothing but a normal amount of "frictional" unemployment, national production had reached a level of 150 billion somewhat inflated dollars and was increasing steadily in spite of critical work stoppages and material shortages.

6

There is no question but that the country and the world *need* all the steel, aluminum, magnesium, synthetic rubber, plastics, construction materials and innumerable consumer goods our enlarged plant can be adapted to produce. Our wants have accumulated to vast and urgent proportions. Normal production for civilian use in lines requiring metals, electrical devices, cotton, synthetics, many chemicals and other critical materials were stopped or greatly curtailed for four or more years, and all that time we were using up our goods, they wore out and broke down without means to replace them; the warehouses and the dealers' shelves are still short of inventories in all these lines; new houses, except for temporary and pretty appalling war housing, have not been built, so that it will take ten years of unprecedented building to make up the shortage; in June of 1945 there were five million less automobiles registered than in 1941 and a majority of those in use were candidates for the scrap heap (allowing for population increase, the backlog of demand was for 15 million cars *); our railroads and airlines are in dire need of repairs and replacement. There is not a single compartment of our civilian economy that is not calling for vast quantities of productive work to be done, and the rest of the world in most cases is even hungrier for goods

* "Automobile Topics," August, 1945.

than we are. In addition to civilian plans, government itself has an immense budget of work prepared in highway improvement, building construction, and the expansion of legitimate government services. There is a stupendous job waiting, one so big that all our men and our tools are not too many for it.

Here in this country we also, individually, have the means to pay for it—assuming that we do not suffer the catastrophe of extreme inflation which would wipe out our accumulated values. Not everybody of course was prudent enough to salt down the high earnings of war jobs, and not all the savings of the prudent will be spent at once. But with full employment at high wages, with billions invested in war stamps and bonds, with private savings of the thrifty reaching astonishing heights, with the prewar consumer debt mostly paid off, our people have a damned-up buying power much greater than we have ever had in our most prosperous times. Private savings which averaged 5 billion dollars a year during the prewar decade had soared to 40 billions by 1944. In the two previous years, individuals paid off almost 5 billions of consumer indebtedness and also drastically reduced their mortgage debts. Liquid resources of the American public increased by the staggering sum of 120 billion dollars, to a total of 170 billions, between 1939 and the end of 1945.* We ended the war with ability to purchase greatly exceeding a full year's national income at the highest hoped-for postwar levels. And surveys show that the spending of much of this money, mostly for durable consumer goods and houses unavailable during the war, has been shrewdly charted in millions of homes and still awaits the stocking of the markets.

In addition we have the improved financial position of most corporations, and their plans for expansion and replacement calling for huge new investments. The Commerce Department reported on July 31, 1945, that 7,000 manufacturers planned an expansion program of more than 9 billion dollars in the succeeding twelve months, while the railroads and airlines planned to spend another 1.5 billion dollars. These programs, it said, might be very much enlarged if the Japanese war ended before midyear

* Report of Securities and Exchange Commission, New York *Times*, March 20, 1945, and *Business Week*, December 15, 1945, p. 16.

of 1946—and it ended within a few days. This huge enlargement of peacetime facilities, added to our usable and converted war plant, indicates a gross national productive capacity of at least 160 billion dollars, and it may prove to be much more.

This private and corporate spending will supply the energizing force for our great productive mechanism during the critical years of transition to an economy of high production-consumption. Once running smoothly, such an economy can be self-perpetuating, the process of production itself generating the means for broad, equivalent consumption. (Provided, of course, that government does not consume too much of our substance unproductively.) Need will be translated into effective demand. By bringing up to the average those lagging sectors of our standard-of-living graph, and pushing it all upward into new levels of well-being, we shall generate the healthiest kind of expansive force within our economy. Here are the new lands to be developed, the fields of investment to absorb those "excess savings" that worried Lord Keynes and Dr. Hansen. To supply more goods to our present population is just as effective an economic stimulant as to supply some goods to more population—and is far more effective in raising the national levels of happiness and welfare.

7

A potential production capacity of 160 billion dollars' worth of goods and services to start with may seem to be just some more astronomical figures among the many that the war has hurled at our numbed comprehension, but they begin to mean something when we reflect that we scraped along on 88.6 billion dollars' worth in that famous Jukes-and-Kalikak boom year of economic history, 1929, and never even came within sight of that amount again until 1940.

To keep the wheels turning at such fruitful speed will need the help of everyone willing and able to work under the less urgent compulsions of peace—about 60 millions in the first postwar years, or 20 millions more than were employed in 1939. Under conditions of full employment in a free industrial society, wages

have never been known to decline, and in fact we are now seeing
them rise even faster than productivity—a process which can be
gravely dangerous unless productivity quickly overtakes wages as it
easily may. If the dollar does not lose too much more of its value
through this and other inflationary influences, there will be immense benefits from a national income raised to some 135 or 140
billion dollars—as contrasted with 70.8 billions in 1939 and 83.3
billions in 1929.*

Production and consumption of the great quantities of goods
represented by such an income will not mean that we shall all roll
in luxury—far from it. Even 160 billions of production will not
begin to fill all our wants, or even provide what we have come to
think of as minimum requirements for everybody. Much will
remain to be done: the appetite for good living grows by being fed,
and there is room for the indefinite generation of incentive to expand. But such an increase in production-consumption, as it
begins to overtake immediate needs, will bring about a general
rise in the American standard of living beyond anything we have
attained before and equal to what a whole generation might be
expected to win for itself at normal rates of progress and with
the best of luck.

So exhilarating a lift in general welfare will stimulate us like
the opening of a new continent or the sudden winning of liberty,
both of which in a sense it will be. It will reflect itself in health,
education, and the arts, and out of this reservoir should come a
richer crop of leadership and creative genius. The "century of the
common man" may reveal itself as a century of decidedly uncommon men.

Even as to our own shrewdness and courage there are grounds
for cautious optimism. There are the clarification of ideas and
ideals to be seen all around us, and our unusual awareness of the
crisis we face. Certainly as a people we can see just as plainly as
Dr. Hansen "the perfectly prodigious capacity of the American
economy to produce," and we aren't overlooking all these conditions favorable to the continued exercise of that capacity throughout the years to come. And we are growing more and more fas-

* *Markets After the War.* See the footnote on the distinction between gross
output and national income, page 49.

cinated by the prospect this opens up to us, beyond the critical gateway.

It is clear that our immediate future is at least as full of un-hatched eggs as the half-century following that other decision, by Carroll Wright, that we had come to the end of our rope. No one can say what future Edisons and Marconis are going to pull out of hats, for our astonishment and gratification; but not counting unpredictables there are enough imminent developments already clearly indicated to lift us to hitherto unapproached levels of well-being. We are standing at the frontiers of limitless unexplored lands, in the realms of power, and the control of power; in electronics, chemistry, metallurgy, engineering—all those sciences that are giving us the ability to knead nature like dough in our hands; in the communication of thought, and the carriage of men and goods everywhere across the face of the earth; in the making of gracious homes and urban communities for the whole population; in bodily health, and the enlightenment and ample furnishing of our minds.

All these fabulous lands wait to be occupied and developed by the same breed of venturesome pioneers who have been opening up all kinds of frontiers throughout our history. They have richer fields to work in than ever in the past. It is a question only of releasing, stimulating, and uniting the energies, immense in combination, of all these virile and ingenious individuals. The results that will flow from a combined national effort are splendid enough to justify any exertion that may be necessary to overcome obstacles and dangers, while they make the obstacles and dangers themselves seem less formidable.

An appreciation of the values at stake may very well be a decisive factor in our preparation for the tests we face. Certainly, as we grow more acutely conscious of what can be ours for the having, the urge to act wisely and successfully should roll up into a compelling force. We shall have an incentive to subject our menacing problems to the most earnest scrutiny, and make any adjustments necessary to achieve social unity. With the will to solve these problems established, we may discover resources of wisdom, restraint, and good will equal to our opportunities.

It will pay at this critical hour to make a quick survey of the prospect that lies beyond that opening door.

PART TWO

PROSPECT

CHAPTER IV

POWER TO DO WHAT WE PLEASE

TODAY there are 18 symbolical horses at work in the service of each man, woman, and child in this country. The 18 symbolical horses of mechanics equal in strength about 24 actual horses. Twenty-four percherons make a formidable team, and it is just as well that the national horsepower isn't parceled out to us in these equal portions. The 18 horsepower quota is chiefly interesting as a standard of comparison: ten years ago, in 1936, we had only half as many, and if we go back forty years further, to 1896, we find that all the power-producing sources of the country added up to only 17 million horsepower, or about ¼ horsepower per person. This figure for 1896, recorded ten years after Carroll Wright concluded that our economic expansion had reached its limits, stands in contrast to our present total capacity of 2.5 billion horsepower. In fifty years we have multiplied our power resources 147 times * and the rate of increase has accelerated swiftly toward the end of the period.

Statistics like these are anything but dry: they are in fact enormously dramatic, and fairly clamorous with significance. They tell the story of an almost fantastic extension of our ability to control our environment and augment our well-being. In practical ability to do work and disseminate its benefits, the 2.5 billion mechanically produced horsepower now at our command constitutes by

* This estimate of current capacity was privately supplied by the late George A. Orrok, distinguished engineer, who contributed the paper on "Progress in the Generation of Energy by Heat Engines" to an important symposium on "Economic Aspects of Power Generation," reprinted from *Transactions of the American Society of Civil Engineers*, Vol. 104 (1939), p. 142. The statistics for 1936 and 1896 are quoted in Mr. Orrok's paper.

far the greatest accumulation of energy sources any people has
ever possessed.

But it couldn't have been either created or utilized if we had
not at the same time acquired an elaborate development of extra-
sensory perceptions. This has given our controls over the application of power a truly superhuman exactitude and sensitivity. It
is on these two factors—power, and precision in its application—
that our present systems of industrial production, transportation,
and communication are based. Without them we could not hope
to supply the quantities of goods and services urgently needed by
the people of this country. With them and the good sense to use
them effectively, we can make a beginning at the gigantic task of
providing a gracious and productive life for the masses of men.

No matter what else we might be failing to do, we have been
getting ourselves ready for this job with scarcely an interruption.
Except for a possible year or two at the very bottom point of the
depression, our power output has steadily enlarged and our controls have improved regardless of the general state of production
activity. In spite of all frustrating influences we have gone on
swiftly and confidently laying up a great reserve of strength
against the day when it should be needed. Its value was demonstrated by the things accomplished when the war put it up to us
to stretch our muscles to the limit. This power is now at our
service for the constructive work of peace, and even in its present
forms it has the capacity to multiply itself many times more as it
is needed. But like a river flowing seawards, it has carried us to
the brink of the ocean of atomic energy: here we shall have resources of power utterly without limit, to make the greatest efforts
of the past seem like mere feeble gestures of an infant.

2

At this critical time of transition, there are reassuring implications in the fact that the increase registered in the past half-century has not only been quantitative, it has been qualitative, it has
been in a very real sense a process of democratization as well. We
have been putting an increasing proportion of newly acquired

power into the hands of individuals and at their personal service. The control of great power—even potentially destructive power— is no longer a strange sensation to millions of Americans.

When Robert Henry Thurston estimated the power-producing machinery in the United States of 1896, he divided it into three classifications—locomotives, marine engines, and stationary engines. In this last class there were only 4 million horsepower, the total supply of power for all production machinery.* As for individuals, they got a real horse or two or they relied on their own unaided muscles. But when Dean A. A. Potter made his report to the National Resources Committee as of June, 1936, he needed seven additional classifications to cover the total national capacity of 1.25 billion horsepower. The earlier categories were still there, much expanded: adding them all together, the original power sources of 1896 had been multiplied by eleven in forty years, to register the respectable sum of 187 million horsepower. But several times that amount are still to be accounted for in Dean Potter's estimate.

The largest increment was in categories which had not existed forty years before, and most of it was under the control of individuals who were using it for their own purposes. Seventy-three million horsepower had been accumulated in the mechanization of farms, and by its aid millions of farmers had had their drudgery lightened and their productivity increased. But most of the new

* The detailed tabulations of horse-power are as follows:

1896		1936	
Locomotives ..	11,000,000	Electric central stations	44,670,000
Marine	2,000,000	Industrial power plants	20,133,000
Stationary	4,000,000	Electric railway plants	2,500,000
		Isolated non-industrial plants .	1,500,000
Total	17,000,000	Mines and quarries	2,750,000
		Agricultural prime movers	72,763,000
		Automotive	965,000,000
		Airplanes	3,500,000
		Locomotives	88,000,000
		Marine	30,000,000
		Total	1,230,816,000

From "Economic Aspects of Power Generation," previously cited.

power sources were mounted under the hoods of automobiles, both trucks and passenger cars, which accounted for the staggering sum of 965 million horsepower—57 times the total power-producing capacity of the country in 1896, and all of it responding to the steering-wheel and foot-pedal control of individual drivers. By this acquisition of power, millions of private citizens have had not only their sense of personal responsibility but their freedom of movement and orbit of life enlarged beyond their grandparents' imagining.

If we agree that the objective of all civil progress is the maturing of the individual and his liberation from irrational limitations, so that he can more freely choose and plan and direct his own life, then this great acquisition of power under personal control must be recognized as one of the most important things that has ever happened to the human race. It is so new that it need not even be justified as yet by any conspicuous betterment of life, although I think it would be easy to prove it has had that effect. Certainly it is only a beginning, but it indicates the kind of process by which we may in time really become the lords of creation we have liked to imagine ourselves.

But farm machinery and automobiles are not the only instruments of this process of democratization, as it effects a betterment of human living. Much of the output of electric central stations, 45 million horsepower in 1936, is delivered into our homes to serve us individually in ways undreamed of before Mr. Edison went into business in Pearl Street—and for a long time afterwards. It has become the most tractable, versatile, unobtrusive and efficient of house servants—and hence, in this country, the most generally utilized of all new technological developments. As late as 1907, only one family in thirty-eight was served with electricity, and that rare family used an average of 300 kilowatt-hours each year, for which it paid 10.33 cents per kilowatt-hour. In 1942 four out of five homes were supplied, using an average of more than 1000 kilowatt-hours per year and paying 3.68 cents per kilowatt-hour.* It is safe to say that in the same interval all

* C. W. Kellogg, President, Edison Electric Institute, "Electric Light and Power Industry in 1942."

other factors that make up the cost of living had risen by percentages big enough to double the total.

This unique record is the result of achieving what all modern industry aims at—more production at less cost. In the first station founded for the production and sale of electric current, Mr. Edison considered ten pounds of coal a satisfactory amount of fuel to produce one kilowatt-hour of electricity: today our service stations have cut their requirements to an average of only 1.75 pounds of coal per kilowatt-hour, and there are late installations that use less than a pound per kilowatt-hour. Similar improvements have been made in the distribution of current, in the devices for its use, and in the more continuous utilization of power-producing equipment. As a result, in New York City, for instance, one cent's worth of current will run your radio for 1 hour and 7 minutes, light a 50-watt lamp for 2 hours and 13 minutes, heat an electric iron for 12 minutes, run a vacuum cleaner for 48 minutes. Considering its practical usefulness, electric power is probably the cheapest commodity we buy today; and it is also the most familiar application of the more abstruse phases of scientific research.

Our power plants were producing three times as much electric current as any other country's in the world in 1937, the last year for which League of Nations reports are available. Since then our central stations alone, under the pressure of war, have increased their output by 100 billion kilowatt-hours per year, so that it amounts now to an annual rate of 250 billion kilowatt-hours, or twice their total output in 1929.* This increase in central station output partly accounts for the doubling of total power-producing capacity between 1936 and today, but there are also great increases all down the line with the exception of automobiles, temporarily restricted by the war. The greatest percentage of increase has been in airplanes, which appeared in Dean Potter's list with a modest 3.5 million horsepower. It is safe to say that the planes in the air today, military as well as civil, add up to hundreds of times the 1936 figure. When we remember that these present machines are forerunners of an enormous expansion of commer-

* "Power," September, 1943, p. 66.

cial and private flying, we realize that we can look forward to a permanent total of aerial horsepower in the hundreds of millions. Again, its direct control will be in the hands of hundreds of thousands of skilled and necessarily responsible individuals.

3

Power of any kind is inherently dangerous, and its expansion raises problems of control which must be solved in accordance with the organizational principles of the society in which it occurs, or those principles will be jeopardized. This is as true of mechanical power as of political power, and authoritarian leaders, taught by Lenin, move swiftly to secure control of the sources of mechanical power as a guarantee of their political rule. The immense expansion of mechanical power production in this country had to be democratically controlled in the interest of a free society, and on the whole we have solved the problem admirably, in a way to make the United States by far the most amply and cheaply served in the world. Unfortunately, in recent years the question of power control has been made a partisan football, and men of statist tendencies have shrewdly moved into this field as the likeliest site for the foundations of a statist structure. They have already succeeded in confusing American thought on the subject to the point where there is a certain not negligible danger that they may be successful.

Nine-tenths of the central station power of this country is supplied by a system of regional power companies, citizen-owned, operating under the surveillance of public commissions which for the most part have been admirably non-partisan and have done a competent job of guarding the people's interests. Power companies undoubtedly have been guilty of their share of skulduggery, as has most big business, and, for that matter, most human beings—certainly the recent activities of the politicians in the power field have provided no shining example of candor, rectitude, or disinterest. Also the agencies of supervision, like any administrative commissions, are subject to faults and deterioration and must be constantly prodded and improved. But the American system of regulated regional power companies, admittedly imperfect like all human devices, has made electric power available to serve much more of the population at less cost than in any other country of the world. It has in fact made our per capita consumption of power more than three times as great as in any other nation.

In addition to the production by citizen-owned companies, about a tenth of the present central station output of current is derived from hydro-electric power plants owned and operated by the government. Much of this is the result of recent government expansion, and a widespread impression has been created, more or less deliberately, that these plants set a pattern for the future of power development. This illusion should be dispelled.

It is obvious that the few great natural sources of water power should be exploited in conformity with standards established by society, acting through government, in protection of its own broad interests. Also their development often is a logical corollary of other unquestioned public functions, which cannot successfully be performed for profit by citizen enterprise, such as flood control, irrigation, and the improvement of navigation. But whether the distribution of power from these sources should become a calculated effort on the part of government to eliminate citizen ownership from the power field through *force majeure* opens up a wholly different and quite fundamental argument.

In this one sector of water power development, Mr. Roosevelt's political and sociological interests were stronger than his adherence to the "mature economy" doctrine, and he went in for expansion of productive capacity. The methods whereby this was accomplished, and the administration of the projects in some cases, make a most disturbing story.* But this great and valuable expansion of our capacity to produce has served us well in ways that could not have been foreseen when it was projected. Much later, when our huge war program was launched, it called for vastly increased production of aluminum, magnesium, chrome, other alloys, synthetic rubber and many chemicals, and all these operations require great blocks of electric power. Where were

* See the uncontested facts presented in the minority section of the Report of the Joint Committee Investigating the Tennessee Valley Authority, April 3, 1939, Senate Document No. 56. Even the whitewash used in the majority section is completely transparent.

great blocks of power, not already allocated, so readily available as at nearly completed Bonneville, Grand Coulee, Tennessee Valley? These reserves proved immensely valuable in the emergency.

This experience goes to prove that it pays to back increased productive capacity, whatever your motives may be and even if there appears to be no immediate necessity for it. The showpiece of these activities, the Tennessee Valley, also is convincing demonstration of another truth: if you take two billion dollars from all the taxpayers of the nation, and spend it on the improvement of a limited area, spend it shrewdly and on the whole intelligently but without any necessity to pay refunds, dividends, interest, or normal taxes, you can do that area a great deal of material good. You can in fact do it two billion dollars' worth of good. But nothing in this whole experience proves that it is in the ultimate interest of a free people for the distribution and allocation of electric power to become a function of the State, with all the control of citizen activities and status which this entails.

Hydro-electric plants, however administered, are not the answer to our future power problems. They will help, by whatever amount of their output is utilized. But the usefulness of hydro-electric plants is strictly limited, in spite of the quantities of nonsense which have been uttered about them in recent years.

In a piece of literature distributed to the nation's school children by the federal government during 1943, there is an account of TVA which contains this remarkable statement: "The use of water power for work is a way of 'getting something for nothing.'" If we could harness the energy generated by "Poor Richard" Franklin spinning in his grave at this educational gem, we might really get something for nothing. But as applied to hydro-electric power sources, a more utterly false statement could scarcely be devised.

For example: the actual cost of TVA has been shrouded in mystery by a system of bookkeeping which would have landed a corporation executive in jail,* but the most convincing answer to the puzzle has been given by Edward L. Moreland, Dean of Engineering, Massachusetts Institute of Technology. He made a

---

* See Report of the Joint Committee Investigating the Tennessee Valley Authority, pp. 264-269.

careful study and came up with the conclusion, amply supported, that the original 11-dam system of TVA will represent an investment *for power generation alone* of $500 per kilowatt of constant capacity.* Other reliable authorities place the figure much higher. The average cost of steam generating plants, on the other hand, falls somewhere between $100 and $130 per kilowatt.† Since the flow of water in the Tennessee River during five months of the year may be inadequate to operate the power plant, TVA includes an auxiliary steam plant and requires reservoirs which permanently cover almost as much acreage as was ever temporarily flooded by the Tennessee before this anomalous type of "flood control" was introduced. Thus the production economies of TVA are questionable and certainly intermittent.

But the principal item in the cost of electrical energy is not its generation but its delivery to the user. Power is most economical when generated nearest the point where it is to be applied, and its cost rises rapidly with the distance over which it is transmitted and soon becomes prohibitive. For distances of 140 miles or more, under most conditions, it is cheaper to ship coal by freight than electric energy by wire.‡ Unfortunately nature and mankind have not gotten together, as a rule, on the location of water power and population—there is only one Niagara in a thickly settled area. The Passamaquoddy project was reluctantly abandoned when it was shown that the cost of transmitting its power to Boston—300 miles away and the nearest area where important use of it could be made—would be 3 mills, whereas the cost of producing power by steam at Boston was only 3.5 mills.

Centers of production and population may grow up in the vicinity of great power sources, the best of which have already been developed or projected. But this depends on many other factors, such as the nature of the terrain, the availability of raw materials and the geographic relationship to major markets. The Tennessee Valley is in the way of becoming an industrial area (although its industrial growth has not been as rapid as in some other unassisted areas of the South) and this may also happen in

* Ernest R. Abrams, *Power in Transition*, Scribner, 1940, p. 227.
† "Economic Aspects of Power Generation," p. 987.
‡ "Economic Aspects of Power Generation," p. 990.

the Columbia River country. Boulder Dam (it was planned and largely built by Mr. Hoover, whose name was removed from it, with execrable taste, in 1933) was justified from the first by the immediate use made of its power and water. Some improvements in the economy of power transmission are foreseeable: the transformation of alternating current to direct current for transmission, and its transformation to alternating current again at the point of use, promise to reduce leakage en route.

But the over-all value of hydro-electric power systems will be as island supplements to the great national power grid. They will not supply any major part of future power needs, vast beyond calculation as these will be. Our line of advance is clearly indicated in another direction. The basic fault of these natural power sources is that they require our submission to conditions as they exist in the world of nature, whereas our progress is aimed at complete emancipation from these conditions.

The same unwelcome bondage to nature will restrict the use of other natural sources of energy—wind, tides, and the sun's rays.

The wind has been made to work for centuries, of course, and is useful for small and intermittent services. But there are few places in the world where winds are strong and constant, and these are not usually also centers of population; and even with steady gales, the sheer bulk of plant required to collect from them the huge quantities of energy required by modern usages makes the process impractical. All the many square rods of canvas on a ship of the line could not drive it half as fast as one diesel plant turning a small propeller: the principle of depending on air currents will scarcely be revived on sea or land.

Much the same is true of tidal power: we cannot tie ourselves to isolated natural phenomena. If the tides rose in Boston Harbor as they do in the Bay of Fundy, a Passamaquoddy project at Boston would have been justified; but in that case no city of Boston would ever have been built on Boston Harbor. The more energetic manifestations of nature do not make comfortable neighbors.

As to the sun's rays, there is less localization and a much greater volume. The power pouring onto the earth from the sun fills all the reservoirs we draw our little cupfuls from—coal, oil, wood, wind, water. The sun's rays deliver on an area the size of Man-

hattan Island enough power to meet the needs of all the world—
if it could be put to work. So far only very crude palaeolithic
attempts have been made to harness it directly, by arranging reflecting mirrors to concentrate enough heat to cook an experimental meal or boil a few pints of water.

It is conceivable that ways can be found, at no distant date,
to collect the sun's energy in the stratosphere and relay it to earth
by wire or by beam. But it is much more probable that we shall
by-pass any such direct use of solar energy altogether, since we
stand on the verge of mastering the process whereby the sun itself produces its prodigious quantities of energy. We should soon
be setting up little suns of our own, disciplined and magnificently
potent.

4

In the immediate future, until the many problems involved in
the control of atomic energy are solved, we shall proceed along
the same line we have followed since James Watt's day, which
is to make more and more efficient use of the latent energy stored
up on earth by the sun in the conveniently portable forms of coal
and oil. The trouble is that until now our methods have been
deplorably *in*efficient, and may of necessity remain so. New-
comen's crude steam engine of 1770 (which can be seen in Mr.
Ford's museum at Dearborn) had a thermal efficiency of .82 per
cent, Watt's reciprocating improvement raised this to 5.6 per cent,
and recent turbines, using mercury vapor in combination with
steam, reach a thermal efficiency of 36 per cent or even a little
higher. This is a big advance, and creditable, but still a long, long
way from the ideal.

The last few decades have seen the swift rise of internal combustion engines. It is only fifty-three years since Henry Ford went
to the Chicago World's Fair to see a gas engine he'd heard about
on a piece of French fire-fighting apparatus. He came home and
by Christmas Eve, 1893, he was able to prove that a one-cylinder
gas engine made from a piece of pipe and clamped to his kitchen
sink would actually run. The history of internal combustion engines is as young as that, and their real development did not

gather speed until after the turn of the century, with the rise of the automotive industry.

Diesels were the first highly successful internal combustion engines, and up to a very few years ago they gave a greater return of power for fuel consumed than any other heat engine. But oil-burning diesels cannot be built as lightly and compactly, in relation to their power output, as gasoline engines, and in most automobiles and all airplanes lightness and compactness are more important than economy. Airplane engines today weigh only a pound or less per horsepower, and while prewar automobile engines averaged six pounds per horsepower, their makers have been going to school to the airplane industry and will cut this ratio by at least two-thirds when they can apply to their own products the lessons they have learned.

But in all these devices there are too many stages between the latent energy in the fuel and that same energy doing productive work, and at each stage some of that energy is lost as unused heat. The elimination of all loss of energy between fuel and work is a manifest impossibility, but it is conceivable that in time the waste may approach the irreducible frictional losses caused by moving parts. We may be a long way from realizing this dream, but it is not safe to say that it will not come to pass; and it is certainly toward this objective that our developments of the early postwar years will be directed.

A large chunk of waste in the early stages of the fuel-to-work sequence can be eliminated in the perfected gas turbine engine— perhaps the most important development in fuel engines since Watt's invention of the reciprocating piston, and undoubtedly significant as a pattern of postwar power sources. Briefly, it is an adaptation of the turbine principle to internal combustion engines. In it, gas from crude oil combined with preheated, compressed air is burned in what amounts to a continuous explosion, exerting its mighty force directly against the fins of a turbine cylinder. The shaft of this turbine at one end turns the air compressor, at the other it is harnessed to useful work. Thus in effect the engine has only one moving part, instead of the thousands in airplane and hundreds in automotive engines; it needs no cooling system and no ignition system; it weighs half as much, costs half as much, burns fuel half as expensive as conventional gasoline engines, and it does not vibrate; it approaches the beautiful simplicity which is the goal of all complex technological evolution, and it realizes the economic ideal of more production at less cost. Gas turbine plants for railway trains will fill only one car instead of the four occupied by the biggest diesel plants, ships will have space for many additional tons of cargo, gas turbine automobile engines should be not much bigger than a lunch box.

The gas turbine is a child of the war's intensive effort, advanced through progress in aerodynamics which enabled men to build turbines and superchargers so efficient that all the energy of the turbine is not used up in turning the air compressor; and through progress in metallurgy which has produced alloys capable of resisting temperatures of 1,200° to 1,700°. Its thermal efficiency does not yet equal that of the best diesel engines, but this will be changed as materials able to resist temperatures of 2,000° to 3,000° are developed for use in its turbine blades. Many stationary gas turbines are successfully in use, most of them of large size and great power. Adaptation of the principle to automotive sizes has not been completed, but its combination with jet propulsion in airplane power plants has had momentous results and may make obsolete all other types of airplane engines.* We enter the postwar period with the gas turbine a proven success, ready to effect its enormous economies in national power production.

5

Engine efficiency is only half of the problem of generating power by combustion, the other half being fuel efficiency. While engineers have been working on the improvement of engines, chemists have been busily engaged in devising better fuels to burn in them, and have even more to show for their efforts. There has been productive research into the better combustion of coal, but the major work has been done on coal and oil derivatives, with immense potentialities for the future.

During the war we have been using our great oil reserves at an

* See Chapter IX.

alarming rate. The output was estimated in September, 1943,* at 4 million barrels a day, and there have been pessimistic warnings that another fourteen to twenty years would see the wells running dry. The discovery of new reserves was 2,392 million barrels in 1936, but only 507 million barrels in 1942—little more than a third of the amount we used per year during the war.

But Cassandra voices have been raised in this same strain before, to be discomfited by the opening up of new reservoirs. Not all the authorities are equally lugubrious, Dr. Frolich † maintaining that the geologists already know where to sink their wells to tap great untouched deposits, and that these, with better utilization of the sources we already have, will bring the available supply to 100 billion barrels, or enough for almost seventy years at the present rate of consumption.

Whenever it is worth while to do so, we can begin to extract oil from shale and sand, where hundreds of billions of barrels more are safely stored up for use. There is more oil to be got out of the world's supply of oil shale than there ever was in the petroleum deposits of the world, even before they were tapped. The process of boiling down shale into oil is now more expensive than tapping an underground lake of oil, but may not remain so once its improvement becomes urgent. The construction of large pilot plants has already been planned.

And the conversion of coal into oil by hydrogenation, a wellknown and proven process, is able to provide practically unlimited supplies for the future. Mr. Ickes, who has had plenty of opportunity to find out and who never chooses to paint a rosy picture if there is any reason to select another tint, says that the coal reserves in this country amount to 3,200 billion tons,‡ which is enough to produce synthetic fuel oils at the rate of 1.5 billion barrels a year, plus a billion tons of coal a year for burning, for 1,000 years. (We have used not more than 700 million tons a year, even in 1943.) If by that time we haven't learned to do without such crude energy sources as coal and oil, something will have blocked our scientific progress, our civilization will have gone

* *Business Week*, September 11, 1943.
† New York *Times*, September 20, 1943.
‡ New York *Herald Tribune*, August 6, 1943.

to pot, and we probably will have reverted to rubbing two sticks together in the woods.

As another stand-by, there is the possibility of synthesizing both coal and fuel oil directly from vegetable matter—dry leaves, corn-stalks, weeds. It has been done on a laboratory scale. Concentrated heat and pressure applied under human control has been able to do in a brief interval what heat and pressure in the earth's crust have accomplished during millions of years. All in all, I don't think we need discount the future on the grounds of an imminent oil shortage.

Of much more immediate interest are the advances made during the war years in oil derivatives designed to obtain the maximum power output from the quantity of fuel used. By refining processes petroleum is converted into gasoline, kerosene, distillate fuel oil, and residual fuel oil, and until recently the refiner was forced to produce some of each as by-products whether or not he wanted them. But the chemists have given him almost full control of the process so that he can adjust the production of each to yield the most economical returns. For many years the trend has been toward a larger proportion of the highest powered derivative, gasoline, and today a refiner by adding hydrogen can turn all his crude oil into gasoline if he so desires. He can also concentrate in the gasoline much more power than ever before.

The Houdry "catalytic cracking" process dates only from 1938. In this process the large molecules of the base stock are split into smaller ones and rearranged to compose a chemical called high-octane gas, although it is not really gasoline at all but a distinctive superfuel. Before the war we produced small quantities of 100-octane gas (normal automobile gasoline rates 70 to 80 octane), but in 1941 the production of this essential aviation fuel was stepped up and since then we have been turning out hundreds of thousands of barrels every day. We have been producing at least 95 per cent of the world's aviation gasoline, far outstripping the Axis at its maximum in both quantity and quality. And in performance: high-octane gas gave our planes quicker take-off, greater speed and higher rate of climb than the enemy ever was able to achieve.

The 100-octane rating quickly became old-fashioned: the military standard rose to 130 octane, with the chemists shooting for 140. Meanwhile they made available a new superfuel called triptane, so much more powerful than the highest octane gas that no engine has yet been built to use it. Before the war triptane was a laboratory curiosity, costing $3,600 a gallon to produce. But we needed more than the enemy's power and speed in the air, and triptane could give us this edge. So keen minds went to work to devise methods of producing it in quantity, with the result that by 1944 it was being delivered to the Air Force as rapidly as needed at a cost of less than a dollar a gallon with the price steadily going down. A very little of it added to high-octane gas enables our propeller-driven planes to get off the ground quicker, fly faster and farther, and maneuver more easily than with any other fuel.

In good time engines can and will be built especially for the use of triptane with results in speed and flying range which will put our propeller-driven planes in a class by themselves. After the war this will mean longer flights, greater carrying capacity and a substantial reduction in time schedules. And there is no evidence that still mightier fuels will not surpass triptane as the chemists continue to tinker with molecules and atoms.

6

If the Manhattan Project had been a complete fiasco, and its great assembly of brains had come to the conclusion that the release of atomic energy was an insoluble mystery, we should still see before us an immense expansion in power production and revolutionary improvements in engines and fuels. We should have gone on generating even vaster quantities of electric power and distributing it more widely and more cheaply, with better controls and more efficient methods of utilization. And we should have gone on concentrating more fabulous power production in ever smaller compass and lighter weight to propel ourselves and our goods wherever we want to go. In fact, we shall still follow this course in the years ahead, with a troubled mind and an eye cast frequently over one shoulder at the atomic laboratories; for the release of atomic energy will not, for a while at least, deflect us from the course we have been following for many years with increasing momentum.

The past six decades, since Carroll Wright argued so convincingly that we had leveled off into a permanent *status quo*, have seen us multiply our power resources in actual use by 15,000 per cent. This lapse of time has been enough for the development of commercial electric power production, with all the mechanism for distributing it and using it where it is needed; and for the development of the internal combustion engine, with its special fuels and a system for purveying these fuels so ubiquitously that in any fairly thickly settled portion of the country one is never more than a few miles from a source of supply.

But neither of these lines of development has yet been followed to its conclusion, or anywhere within sight of a dead end. The internal combustion engine has been advanced to a high degree of efficiency, but this has been done by allowing it to acquire an extravagant complexity. Now the gas turbine and jet propulsion motor would seem to have turned a corner and restored the possibility of a fundamental simplicity which can only result in more power at less cost, obtained with greater ease. If this is true we are at the beginning of a new cycle of development in internal combustion engines more productive than the one just ending.

Again, the study of oil derivatives has presented us with fuels much more potent than anything we have had before, and there has been no opportunity to take advantage of them in normal peacetime activities. This too is a line of development not ending but just beginning, with an unpredictable influence on the productivity of the future.

Even if nothing more radically new than these advances in engines and fuels had invaded the power scene, we should still have the means to project ourselves several turns up the ascending and swiftly expanding spiral of racial well-being. And we are not to be diverted in a moment from a line of advance in which so many forces converge.

But the egg of atomic energy has been laid on our doorstep and it intrudes itself into every calculation of the future. It was conceived as a military weapon and it introduces a hazard of the first magnitude into the fortunes of the race. But assuming that we are successful in dealing with atomic energy as a threat of destruction, we still have the problem of dealing with it as a servant of man. In this capacity it will require the most drastic adjustments we have ever made, and introduce us to potentialities we cannot yet conceive except as huge forms looming through a fog of complete inexperience. The accommodations we shall have to make will be so radical that they cannot be made swiftly; fortunately (granted peace) the age of power as we have learned to know it still has years to run its normal course, familiarizing us with greater and greater might at our command, before we pass over into the strange scenes of a world where men have literally God-like power in their hands.

CHAPTER V

AND NOW WE UNLOCK THE ATOM

WHEN the writing of a book, even as simple a book as this, must be done in odd moments of spare time salvaged from a busy professional life, it is a long-drawn process. Much of it had been written long before the world was abruptly inducted into a new age on August 5, 1945, and included in that pre-atomic script was a discussion of the possibility that our power resources might soon be augmented by the release of atomic energy. What I said then is still sound, as far as it goes, and has a certain interest as indicating sketchily the atomic facts which had become available to unscientific laymen like myself before a curtain of silence was dropped over this subject by the scientists in 1940. It also has some significance as indicating how popular attention had been concentrated, up to that time, on the constructive possibilities of atomic energy rather than on its dreadful military potentials. I wrote then as follows:

"Physicists as well as chemists are manipulating atoms, and are playing for much higher stakes. If they should succeed in devising a practical method of releasing and applying the energy stored in the atom itself, they would make mere combustion fuels such as coal, gas or triptane as obsolete as stone axes. A ton of coal when burned may release 13,500 'British thermal units.' But stored in each *pound* of that same coal is *atomic* energy equal to about 40,000 billion B.T.U.S. If all that atomic energy in one pound of coal could be released—which God forbid, unless it could be done slowly over a long period of time so as not to blow up the world— it would equal the burning of almost three billion tons of coal. Every pound of any kind of matter contains approximately the same prodigious quantity of atomic energy. To get even a little of this energy out, and make it work, has been the ultimate ambition of physical science for many years. It has been an objective so seemingly remote, so doubtful of attainment, so completely revolutionary in its implications, that physicists have been cautious even in discussing it. If it can be done, we shall have our miniature suns, making cheap power in unlimited quantities universally available.

"And it has been proven by actual laboratory tests that it *can* be done.* The energy so far obtained from a tiny particle of uranium 235 has been far from the total in that particle, and too minute to be of value in itself; but if a whole pound of uranium 235 could be subjected to the same treatment with the same proportionate result, we should obtain from this partial disintegration a heat output equal to the burning of 1,370 tons of 13,500-B.T.U. coal. If an automobile that now gives fifteen miles to the gallon wears out in 50,000 miles, one pound of uranium 235 would drive eighty of them in succession from the factory to the scrap heap: instead of fifteen miles to the gallon, four million miles to the pound.

"When a thing has been done experimentally, the odds are that it will be done on a serviceable scale."

I then mentioned briefly the work of Rutherford and Bohr in revealing the structure of the atom, and of Lawrence in splitting the atom by means of his cyclotron. Then followed the typical description of atomic structure which since has become old, familiar stuff to all newspaper readers, and the usual account of how the emission of energy which is characteristic of certain radioactive elements can be induced in others by bombarding their atoms with atomic particles. And I went on:

"In most elements the amount of energy generated in this way is less or no more than that energy required to fire the projectile. It is an ironic fact that to shoot at targets so small that a billion of them could be piled on the point of a pin, Dr. Lawrence requires a machine weighing 4,900 tons, with elaborate safeguards for the operators.

* "Uranium 235—Power Fuel of the Future?" by Philip W. Swain, *Power*, July, 1940, p. 56.

"This would seem to be an impractical disproportion. But uranium 235 is different. A direct hit splits its atom in two, and each half flies off with terrific speed. When they collide with an obstacle—water stops them—their velocity is turned into heat equal to several billion times the energy of the projectile that split them. And if the first shot were fired into a mass of one to five pounds of uranium 235, it would set up a chain action, one atom exploding another, which would go on automatically until all the 37 billion B.T.U.s per pound were released. Endless streams of water could be turned instantly into steam by this heat. Also it is possible to control the speed of the chain action—a reassuring point—by proper disposition of the water throughout the mass of uranium. Uranium 235 would seem to be the ideal energy source, and is—the only hitch being that so far there is available in the world no more than a speck of uranium 235.

"It is not exactly rare, being present in all pitch-blende deposits. But it exists in combination with its isotopes, uranium 234 and uranium 238, which are no good for this purpose, and it is extremely difficult to isolate. No one has yet found a way to accumulate the first pound, not to mention the first five pounds. But a few years ago, the extraction of magnesium from brine was little more than a laboratory experiment, and now we are producing many thousands of tons. Since a ton of uranium 235 would be as useful as 2.7 million tons of coal, the chances are that we will find ways of scraping it together. Research has been carried on secretly but intensively during the war, and there are rumors that it has been momentously successful."

No rumors were ever better founded than those, but my remark does not indicate any inside information. I knew no more about the Manhattan Project than the most uninformed citizen of Patagonia, but one could not escape a feeling in the air, partly inspired by the dense silence on the subject, that something momentous was impending in the field of atomic research. This thought was exchanged by many people who had no inkling of what was going on at Oak Ridge and Hanford and Los Alamos. That it would eventuate as the most destructive weapon man has ever devised, instead of an engine of beneficent power, was a complete and bleak surprise.

Again we see how the impulse to survival in war exceeds in urgency any peaceful ambition to achieve a better plane of living. The basic facts which led to the obliteration of Hiroshima and Nagasaki in 1945 were all in the possession of nuclear physicists in 1940, and they might have remained in the realm of theoretical knowledge or laboratory experiment for many years if the necessities of war had not placed immense resources at the disposal of the scientists and incited them to a prodigious and concentrated effort. The menace they have let loose in the world is terrible enough, God knows, and finds us grievously dubious of the ability of human wisdom to cope with it. But if we think too exclusively of this danger we shall only augment it: one does not avoid calamity by letting it become an obsession. Atomic energy can become as mighty for beneficent works as it is for obliteration, and if we can fix at least a part of our attention on this phase of the truth and the possibilities it opens up to us, we may find it easier to avoid applying atomic energy to racial suicide.

2

The story of the Manhattan Project is distinctly epical, and Professor Smyth's matter-of-fact official account * of its organization and its accomplishments will become one of the great documents in the history of science. Many other accounts have been written, but Professor Smyth's will remain the original log of the first large-scale expedition into the uncharted but hypothesized realm of nuclear fission.

It was a mammoth expedition, this one that undertook to open the universe's smallest gates to the universe's mightiest forces. It was directed by the greatest international staff of scientific minds ever mobilized on one project, and this staff was required to solve out of hand problems that until its own generation had been considered outside the range of possibility; it required the working

* H. D. Smyth, A General Account of the Development of Methods of Using Atomic Energy for Military Purposes, War Department, Washington, 1945, Princeton University, 1945. One of the best popular symposiums on the subject is the "Nucleonics Issue" of the Monsanto Magazine, not dated.

out of intricate processes about which almost nothing was known except that they would be exceedingly dangerous in many subtle as well as violent ways; it called for the designing, building, and equipping of huge new and entirely unprecedented plants for carrying on these processes on an immense scale in absolute secrecy; the recruiting of a hundred thousand workers and their training in operations that had never been tried before; the building of three complete communities in isolated spots to house these workers and their families; the enlistment of all the technological resources of American industry and the laboratory facilities of American universities as needed to supply unique equipment and solve novel operational problems.

This vast undertaking grew with astounding speed, rather like the great mushroom of smoke and dust that rose over Hiroshima six years later. It started from conversations between nuclear physicists in Princeton, New York, and Washington in the spring of 1939, and the first Committee on Uranium was appointed by President Roosevelt, largely through the influence of Albert Einstein, in the autumn of that year. Research had opened up such dangerous possibilities by the spring of 1940 as to convince all nuclear physicists concerned that it would be highly desirable to restrict knowledge of further developments to those who were working under the aegis of the government. A voluntary censorship was established, but behind a curtain of silence the studies proceeded with gathering momentum.

By the end of 1941, enough certainty had been achieved to warrant the organization of an all-out effort to produce an atomic bomb before our enemies beat us to the draw. A special section of the Office of Scientific Research and Development was set up by Dr. Bush and Dr. Conant, and into it were drawn all the competent nuclear physicists of America, Britain, and Canada, with a number of critically important scientific refugees from Fascist Italy and Nazi Germany.

In the summer of 1942 the Army Corps of Engineers entered the picture to supply engineering and procurement services for the vastly expanding project, and organized a special section for the purpose known for security reasons as the Manhattan District. In May, 1943, the Manhattan District under General Groves took over full responsibility for management from OSRD, and the whole enterprise came to be known, irrelevantly, as the Manhattan Project.

3

At the time the momentous step was taken in December, 1941, the job to be done would have staggered all but those for whom the unknown has no terrors.

It had been established only two years before that the atom of uranium 235 can be split, with release of great amounts of energy, if its nucleus is hit by a fast-moving neutron; and that in the splitting extra neutrons are catapulted off, possibly to split other nuclei and thus start a chain reaction. It was also known theoretically that if a certain quantity of U-235 could be assembled, this chain reaction would have a field in which it could sustain itself. It was even known how this "critical mass" could be calculated, if enough experimental data could be accumulated as an accurate base for calculations. Supposing this critical mass should turn out to be a practical size for a bomb—say, one to 100 kilograms—a wholly new order of offensive weapon would be possible. If all the atoms in one kilogram (2.2 pounds) of U-235 could be split, the explosion would equal that of 20,000 tons of TNT; so that if only one per cent of the atoms in whatever the critical mass might prove to be were split, the result would be something quite literally out of this world.

But there are only 14 pounds of U-235 in a ton of uranium, and so little uranium of any kind had been refined by 1941 that its melting point was not even known, and no practicable method had been found to isolate the tiny portion of U-235 from its more abundant and chemically indistinguishable isotopes, U-238 and U-234.

A significant fact had been discovered: that when a *slow* neutron hits the nucleus of U-238, it is absorbed to form a new isotope, U-239, which is highly unstable and quickly loses an electron to become a wholly new element of atomic number 93. The new element was named neptunium. Reaction doesn't stop there, as neptunium is still unstable, quickly gives up another electron and becomes another new and relatively stable element of atomic number 94, christened plutonium (Pu). Now the atoms of plutonium split even more easily than the atoms of U-235, with equal energy output, and since it is a distinct element it can be isolated more easily than U-235. Therefore if a chain reaction could be set up among the nuclei of U-235 in a quantity of normal uranium, and their fast-flying neutrons slowed down by use of a "moderator" so that many of them could be absorbed in the nuclei of U-238 atoms to turn them into plutonium atoms, the total amount of explosive energy to be gotten out of a given quantity of uranium would be increased about one hundred-fold.

Heaven help the man who sets up a chain reaction among the atoms without being able to control it—an uninhibited chain reaction is what happened to Hiroshima and Nagasaki. It was known that a "moderator" would be an effective means of control. Water, as I said in my early recital, is such a moderator: it slows down flying neutrons just as it slows down bullets. But "heavy water" (deuterium oxide) will do the job still better, and so will beryllium or carbon. But in 1940 only a few quarts of heavy water and 700 pounds of beryllium were produced in this country, and great quantities were needed: clearly carbon in the abundant form of graphite offered the best bet. But to be effective, all these substances must be so pure that only a very few parts of impurities appear in a million parts, and graphite had never been produced in anything approaching this degree of purity and no one knew how to do it.

Suppose they were able to get the materials and produce and control a chain reaction, then where were they? Says Professor Smyth: "The technological gap between producing a controlled chain reaction and using it as a large-scale power source or an explosive is comparable to the gap between the discovery of fire and the manufacture of a steam locomotive." Yet the gap was bridged in five years.

4

In a race with the Germans, there was no time to take up all these problems in deliberate, orderly sequence, so the scientists split themselves up like their favorite atoms into separate nuclei of tremendous energy to tackle all the problems simultaneously. Each group had to assume that all the others would do their jobs successfully, and solve its own problems on that assumption. The results of some of these efforts would be eliminated in favor of others, but a high degree of waste also had to be cheerfully assumed.

At the start and through most of 1942, neither the ham nor the eggs were available for the desired ham-and-eggs. The few grams of good uranium which had been produced by Westinghouse at a cost of $1,000 a pound had to be built up into daily deliveries of hundreds of pounds of pure metal at low cost. By the combined efforts of many of the leading chemical plants of the country this was accomplished during 1943.

Heavy water and beryllium were eliminated for the time being as moderators, due to the hopelessness of any quantity production in a reasonable time, and efforts were centered on the purification of graphite. Again the chemical industries and scientists combined their efforts and the problem was solved by midyear of 1942. In November, 1942, Dr. Compton at the University of Chicago laid up the first "exponential" pile of six tons of uranium in a lattice arrangement of relatively pure graphite for the production of plutonium. And on December 2, 1942, the first self-maintaining nuclear chain reaction ever to be initiated by man was set in motion.

Plutonium was produced in this first pile, but at a rate that would need 70,000 years to make enough for a bomb. To make and separate a gram of plutonium a day would require between a half-million and a million-and-a-half kilowatts of electrical energy in a plant operated entirely by remote control because of the dangerous radioactivity of the materials, and stupendous quantities of heat generated in the process would have to be dissipated. To design such a plant was roughly comparable to designing the Grand Coulee hydro-electric plant on the basis of prior experience with a Leyden jar. The du Pont Company accomplished the feat by September, 1944, first by building a pilot plant at Clinton, Tennessee, and then building and operating a full-scale plant on the Columbia River in Washington. By its own stipulation, its profit on this gigantic undertaking was one dollar.

While the production of materials was being accomplished, work on the separation of isotopes of uranium—one of the most baffling of all the problems involved—proceeded simultaneously. A number of alternative methods were proposed, and large plants were built for trying out all the more promising. These activities, with all their related problems of health protection and thermal diffusion, eventually were concentrated in the Clinton plants at Oak Ridge, Tennessee, which became a sprawling city of many strange factories, dense mystery, and a hastily recruited population of 75,000 covering more than 70 square miles. At the same time, a third center grew up on the New Mexican desert at a spot called Los Alamos where work on the development of an actual atomic bomb to use the assumed explosive was carried forward under Dr. Oppenheimer.

Most of the leading industries of America were involved in some phase or other of the proliferating undertaking, designing, building, and operating plants, creating special machinery, instruments, controls, devising methods and processes. The research has been immense—it has been said at Oak Ridge that 5,000 new and improved procedures for industry are available on government release; great advances in radioactive treatment of diseases were made possible; the report of the important researches carried on by the Metallurgical Laboratory section alone will fill thirty volumes. The "secret of the atomic bomb" has been in reality the disclosure of ten thousand secrets.

I can imagine few more dramatic moments in history than the hour before the dawn of July 16, 1945, when some 150 scientists responsible for the guidance of this prodigious effort waited in a lonely stretch of desert at Almogordo for the first practical demonstration of the theories on which all their work had been based. I can imagine no more spectacular anticlimax if the Almogordo bomb had been a dud. It wasn't.

5

At Almogordo the development of atomic energy for military offense reached a dead end: Hiroshima and Nagasaki were mere confirmations. It is true that much more devastating atomic bombs have been concocted and worse yet can still be made. But Almogordo proved that the total destruction of all an enemy's surface installations is entirely possible within a matter of minutes or hours—and you cannot go beyond total destruction. The world must adjust itself to that ultimate concept of war.

War between nations armed with atomic bombs can only bring catastrophe to everybody involved. You may by a surprise attack destroy all an enemy's surface concentrations in an hour, but, as Dr. Compton has pointed out, the enemy from his hidden and untouchable bases can destroy all your surface concentrations in the next hour. There is no wall, no defense that can protect us from atomic bombs in the hands of an enemy minded to use them. To duplicate our achievement in the Manhattan Project will not be as easy as many people think, but there are nations which will be able to do so if it appears that they must. Unless we wish to be devastated as surely as we devastate, control of the military applications of atomic energy must be lodged effectively in an international trusteeship dedicated to peace, and must remain there.

I do not agree with Stuart Chase * that this means the end of independent sovereign States, patriotism, and free enterprise. Mankind does not make any such radical alteration in its institutions or its mental habits so abruptly. A true World State, obliterating the divisions between existing nations and extending the emotion of patriotism to include the globe, is inevitable in time if the civilization of the human race continues to progress. All our advance from its beginning has been marked by a continuous expansion of the community—from the family to the tribe or clan, to the demesne or the city, to the league of petty lordships and so by successive enlargements to the sovereign nation

* *Common Sense*, October, 1945, p. 28.

as we know it in modern times. War between contiguous units has been inevitable at all stages of this series, and the same cantankerous spirit is still active in mankind.

Today the nations of the world are interdependent, and recognition of this vital fact is growing. But a true World State will be achieved only as men agree on human rights and on methods of safeguarding such rights as it is agreed that men should have. With the world sharply divided in ideological conflict as to the relative status of the individual and the State, we need not expect either side suddenly to toss in the sponge in surrender to the opposing school of thought, as Mr. Chase's prediction assumes. Certainly those who believe that life without liberty would be worthless will not do so: no threat, not even the threat of total destruction, will induce men to yield to a World State rights which they have not been willing to surrender to their own native State.

We are approaching the psychological conditioning of the Thirteen Colonies in 1787 when they reluctantly agreed to sink their bitter rivalries and deep suspicions in a federal union. But we must bear in mind that the colonies were already agreed on just those fundamental principles which split the modern world wide open, and the nations must get together in their thinking as closely as the colonies did before we can hope to set up a world federation as stable as the federal Union of 1789. We must also remember that even that Union did not preclude at least one bitter internecine war before it was finally cemented.

It will take time for the world to reach agreement on the question of whether the State is to exist for the service of the citizen or whether the citizen exists to serve the State, but there is no reason why the argument cannot proceed in peace and be decided at last by factual demonstration rather than by dialectics or force. The United Nations Organization provides a parliament in which the issue can be exposed and areas of agreement gradually enlarged. But this slow process of working out a universally acceptable pattern of human relationships will be inhibited if each nation must keep a wary eye on the atomic bomb in its opposite number's back pocket. This is a hair-trigger weapon too dangerous to tolerate—it must be checked at the door.

It is a mistake to assume that the control of nucleonic explosives must be involved with all the other administrative details of a World State. We face an emergency which should be dealt with by itself alone, so that we can give our attention to other less clean-cut issues. It should inspire agreement at least within its own limited area—effective unity on this one point should be attainable at once. If so, it may prove to be a beginning to which other agreements will attach themselves.

It should be possible to set up a trusteeship to discharge this single responsibility, a board composed of delegates whose probity and ability are recognized by all the nations: practically every country can produce at least one such man. To this board all atomic bombs in existence can be entrusted, with the relatively simple means to use them if necessary. And to it can be handed over all plutonium produced in industrial applications of atomic energy, with authority to license and inspect all such applications and all plants and laboratories which might be adapted to the production of nucleonic explosives.

The production of nucleonic explosives is no hole and corner affair. It is a huge undertaking which cannot be carried on in cellars and attics, and if barriers to intercourse are reasonably relaxed in a peaceful world it can scarcely be carried on in secrecy. The natural deposits from which uranium is obtainable can be charted for the world and their exploitation supervised by the Atomic Trustees. With international co-operation a roster could be made of all competent nuclear physicists in the world: they are not many, they are known to each other, and new recruits cannot be trained overnight. It is possible that all these physicists should be required to meet at one spot for a week every six months: if they were locked up together in a Bretton Woods or a Dumbarton Oaks for continuous discussions it is safe to say that, being pure scientists, they would have few secrets from each other when they parted.

The control of nucleonic explosives is not an impractical task if the nations are willing to dedicate themselves to that one undertaking alone, uncomplicated by other commitments. It would be much easier, for instance, than control of the opium traffic. Whether or not it will be accomplished depends, like so many other phases of future progress, on the quality of realistic wisdom brought to bear on the problem at this time of critical decisions.

6

All tools and all power sources are potentially dangerous. If all the skulls that have been broken by hammers since a stone was first tied to the end of a stick could be collected in one heap, the pile would make any Rocky Mountain look like a mole hill. In the long history of man's use of fire, fire has caused more deaths and suffering than can ever be charged to atomic bombs even if they should wipe out all the civilized peoples now living. No one would suggest that the use of fire and hammers be abandoned for these reasons. It is not likely that the application of atomic energy to useful work will be prevented because atomic energy can be manipulated into the most dangerous explosive ever invented.

On the contrary, it is entirely possible that atomic bombs may never again be used in warfare, while atomic energy as a power source may become one of the great liberators and perhaps the most useful servant of the human race. The possibilities of good that lie along this line are immense and still unpredictable, and one of the best safeguards against atomic destruction will be to concentrate our thought and efforts on the realization of these possibilities, too little stressed in all the current discussions of atomic fission.

In nuclear physics we have reached about the same degree of advancement as Faraday had attained in electricity a century ago, but it will not take a hundred years for nuclear physics to cover as much ground as electricity has gained since then. We work fast these days, and the development of atomic energy for useful work may come with startling speed.

We have Dr. A. H. Compton's word for it that it would be quite possible today to build an atomic plant for the generation of electric power. Immense quantities of heat were produced in the reaction piles of the Manhattan Project, and wasted because power was not the objective. But a reaction pile could be built for that sole purpose, and a heat transfer medium passing through it—water, air or liquid metal—could be used to produce super-heated steam for driving a turbine.

Blocks of uranium enriched with U-235 or plutonium in a chain reaction can be maintained at any desired temperature no matter how fast the heat is removed, and as much heat can be drawn in this way from a pound of uranium as from more than a thousand tons of coal. This means that only a small-size heater unit will be needed for almost any purpose, and its fuel consumption will be negligible. Its temperatures can be controlled accurately and with ease by means now available, and it is perfectly safe from unplanned explosions. Such a plant would emit no smoke or fumes, require no stoking, and be as clean as an operating room.

What, then, is stopping us? Principally the fact that the plant emits something far more deadly and less palpable than smoke or fumes—the ionizing rays given off by the chain reaction pile and contaminating everything that comes in contact with it—metal, air, the heat transfer medium. The plant itself and everything that comes out of it are dangerous to human life. Injury can be prevented: not a single case of serious exposure occurred in the half dozen plants operated by the Manhattan Project. But protection as it is understood today places an impractical handicap on atomic power sources: it takes five feet of solid steel to confine the deadly rays, so that even a one-horsepower atomic plant would weigh at least fifty tons. Atomic motors for airplanes and automobiles are out for the present, and only very large installations in areas where other fuels are not available—the Arctic, for instance—are economically feasible at the moment.

How long this moment will last no one can be sure. A great deal remains to be done to make atomic plants small, portable, safe and capable of effecting their potential economies. The use of atomic energy as a direct source of power, eliminating the heat-to-steam phase of the cycle, which is the ultimate objective, may lie far over the horizon, but Professor Dunning of Columbia has said that we will have atomic power plants for ships and planes within five years. Dr. Millikan is skeptical. Even if the five-year forecast is optimistic, we can be confident that, if research is allowed to proceed unhampered, all obstacles will be overcome in due course and the ultimate fountains of all the energy in the universe will be systematically tapped to serve our needs.

The outcome does not depend on a continued Manhattan Project, or anything like it. The amazing success of this concentrated effort has led to the foolish conclusion that all research should be organized and directed in the same manner. Nothing would be more calamitous to the progress of science. This project had a single, clearly defined objective, a practical and not an abstract objective, difficult though it was. Pure scientific research does not follow any such charted line: it wanders as the imaginative vision of many inspired minds may lead it, feeding on the knowledge voluntarily pooled by these isolated but co-operative workers, but never certain of what may lie a few steps beyond in the darkness. All the basic facts of nuclear physics with which the Manhattan Project worked had been accumulated in advance by this kind of independent, exploratory effort, and in spite of its great achievement it made no basic contributions to knowledge as important as those with which it began. Directed research can be immensely valuable, but it will arrive at a series of dead ends unless it is fed by wholly free and unhampered studies. Industry recognizes this truth in its own research activities, and free academic and industrial research can be depended on to put atomic energy to work for us as fast as we can accommodate ourselves to its use.

What this will mean to the human race will reveal itself only as it is approached. It is easy to see now that it will mean a further great reduction in the amount of physical labor required of men, and a further great expansion of our power to control our environment—even, perhaps, to the extent of enabling us to "do something" about the weather. It will multiply the productive capacity of the world to the point where the needs of all the people in it can be abundantly supplied. It will in time give man absolute mastery of his destiny on earth.

Power such as this will make demands on human wisdom and restraint beyond any of the minor exactions of the past and present. How to measure up to them? Dr. Compton calls for wider and deeper education—encouragement of the individual to seek his maximum development, to prepare himself for "advancement and leadership"; a more active spirit of co-operation and a keener sense of its necessity; a more complete dedication to the general good—a realization that a man's first objective "is to contribute to the common welfare the maximum that his abilities make possible." This is a program of stimulation and release, with no vestige of repression or regimentation. And the wise doctor concludes that the aims of progress in these directions will be served only by the fullest realization of the national destiny: "The best assurance of national safety in the atomic age, both before and after the establishment of a world government, is to develop the nation's maximum human and industrial resources." What need be added to that summing up?

CHAPTER VI

WE TRAVEL THE FIRST INCH OF A MILE

DURING an earlier crisis in the history of the Republic, Eli Whitney, inventor and Connecticut gun manufacturer, received an order for 3,000 muskets. Faced with the necessity of delivering 3,000 guns as quickly and cheaply as possible, he had a brilliant idea: he would not make each gun as a bench job, beginning and finishing it apart from all the others, as was the universal custom; instead, he would break down a musket into its component parts, and then duplicate each of these parts 3,000 times; and he would make all the pieces of each kind so accurately, so much alike, that the whole lot could be assembled into 3,000 muskets with a minimum of filing and fitting, at great speed and low cost. He had formulated the basic theory of mass production.

But anything that could be done along this line in the mid-nineteenth century was a very crude example of the real thing: mass production had to wait for the twentieth century before it could hit its stride. It had to wait for supplies of power, and exact controls of the application of power, far beyond anything known to Eli Whitney or his successors for many years. The things that are done today in the ordinary, everyday processes of mass production could not have been imagined even fifty years ago—and they have more than a touch of the fantastic even now.

When we see 3,000-horsepower airplane motors grow as they follow one another down the assembly line, their thousands of parts arriving from fabricating sources near and far to be fed into the assembly at just the right points; and we see these parts fitted into place without the slightest alteration or adjustment but with uncanny exactness; and we realize that lives and fortunes can be confidently staked on the expectation that when finished each of these complexes of intricate and violent movements will go through its cycle without failure and without a shadow of variation in its split-second timing in all kinds of weather for hours on end—there is inspiration here for rather awesome respect. We realize that we are in the presence of an esoteric craftsmanship commanding kinds and degrees of precision that are new in the world. Airplane engines are dramatic examples, but they are not exceptional: all the typically modern things we do in the fields of manufacture, transportation, and communication are demonstrations of this very practical necromancy.

What we have acquired in modern times, never known in the world before, is an immense extension of our perceptions and our sensitivity. The innumerable machines we use are not only substitutes—and much stronger, tireless, precise substitutes—for our muscles, they are also projections of our five senses into realms that have been completely beyond our reach in the past. The processes of modern manufacture by which we are multiplying the wealth available to all people depend on a weird array of instruments that detect what no eye can see or finger feel; and so do all our modern means of carrying men and goods, communicating across space, combating disease and extending knowledge. We have devised any number of new controls of power and new enlargements of our faculties which must be placed in a category that is quite literally superhuman.

And now the prospects opening up before us make all our past performances look like the gropings of the blind. Over this whole field of extra-sensory achievements is spreading the light of the science of electronics, and we are beginning to have a feeling that we encountered our old tools in the dark and learned to use them by the sense of touch. For a time the light spread slowly, but of late it has grown with the abruptness of a tropical dawn. It is not surprising if we are still not well adjusted to the realization that we are all set to move farther and faster than most people have supposed would ever be possible.

2

Although a new science itself, electronics is the parent of a terrible baby—neucleonics—and the baby's deadly rattle, the atom bomb. Electronics deals with the minute units of energy in the outer orbits of the atom—the tiny charges of negative electricity that whirl around the nucleus like planets around the sun. Neucleonics penetrates deeper and deals with the energy locked in the tenacious nucleus itself. Electronics thus has the more tractable material to deal with, the ultimate unit of energy, the smallest and most abundant identity in the universe, inexhaustible and indestructible, so plentiful that the number of electrons which streams through the bright filament of a 100-watt lamp every second is represented by the figure 6 followed by 18 zeros.

But when electrons flow through metal conductors they are within the province of another subdivision of electronics, the practical science of electricity. Electronics proper is concerned with streams of "free" electrons flowing through air, gas or empty space. Get enough of them going one way and they become immensely powerful, but a stream so weak as to be far below the level of human perception can be made to do prodigious work. The direction, control, and amplification of streams of free electrons is the immediate utilitarian function of electronics, but it must not be forgotten that within its cognizance are all arc and spark discharges including lightning, ionization phenomena, atomic fission, the generation of energy in and by the sun. Since it has to do with the energy of which all matter is composed, and its release and manipulation, it is basic in physics and is drawing all sciences toward and into itself—large sectors of chemistry, metallurgy, biochemistry, astronomy, medicine already have been taken over. It may be that electronics in time will effect a synthesis of all science, and reveal the nature of life itself.

In the technological field it has already given us a fabulous and variegated set of tools, and is responsible for as disparate a flock of offspring as can be imagined: for the great power-conversion job at Bonneville, for the pint-sized radio by your bed and the neon sign on the drugstore at the corner, for sound-movies and television and radar and for the electronic microscope which magnifies 100,000 times and will do ten times better: for rapid bonding of plywood and welding of aluminum and variable speed control of machine tools; for your dentist's X-ray apparatus that reveals a cavity in your molar and for the million-volt machine that detects a flaw buried eight inches deep in solid steel; for the light-meter you use in timing your snapshots and for the Manhattan Project's achievements in the transmutation of elements and the release of atomic energy.

Electronic frontiers are being pushed out frantically toward all sorts of cosmic horizons. "A careful analysis would probably show," says Mr. Chubb, Director of Research for Westinghouse, "that there has been more expansion of personnel for the study, research, development, and production of electronic devices than in any other war development." * Electronics as an industry is estimated to have reached, already, the size of the prewar automobile industry; as applied science it has quickly overcome all sorts of conservative reluctance and established vital controls in industry, aviation, and navigation as well as in communication; it has become a major deadly weapon in combat; and the way has been prepared for drastic technological revolutions, having a profound influence on our lives. And yet it has been said with authority that if the potential development of electronics is conceived as a mile long, the part so far covered is about an inch.†

3

Practically all sciences are new, in the sense that what has happened to them in the past half-century overbalances everything that went before. And, of course, electronic phenomena have been observed with attention ever since our first shaggy ancestor was frightened by a flash of lightning. But a science begins when you measure something that has never been measured before, and to do this you must have manageable material

* *Electronics*, March, 1943, p. 7.
† *Science Digest*, October, 1943, p. 36.

to work with. Lightning is far from manageable. The starting point of electronics as a science was established all unknowingly in 1883. In that year Thomas A. Edison put a plate of metal in one of his vacuum lamps, and although the plate had no connection with its neighbor, the incandescent filament, it became charged with electricity across the void that separated the two. This mysterious transfer of electricity through empty space came to be known as the "Edison effect," and it led a procession of curious phenomena which were sufficiently baffling to inspire systematic and increasingly earnest investigation. Gradually, apparently unrelated facts began to fall into place and fit themselves together into a coherent body of knowledge.

Hertz's and Hallwachs' revelation of the photo-electric effects of ultra-violet light, Roentgen's accidental discovery of radiations from uranium so mysterious that he called them X-rays, J. J. Thomson's identification of the electron (he coined the word) and his measurement of the ratio of its charge to its mass leading to his propounding of the electron theory, were important milestones up to 1900. In 1907 Dr. de Forest developed Edison's "effect" into the first electronic tube and gave the science its all-important working tool, and Milliken's exact determination of the charge carried by the electron, and hence its mass, provided the basis of accurate measurement any science must have as its foundation.

Most of the electrons put to work by electronics are abstracted from metals. Electrons in the atoms of metals are comparatively footloose, and, once you know how, it is not difficult to induce them to flow out freely as a current of negative electrical energy. As a General Electric primer puts it, one way of doing this is by "yanking them out with a high electric voltage": this is the method used in the oldest of electronic applications, the X-ray machine. Another is by "scaring them out with a beam of light": this is the method used in the various kinds of photo-electric tubes, in which an input of radiant energy, or light, is transformed into an output of electrical energy. But "the easiest and most common way is by boiling them out with heat." This is the method used in hundreds of "hot cathode" tubes used in radio, power control and conversion, and a constantly growing number of industrial applications.

Electronic tubes are the characteristic tools of electronic science. There are upwards of 800 kinds of them ranging in size from little pliotrons not as big as your thumb to huge steel-jacketed jobs as big as a man. Some enclose a high vacuum, some are filled with gas. There are tubes with hot cathodes, cold cathodes, mercury pool cathodes and light-sensitive cathodes; tubes activated by electrical energy to give out light, others activated by light to give out electrical energy, and the largest class of all activated by very slight electrical energy to regulate much greater volumes of electrical energy. But all these electronic tubes are descendants of the first one invented by Dr. de Forest in 1907.

Working along the lines of the "Edison effect," Dr. de Forest placed a metal filament called a cathode and a metal plate called an anode side by side but insulated from each other, in a high vacuum tube. If he then heated the cathode by an electric current and charged the anode by applying a positive voltage, electrons would boil out of the hot filament and flow across to the anode, attracted by its positive charge. But Dr. de Forest went further and placed between the cathode and anode a metal screen or grid through which the electrons must pass as they leap the gap. He found that according as the grid was positively or negatively charged by a weak current of low-voltage electricity, it was able to interpose an impregnable barrier to the stream of electrons, or allow them to pass as freely as if it weren't there, or allow any desired volume of them to get by.

This grid is usually compared to a Venetian blind, and its valve action to the opening and closing of the slats of the blind. But an electronic grid is infinitely more subtle and flexible than any mechanical shutter could possibly be. It can fluctuate thousands of times a second, opening and closing in a full range of variability from complete opacity to transmission of the passing current at its maximum strength. Thus an electronic tube introduced into an electric circuit becomes essentially a valve, adjusting the strength of the current that flows through it in exact proportion to the characteristics of the very tiny current in the grid. In this way it has been found that a minute fraction of a watt in the grid will absolutely control the passage of hundreds of thousands of watts. In a great many applications this valvular action is the objective desired, and electronics becomes a means of controlling much with very little, in the way an army of millions may move to the commands of a single man.

But in many other applications, while the valvular action is the same, its objective is different. Instead of our motive being the regulation of the big current, we are primarily interested in reproducing the little current on a larger scale. In your radio tubes, the grid is charged by the faint impulses collected from the ether by your aerial, and these varying impulses are reproduced in corresponding variations of the strong current that flows through the tube and goes on to be translated into sound waves in your loudspeaker. Here the objective is amplification—the same sort of thing that happens when light passing through a tiny film in a projector throws on a screen a vastly enlarged version of the picture on the film. If you can imagine a 16-millimeter film being projected with perfect clarity on a screen a mile high, you will have a crude comparison of what an electronic tube is able to do in the way of amplification. But this simile is absurd, because the amount of light that can be concentrated and passed through an aperture equal to the film's area is extremely limited, and once past the film, its intensity diminishes thereafter by the square of the distance it travels. In electronic amplification there is theoretically no limit to the degree to which the activating current can be magnified: any amount of power can be fed into the primary stream to reproduce the fluctuations of the tiniest of grid currents, so that something very much fainter than a butterfly's pulse can be made to swing a battleship in circles, and the gnawing of a worm can be expanded into a roar that will be heard in the next county.

The fantastic possibilities of this type of power control and amplification can be imagined—that is, they can be imagined by a few scientists with enough information to work on; the rest of us are left panting far behind. The basic means would seem to be simple enough: a valve, or a magnifying lens. All the applications of electronics are variations on these apparently elementary tools. But they represent all that we have been striving for in our

ancient struggle for means to subjugate the world and its unfriendly forces—absolute and instant control of power in any
quantity, sensitivity infinitely more acute than our own, speed
transcending human nerve reactions even so far as the speed of
light. With these capabilities in hand, applicable to every phase
of our efforts in making and building, communicating thought
and moving weights, we should be able to bring nature to heel
and make ourselves whatever kind of a world we want.

4

This is a long-range objective, but the immediate effects will
be drastic enough. There has been much discussion of whether
the manufacture of electronic devices will remain one of the great
new industries we need to keep everybody busy after the war.
The truth is that there is no limit to its expansion yet in sight,
since we have not yet begun to recast our industrial economy
in terms of electronics. But this issue is unimportant compared
to the effect electronics will have in expanding and accelerating
every other phase of our activities. We are in line to see productivity stepped up to undreamed-of levels, our physical welfare
enhanced, and the civilized world brought into the intimacy of
a rural village at will—only at the will, fortunately, of each individual.

In our own lifetimes we have watched the swift expansion of
radio. It is sobering to realize that the two decades of the "Long
Armistice" were enough to bring radio to its present ubiquitous,
frequently distressing but indispensable place in American life.
In that short time we acquired the world's most complete system
of radio communication, with 55 million receiving sets shattering
the silence of our homes, 900 broadcasting stations crowding the
ether and an industry employing half a million people.

But up to now radio has given an imperfect and largely local-
ized service. With the general use of ultra-short-wave broadcasting after the war, making it possible to use modulations and
systems not otherwise practicable, radio reception will become
practically perfect in its quality, and devoid of atmospheric or

other disturbing noises. Distance will mean nothing and the broadcasts from Moscow and Chungking will be heard as satisfactorily as those from your neighborhood station.

If you had the choice of conferring either sight or hearing on a man who had neither, you would certainly give him sight. The imminence of television puts us in the position, in respect to broadcasting, of a people who have been able to hear and are now about to acquire vision. More exactly, it is as if the pictures were just about to be added to sound in the movies. There is no question but that the new gift has greater potentialities than the old.

Many of the limitations that have hampered the development of television have been overcome, and we shall have cheaper receiving sets, bright, sharply focused images on larger screens, and a broadcasting range comparable to that of radio. In due time color will be added, and three-dimensional pictures are entirely possible by using principles already known. We shall not only be able to hear about historic events, we shall actually see them happen, and they will be preserved so that posterity too can see them. Television will have a profound effect in tightening the union of the human race, as it gives us that familiarity with our fellow men of other races which is the basis of tolerance and understanding. It will facilitate democratic processes, as it gives them the intimacy of a town meeting. With moving pictures and radio it will constitute the apparatus of a wholly new educational technique.

As a phase of television the transmission of facsimiles will make it possible to send great masses of documentary information, whole books, over the air waves as fast as you can turn the pages, to be permanently recorded at the receiving end. This will be especially important to the great nation of China, which has no alphabet but thousands of word-symbols making code transmission of messages laborious to the point of impracticability. China is already planning to install facsimile transmission in place of the telegraph throughout the land.

The instrument of television is the cathode ray tube, in which a stream of electrons is sharply focused into a narrow concentrated beam. This beam is swung back and forth many thousands of times a second across a fluorescent screen at the end of the tube. The strength of the current in the beam fluctuates with the current in the grid, making the screen bright or leaving it dark as it passes. Thus the beam recreates a picture which is being "scanned" in identical back-and-forth swings by a beam at the point of broadcasting.

The development of cathode ray tubes, with the necessity of focusing beams of electrons in much the same way that light rays are focused by a glass lens, has given rise to a science of "electronic optics" which uses electric and magnetic fields instead of glass for lenses. There is an astonishing similarity between the laws of electronic and light optics, and it is possible to duplicate electronically all types of light-lens apparatus. But there is one great difference: the electronic apparatus is vastly more powerful than the light-lens apparatus. Already electronic microscopes are in use that are 100 times better than the best light microscope, and they may be built 1,000 times as powerful. With them atoms and molecules and even the internal structure of large molecules and viruses become visible. Already important advances have been made in bacteriology and immunology, industrial chemistry and metallurgy by means of electronic microscopes although only a few have been built and the exploration of the hitherto invisible worlds they open up has only just begun.

If electronic optics can concentrate current in a beam and direct it at will, the possibility is opened up that large volumes of power may be projected through space in this way. The revolutionary implications of such a prospect are drastic, and it is just as well that we can approach them not too swiftly. But already cathode ray tubes, like all electronic tubes, do a surprising variety of things, all related of course to translating electrical impulses into tiny beams of light or vice-versa. They change sounds, vibrations, or electrical currents into wave pictures—dancing lines of light—so that their characteristics can be studied and compared. They make it possible to measure millicycles and milliseconds, and magnify them into easily visible recordings. It is by their help that the doctors can see the wave patterns generated in a specific area of your brain: already they know what the normal patterns should be, and what the aberrations mean, so that they can detect any incipient tendency to degeneration of the brain tissues before it becomes evident to the patient himself or to anyone else. The mental health of mankind may be safeguarded and the asylums emptied in the future by developments of this instrument that staggers under the name of electroencephalograph.

By vibration studies the fatigue of metals can be measured, and the lifetime of a machine part in service exactly predicted. In this way, and by the thorough testing for flaws and the accurate reporting on stresses which electronics gives us, machines can be designed in future without regard to the "factor of safety" we have been building into them. Our methods of testing have been so crude in the past that we have felt obliged for safety's sake to build all structures, from automobile frames to skyscrapers, much stronger than our calculations indicate as necessary. This "factor of safety" may be a multiplication by any number from two to ten. Thus we have been using much more metal and carrying much heavier weights than we should because we couldn't depend on our methods of analysis, and this in itself has introduced an element of hazard as well as a frightful waste. In the postwar era a whole new school of design will produce lighter planes, automobiles, machines and buildings on a basis of exact knowledge of how far materials and parts can be trusted.

The large class of photo-electric tubes are put to doing all kinds of jobs in industry. It is a long way from recording the wave patterns of your thoughts to sorting beans, but electronics does that, too—tossing the good beans one way, picking out the bad beans and tossing them another. Photo tubes have no hot filament: their cathode is sensitive to light and the stronger the light, the more electrons stream out of the cathode. Thus by shining a light on it, or interrupting a light beam that strikes it, the tube can be made to do any number of things—count, record, inspect, sort, protect. Sheet steel races out of the rollers at 1,000 feet a minute, but if there is a pinhole $\frac{1}{64}$ of an inch in diameter in that sheet a photo tube will discover it and mark its location. It will count up to 50,000 units a minute. It opens doors and sounds alarms and prevents machines from being operated while the machinist's hand is in a danger area. It translates a line at the side of a movie film into Garbo's or Bob Hope's or anybody's voice. Also it peers into furnaces and crucibles and exactly controls the heat of a molten alloy or a chemical combination by analyzing the light it gives off. The synthetic rubber program has been accelerated by the use of these spectometers. Every day fresh and profitable ways are being found to apply the principle of light-into-current and current-into-light.

5

The same kind of pliotron tube you use in your radio (but differing in design and potency) is used in induction heating and resistance welding. Radio waves are made to bombard the molecules of a bar of metal or a layer of plywood so as to set up a terrific commotion among them, which commotion is heat. If a very low frequency is used, the surface and only the surface is heated instantly, so that metal can be given a "case-hardened" surface with the inside remaining strong and tough. If a high-frequency current is used, the heat is generated *within* the metal or plywood, evenly all the way through, in contrast with the old method of applying heat to the outside and letting it gradually soak in. The bar can be heated white hot in seconds, so rapidly that if the heat is applied at only one spot, the bar will remain cool only a few inches away. This is enormously valuable in welding, especially in the case of metals like aluminum which would melt on the surface before they would weld by the old torch methods. There are electronic welders which stab their current through the metal as often as 1,800 times a second, literally sewing the parts together. Heavy layers of plywood are bonded in minutes, as compared with hours required before.

Induction heating dries paints, cures tobacco, dehydrates foods. It is quite possible that it may in time revolutionize cooking: a 15-pound roast could be roasted evenly through and through in a matter of seconds—no "15 minutes a pound" roasting time any more. Foods could be cooked in cold dishes, and served that way, and the exact degree of "doneness" could be controlled much more accurately than on any range now built. All this would be worth while in a servantless world. This is an undeveloped field as yet, and there are many doubtful points to be cleared up. Maybe time of cooking itself is a factor in the palatability of foods—we haven't done enough experimental work on the subject to know. But don't lay any bets that you won't be cooking electronically before you are many years older.

Certainly you will be cleansing the air in your home by means of the precipitron—removing from it all particles of dust, smoke and pollen, lightening the dusting job and doing no end of good to your hay-fever. And you will also be disinfecting the air with sterilamps, which kill the bacteria within a certain range. Schools equipped with sterilamps will reduce the contagious diseases of childhood, sterilamps in places where people congregate will put a brake on the common cold. And precipitrons in all chimneys— required by law—*can* make Pittsburgh and Chicago as bright and shining as Pasadena or Miami.

When we suddenly needed to convert huge quantities of current from AC to DC at Bonneville, Grand Coulee, and Tennessee Valley in order to make aluminum and magnesium, there were neither critical metals nor time to build the huge rotary converters which always had been used for this purpose. But a battery of ignitron tubes, cheap, with no moving parts, could do the job even better, and they have proved it in many months of heavy-duty service. There is no reason why rotary converters should ever again be built, by comparison clumsy, expensive, and wasteful as they are. The postwar era will see our whole national power system adapted to electronic controls of all kinds, with an immense gain in flexibility and economy.

But current conversion is not always on the Bonneville scale. There are many machine tools which require AC at some points in their operations and DC at others, and it has been an expensive business to equip and wire great industrial plants to supply both kinds of current. Now a little thyratron tube, no more trouble to install than an incandescent lamp, will make the conversion to DC at the exact point of use. Also electronic speed controls are being rapidly applied to all machine tools. Hitherto variable speed control of electric motors by mechanical means or rheostats has been a clumsy makeshift, but a thyratron tube will give an infinite range of speeds from zero to maximum, and once adjusted it will hold the machine at a fixed speed no matter what load is put on it. These advances may not seem important to you if you are a novice in industry, but they affect you directly because they mean better and cheaper products of all kinds.

6

This chapter has tagged a very few of an enormous number of feats that electronics is performing in a few phases of our economy, particularly in communications and industry. I have barely waved a hand in the general direction of medical science, the airplane, automobile, merchant marine, railways, domestic life— all of which will go through an electronic rebirth of new forms and habits. Some of these applications I shall talk about later, because they are too important to ignore. But all of them put together add up to a few minute fractions of the big inch we have already traveled. We can see a few inches ahead, with a feeling that we'd rather not talk about them just yet. This is not an uncommon mood in the face of modern science: it hushed the General Electric representatives who, in August of 1943, had just completed a 100-million-volt X-ray machine and were reluctant to discuss what it might be expected to do. They felt themselves entering a new phase of exploration into atomic energy —"a world where nothing exists, only events occur."

But beyond us now stretches the long mile of electronic developments. By comparison has there been any achievement in the past fifty years that was anything more than a baby's first staggering steps? What price population increase, or new farm lands, or any industrial growth we have had as yet, when we stand at the threshold of an empire of power and power controls such as this that is opening up before us? In terms of an expanding economy, we have laid the first few bricks of a skyscraper; and all the rest of the materials are ready at hand, waiting for us to put them in place.

CHAPTER VII

WE CAN MAKE THE MATERIALS WE NEED

THE POPULAR conception of a chemist is a man in a white coat who pours a little of this and a little of that into a beaker to concoct something that tastes bad, smells bad, or explodes; and the popular symbol of chemistry is a crooked-necked retort—as seen in the insignia of the Chemical Warfare Service—which alchemists invented in the Middle Ages and not one chemist in ten has used since his early college days. Physicists and metallurgists do not call to mind any pictures or symbols even as antiquated as these, their functions being wholly vague in the public mind. Engineers are less unfamiliar because there are more of them, but the name is more likely to suggest a man who builds dams or drives a locomotive than one who designs the minute gear trains of a high-speed camera shutter or the automatic mechanisms of a turret lathe.

And yet these four little-publicized professions are the four caryatids who carry on their shoulders the whole structure of modern production. If chemists, physicists, metallurgists, and engineers with their skills should be withdrawn from our industrial system, it would not only cease to progress but its structure would collapse in no time because it would not be possible to keep the machinery running in good order, the supplies up to standard and the products usable. On the other hand, if they were left in action but the whole existing plant wiped out, these four professions alone could rebuild it from the ground up and get it running again. It would be a laborious undertaking of course, but these specialists, and they alone, could do it. They are the dynamic force animating the whole exercise in applied science we call modern industry, and without them it could not have been created and could not now continue to function.

With these truths in mind, one stumbles in astonishment over a bland reference by Mr. Harold Laski to "that hostility to new invention which is endemic in a capitalistic society." * The phrase is stock with Mr. Laski, being repeated more than once in identical words, and he may never have thought of applying a simple factual test to something he would so much like to believe. It would be generous to suppose so, but however you explain so stupid an untruth, either his perspicacity or his intellectual integrity is discredited; as by many other things in a work which has the present-day relevance of an early film by Cecil B. DeMille.

Whatever else may be true of modern capitalist industry, it should be plain to the dullest wit that its prosperity is founded on invention, on the encouragement and exploitation of invention. "Hostility to invention" if it ever appeared has never had time to become "endemic": the first infection acted on the particular victim like a fine shot of arsenic.

Our early industrial history is a record of brilliant inventions, often made obscurely and usually with the most meager means, but immediately proliferating into huge activities that have had a drastic effect on human living. Trace almost any major industry to its beginnings and you will find individual inspiration, sometimes amounting to genius, as its source: agricultural implements originate in John Deere and Cyrus McCormick, rubber products in Charles Goodyear, the telegraph and telephone in Morse and Bell, mass production of printing in Hoe and Mergenthaler, mass production of automobiles in Henry Ford, mass production in the "needle trades" in Elias Howe, the electric power industry, electric lights, sound recording, and motion pictures in Thomas A. Edison. The list could be extended interminably and carried

---

* Harold Laski, *Reflections on the Revolution of Our Time*, Viking, 1943, p. 50. Mr. Laski is heretical. Marx and Engels said a hundred years ago (*Communist Manifesto*, 1848), "The bourgeoisie [i.e., capitalistic society] cannot exist without constantly revolutionizing the instruments of production. . . . The bourgeoisie, during its rule of scarce one hundred years, has created more massive and more colossal productive forces than have all preceding generations together." Which revolutionary do you read?

down through countless less spectacular but still invaluable beginnings.

The principal equipment of most of these pioneers was vision
and tenacity. Few of them were well trained for what they undertook to do, they often were supported by nothing more substantial than their own convictions, and they were frequently assisted
—as in Goodyear's case—by the kind of lucky accident that happens when you have arranged all the circumstances so that it *can*
happen. Their achievements, in most instances, resulted from an
imaginative ability to conceive new ways of meeting old needs,
and the ingenuity to combine known elements in unprecedented
arrangements: they did not, except in Edison's case, engage in
what we now consider scientific research.

It is astonishing that so much could have been accomplished
during the nineteenth and early twentieth centuries by this kind of
pertinacious but fumbling effort. But in practically every instance
the value of the new concept was recognized the instant it was
demonstrable, and it was incorporated into our capitalistic scheme
of living with exemplary promptness no matter what ancient interests, habits and customs it might displace. Our modern fertility
in invention has been equaled only by our receptivity to it. And
fortunately we have progressed from receptivity to stimulation.
We no longer depend for advancements on the vision and per-
sistence of lone pioneers: we cultivate our inventions in forcing
frames.

2

One of the things that make our present period different from
any preceding is the deliberate incubation of advancements. This
is not to say that creative imagination and individual genius are
no longer potent factors, but they are not left to their own devices. Research and invention now are carefully programed, adequately subsidized, and pressed home to the desired conclusions.
Today it usually happens that a need is recognized by specialists
before the public is aware of it. An unfilled need is a business
opportunity. So it is analyzed and defined and a staff of competent men assigned with all necessary facilities to find a way

of supplying it. This is the more common method whereby important inventions are now achieved, and it is a usual procedure in major and even minor corporations.

The lone-wolf inventor still occurs, and occasionally makes a ten-strike. But more often than not when he submits his findings, he learns that they have been anticipated in the routine work of an industrial laboratory. Sometimes even worthless inventions may be bought in order to avoid patent complications, and the inventor who never hears of his brain-child again may not realize that it has had only nuisance value and may think that it has been ruthlessly suppressed. When he has a really new and valuable idea, he may be invited to use an industry's facilities to develop it, as happened to young Mannes and Godowski when they took to the Eastman Kodak Company the idea of suspending dyes in layers of gelatine which led to the making of Kodachrome films. But this inspiration was exceptional, and the chance of a free-lance exceeding the thorough coverage of professional investigators today is slight.

We can thank subsidized research directed to specific ends for the past quarter-century's swift progress in many fields. The rapid advancement of radio, television, telephonics, fluorescent lighting, sound and color movies, the industrial applications of electronics, the synthesis of rubber, plastics and sulfa drugs, the isolation of magnesium from sea water and nitrogen from the air, improvements in motor fuels and planes, development of the gas turbine, air-conditioning, prepared foods—all these are typical and by no means exceptional examples. In each of these instances, years of the time of many gifted men and great sums of money were devoted to the solution of well-defined problems. And often the knowledge that more than one group under different auspices was working on the same problem gave the effort the eager intensity of a race against time and able rivals.

But research in industry is not always restricted to specific programs: it may be turned loose with at least as much freedom as it enjoys in institutions of learning devoted to pure research —and often with more ample facilities. As Dr. Kenneth Mees has said, "Let the research man follow his inquisitive nose from fact to fact, no matter how far afield it may lead him." This is done in a spirit of healthy self-interest, with confidence that any exact knowledge turned up will prove to be usable, or will fit itself into a pattern of knowledge which thereby is given practical applicability.

Thus we can account for the rather surprising fact that both the Eastman Kodak Company and the Bell Telephone Laboratories have made important contributions to the synthesis of vitamins, and the former is now the largest producer of certain types of vitamins. There would seem to be very little connection between snapshots and vitamins, but a continuous series of links exists if you take the trouble to trace them. Also a distinguished chemist in a du Pont laboratory endeavoring to construct molecules as big as nature's biggest would seem to be a long way from nylon stockings and more durable paint brushes, but his efforts led directly to these results. And the Radio Corporation of America is not in the glass business but it does specialize in electronic optics and one of its scientists saw for the first time a network of solid silica on the surface of ordinary glass. It is only $\frac{1}{50,000}$ of an inch thick and understandably had escaped notice up to this time, but it cuts down the transparency of glass materially. It can be removed by a treatment with hydrofluoric acid vapor during manufacture, and glass will then pass all but $\frac{1}{500}$ of the light that strikes it—a discovery which means that we shall have better window glass in the future than ever in the past.

Planned industrial research is comparatively recent—little more than a generation old. It was not until the early years of this century that industry got tired of waiting at the back door of science for handouts, and began moving into the kitchen to cook its own scientific sustenance. Then came World War I, with its sudden urgent need to supply ourselves with dyes, drugs, potash, nitrates, and other chemical products we had been lazily importing from the rest of the world. Research was equal to this call, and proved its immense value. It has been expanding and accelerating ever since. Just before the war, in 1940, there were 2,200 laboratories operating in industry, employing an average of more than 33 scientists each (some have staffs of hundreds) and spending more than 300 million dollars a year.* These figures may not be breath-taking, but it should be remembered that research is not measured in manpower or dollars but in results. Only ten men assisted Dr. Carothers in his epochal tinkering with long-polymer cells.

The "pure" research carried on by universities and foundations also contributes large and very valuable items to the resources of industry with surprising frequency. The isolation of penicillin, now in mass production, was an academic achievement. The irradiation of food products to increase their vitamin content was a university development but it immediately became general practice in the dairy and other food-processing industries. Dr. Lawrence's experiments with his cyclotron were directed with complete indifference to anything but the advancement of science, but the special science they advanced was electronics and electronics as we have seen is revitalizing industry like an infusion of blood plasma. In the same field, Dr. Millikan's earlier work in measuring the speed of light led directly to the photo-cells that detect flaws in tin-plating and turn on the lamps when daylight lessens in our more up-to-date schoolrooms. It appears that knowledge can scarcely be so pure that it is not also of practical value.

This war brought about a mobilization and amalgamation of both university and industrial research under a single head, the Office of Scientific Research and Development, as described briefly in an earlier chapter of this book. University professors and scientists in industrial employ were shifted about and put to work where their abilities would be most productive, laboratories were taken over and their staffs enlarged or replaced as seemed best, and everybody was assigned to whatever tasks were most urgent. Back of this combined effort stood the whole system of the nation's industry, ready to put the scientists' conclusions to work as fast as they were handed over. And there was a pooling of patents and a free exchange of knowledge and experience such as never were seen before.

* There are a number of large, well-staffed laboratories, such as those of the Armour Institute, prepared to undertake specific research for smaller corporations which cannot afford to maintain private laboratories of their own.

We shall not realize the value of all the achievements of this united effort until years after the war, but we know already that it was greatly productive. Any number of dire needs would not have been so swiftly and amply supplied if it had not been for this superb teamwork—the rapid solving of intricate problems, the instant translation of new knowledge into great volumes of production.

This mobilization, so successful and so inspiring to everyone concerned, may never again be completely unscrambled. After all, the ultimate purpose of all research, pure or applied, is the enhancement of our racial welfare, and the quicker any new-found fact can be put to work the better—and the more gratifying to the finder. Now that the industrial scientists have gone back to drink at the springs of academic learning, and the professors have had the sensation of unlimited materials, funds, and machinery at their command, why should either group be willing to return to its separate compartment? My guess is we have seen a merging of scientific effort that will be the rule from here on, with the universities overlapping and co-operating with industry in the quick conversion of all knowledge to human betterment.

3

Our synthetic rubber program is a dramatic example of what can be accomplished by an all-out union of chemical research with industrial production. The enemy undoubtedly counted on the stoppage of our rubber supplies—along with the stoppage of tin, quinine, camphor, copra, hemp, and sisal—to help mightily toward our defeat. And if industry had not been far better prepared than government to deal with the emergency the enemy might have been right. We used two-thirds of all the rubber produced in the world and raised none of it ourselves. In 1940 we imported 700,000 tons of caoutchouc—raw rubber—all but a bit of it from the shores of the Southwest Pacific. You might think that with war obviously turning into our street we would have officially prepared an ace in the hole, just in case. The Nazi government did so from the moment it came into power in 1933, but our government was not so far-sighted. Almost a year of delay, confusion, and bickering passed, even after Pearl Harbor, before the situation was officially dealt with.

Fortunately, several industrial corporations had been carrying on research in rubber substitutes for years. They had succeeded in synthesizing molecules to compose several substances that were not rubber and differed radically from each other, but among them had all the properties of rubber and some that rubber does not have. They all cost more than natural rubber, especially in small quantities, so it had been practicable to produce only enough to supply specialized needs which rubber would not serve —such as the need for resistance to oil, acid, and sunshine, or the need for thin, transparent, waterproof sheets. Not more than 3,000 long tons were manufactured in 1939, and the 1941 output stood at 12,000 tons. But the formulas were tested, the art had been learned. When the government finally made up its mind, toward the end of 1942, to release the materials and funds for an adequate synthetic rubber program, American industries were all set to build plants and swing into production on a mammoth scale.

It takes seven years for a rubber plantation to reach the bearing stage; it took less than two years for industry to supplant all our imports. In 1943 we produced 231,000 long tons, in 1944, 763,000 tons—more than we ever imported in a year prior to 1941. "The rubber industry," says Dr. John T. Blake, chairman of the rubber division of the American Chemical Society, "has accomplished in approximately two years with new substances what it took more than 100 years to do with natural rubber." *

By far the greater part of this output is a product known as Buna-S or GR-S (the GR stands for Government Rubber) made principally from butadiens and styrene, which are derived from petroleum, alcohol, or natural gas. It is similar to the German substitute, but better. It is not possible to say as yet that tires made from GR-S are quite as good as tires made from natural rubber for all purposes, and they are not yet as cheap. But after all, we didn't learn to make tires from natural rubber overnight.

* New York Times, October 6, 1943.

A tire made in 1908 cost $35 to $125, according to size, and usually was good for 2,000 miles of service. By 1936 industrial research had cut cost to $8 to $25, and increased the service to an average of 20,000 miles, with much greater safety and comfort. Give the rubber industry's chemists a fraction of that length of time to improve their pet molecules, and they may very well realize Dr. Gustav Egloff's prediction that postwar synthetic tires will outlast the cars they carry, and Rubber Director Bradley Dewey's prediction that postwar synthetics will undersell crude rubber by several cents—dropping to twelve cents a pound.

Whether these results will come to pass depends more on politics and chance than on science. At one time our then Vice President expressed the hope that after the war our 900-million-dollar synthetic rubber plant will be scrapped so that the Far East may have its market back; the Rio de Janeiro Agreement provides obliquely that we will abandon synthetic production if other American countries raise the natural product: and Mr. Roosevelt once said that he hoped no effort will be made to give postwar tariff protection to the synthetic industry.* The President was basically right. Certainly synthetics should compete with the natural product, both as to quality and price, in a fair field, with no favors. But if the chemists haven't had time to finish their work and perfect their syntheses before the natural product starts flowing in volume again, we can venture to hope that they are given a reprieve to do it.

If the synthetic industry is able to survive on its own merits, it may attain volumes of production and wide usefulness much greater than any planned now. For we must remember that synthetics can be designed to do many things that natural rubber will not do; and we can foresee cheap tires "that will be nonskid, puncture-proof, good for 100,000 miles"; † and an age of universally resilient floors, and resilient pavements, and other broad applications for a material that is tough, elastic, waterproof, adaptable, abundant, and cheap.

* New York Times, October 18, 1943.
† William Haynes, The Chemical Front, Knopf, 1943, p. 190.

4

The science-plus-industry record in rubber substitute production does not stand alone. During this war the partnership has done as well in supplying special steels, aluminum and magnesium; great quantities of atabrine as a substitute for quinine—more than a quarter of a million pounds a year—without which our armies could not have fought in the malaria-infested Southwest Pacific islands; 5 million pounds of camphor a year, formerly imported from the Japanese island of Formosa; indispensable sulfa drugs and the magical penicillin. And our spectacular achievement in snatching great quantities of nitrogen from the air rivals synthetic rubber production in scale and may have an even greater influence on our postwar economy.

Almost four-fifths of the air we breathe is nitrogen, and all fertile soil and we ourselves are full of it. We smell its presence in the ammoniacal odor of the stable manure that enriches our fields. We cannot live without it, but it's a case of nitrogen, nitrogen everywhere but not a drop to assimilate. We can get it into our systems only by eating plants which can and do assimilate it, or by eating other animals which have gotten it by eating plants—which is why our meat supplies are provided by herbivorous animals. Cultivated crops take more nitrogen out of the soil than nature puts back, and if we did not replace it by applying stable manure and chemical fertilizers we should soon find ourselves in a state of famine through exhaustion of farm lands.

But nitrogen is also essential in many phases of industrial chemistry and especially in making military explosives. Some freak of nature has deposited great natural beds of nitrogen in Chile, and for many years we imported it from this source. The difficulty and expense of supplying our increased needs from South America caused one of the great crises of World War I, but with the early ending of that conflict our efforts to establish production here at home were allowed to lapse. The methods employed then were crude and expensive, anyhow. In the late twenties industrial enterprise undertook to compete with the Chilean supply by drawing on the limitless quantities of nitrogen in the air all around us. The original derivative is a gas called ammonium hydrate, which in one form gives us our "household ammonia" and in others enters into all sorts of products from nylon to meat preservatives and refrigerants. As nitric acid it combines with soda ash to make sodium nitrate, or with the original ammonia to make ammonium nitrate, both excellent fertilizers.

By 1939 our production of nitrogen in the pure state was a little more than half a million tons, but by 1943 our plants were delivering more than 1.3 million tons. Munitions had first call on this vast quantity and farmers were on reduced rations of nitrogenous fertilizers. In peace times, production on such a scale will provide a much greater tonnage of chemical fertilizer than we have ever used in this country, and some authorities think it will be more than we can possibly consume. But the fact is that our farmers have never used enough, largely because of the expense, and we have little idea of what can be done with cheap and abundant supplies of these essential aids to agriculture. Dr. Charles M. A. Stine, du Pont's Adviser on Research and one of the nation's most eminent chemists, says it may well change "the basic trends of agriculture." It is true that we have here a possibility of foodstuffs plentiful and cheap beyond our fondest hopes. This in combination with the innumerable industrial uses of nitrogen compounds gives Dr. Stine reason to believe that in the postwar world "the high-pressure synthesis of ammonia, one of the major chemical exploits of the century, will have taken on an industrial status that, in terms of new producing capacity, may be comparable to the discovery of a sixth continent."

The "basic trends of agriculture" are overdue for a change. Agriculture from its beginning has been the business of raising food for man and beast. The new trends may direct it toward other great objectives as well.

Even when all our people attain the varied and abundant diet which all should have and only a comparative few have enjoyed in the past, there will still be a definite limit to the amount of foodstuffs the nation can eat. In the past, when production exceeded consumption in our domestic market, the only way to dispose of the surplus aside from the idiotic expedient of plowing it under has been to sell it abroad, and that often has been impossible. So we have witnessed the vicious absurdity of unsalable surpluses of foodstuffs, and agricultural depression, in an underfed world.

The cycle of increased production, lower prices, greater consumption and surer profits should operate in agriculture as it does in industry. It should spur on a progressive agriculture to greater productivity, and agricultural prosperity should be one of the bulwarks of national prosperity. But the cycle has not operated for the farmer, because in his restricted market consumption does not expand as fast as production, and the more the farmer has raised the lower have been his prices and his profits both.

It might seem that the highly efficient agriculture of the future, scientific, mechanized, and supplied with cheap and abundant fertilizers, would only make this situation worse. But not when the farmer finds a great new market eager for all he can raise. He is about to discover that his crops are only incidentally foodstuffs: fundamentally they are chemicals known as proteins, carbohydrates, and cellulose, and there is no limit in sight to the quantities of these chemicals that can be consumed in the future as industrial raw materials. The farmer in the postwar era will send his products to the same market as the coal miner and the iron miner, and the cheaper they are the more he can sell and, with cheaper production, the more money he can make.

This integration of agriculture with industry will be one of the major revolutions in human history, and it is not far off. Its coming has been hastened by the swift development of industrial chemistry as it prepares on the one hand to lower the farmer's production costs and on the other to expand his market.

5

The fixation of nitrogen from the free air is the perfect type of modern chemical operation, because it is knowledge at work with great quantities of power—power under precise controls to provide heat and pressure—on a raw material that costs nothing. Abundant power, plentiful and cheap raw materials, exact knowledge—all these are characteristically modern. But power is only relatively greater than in the past, the raw materials have always been ready to hand: the one new and determinant factor is the extent of the modern scientists' factual equipment. What the industrial scientist possesses now, as the result of organized research, and what never existed until recent years, is a mature working technique.

When a chemical objective is defined, the approaches to it usually are clearly indicated and they can be taken step by step. There still are large gaps in our knowledge, of course, and some of the steps to an end may require careful fishing in dark places before we are quite sure of our footing. But chemists, physicists, metallurgists are now dealing with fundamental building blocks of nature about which they have a large fund of exact information, and their problems are much more like those of an architect who is combining well-known materials into a planned structure than like the bewilderments of early investigators who weren't sure as to what they were handling.

Charles Goodyear learned how to vulcanize rubber by forgetting to remove a mixture of rubber and sulphur from a hot stove. It was an accident, although no one else would have been fooling with rubber and sulphur on the kitchen range. But today, when the need to synthesize a substitute for rubber arises, the chemist knows exactly what kind of polymers (groups or chains of molecules) are required to compose a substance with the same properties as rubber. These polymers must be big molecules made by the union of small molecules to form rubbery, elastic masses, which give rubber its stretch. With detailed knowledge of these molecule-groups in mind, the chemist must discover what atoms of gases or fluids will coalesce to form polymers of this type, and he observes that the polymeric reaction is affected by factors such as catalysts, temperature, pressure, and reaction time. He also finds that chemical substances known as modifying agents and regulators affect the rate of polymerization, yield, and quality. The process of synthesizing a satisfactory polymer is thus an involved and delicate one, but since the chemist has the key the problem is not insoluble. Within limits, it is possible to design synthetic rubber to specifications, and the same thing is true of any other type of molecular structure desired. Modern chemistry, says William Haynes, is "the great business of making molecules to order." *

Not all chemical raw materials are as free as the air, but those used in any great quantity are easy to come by. The chemist no longer deals with rare essences and tinctures of the Orient—he performs his wonders with the most common and plentiful of raw materials, and the supplies of elemental sow's ears he requires are literally all around us and under foot and practically unlimited.

The atoms of about ten elements are all the chemist needs in any quantity for the making of whatever molecules he designs. Nature seems to have shared his preference: in fact, four of these elements—oxygen, nitrogen, hydrogen, and carbon—suffice in nature to build practically all of our organic compounds, including ourselves. These and the other most serviceable elements can all be gotten from a half-dozen cheap and abundant sources.

The air supplies nitrogen and oxygen, water supplies oxygen and hydrogen, coal supplies hydrogen and carbon. Calcium we have in vast limestone beds—3.5 million tons were quarried in peacetime years, making no more than a dent in the whole. As to sodium, much of the Central Valley and Gulf areas of the United States are underlaid with beds of sodium salts often thousands of feet thick. Potash-bearing salts are present in associated deposits, to supply all the potassium we can ever conceivably need. And in the Gulf region there are enormous beds of sulphur which we melt electronically underground and pump to the surface. Magnesium is present in every gallon of sea water, as in fact are traces of every other element and some in substantial quantities. Great quarries of phosphate rock yield millions of tons of phosphorus every year, as much as our phosphate plants can process and the market absorb.

These ten elemental atoms—oxygen, nitrogen, hydrogen, carbon, calcium, sodium, magnesium, potassium, sulphur, phosphorus—are thus available in what to all intents and purposes are in-

* William Haynes, *This Chemical Age*, Knopf, 1942, p. 27. A fascinating book.

exhaustible quantities, and the four most used are happily the most abundant. The limitless air and water and our thousand years' supply of coal—100 million tons were fed into our chemical industries in prewar years—are guarantees that any number of chemists and chemical manufacturers will continue contentedly productive through many lifetimes. And since Dr. Ernst Berl has synthesized perfectly good coal and oil out of dried leaves, weeds and old cornstalks,* we are safe in assuming that our supply of annually renewed carbohydrates will last as long as the supply of air, water, and sunshine.

6

The chemist does not often find his atoms segregated, in a pure and exclusive state. He may find them combined with atoms of other elements to form molecules, and if he wants to isolate them he knows how to do so. But since he is interested in the reconstruction of molecules, he usually can start to build with molecules as he finds them. Out of the 92 elemental atoms, an infinite variety of molecules can be constructed, and nature herself has tried out an extravagant number from very simple to very complex. The one chemical formula known to anyone who can read—H_2O—means that the molecule of water is composed of two atoms of hydrogen and one of oxygen. The Chemical Warfare Service's insignia, in addition to the retorts, contains a hexagon which is the symbol of a benzene molecule—six carbon atoms linked in a ring, each with an atom of hydrogen attached. These are simple compounds, but the molecule of haemoglobin, the substance in our bloodstream that carries oxygen from the air to all parts of our bodies, is composed of some 10,000 atoms, all essential to its function even when, as in the case of iron, there are only four in the whole crowd.

The number, kind, and arrangement of atoms in its molecules give any compound its peculiar quality and characteristics—its identity as distinguished from all other compounds. Arrangement is important: the atoms may occur in chains, in closed rings, in

* *Science Digest*, February, 1944, p. 29.

branching groups of chains, in compact masses. But all these
factors of number, kind, and arrangement of atoms are rapidly
coming under the chemist's control. He has found that he can
add atoms to molecules or take them out, he can rearrange them
from chains to compact groups, he can hook chains together to
make longer chains or branching systems, he can break open
closed rings so as to hook on new atoms, chains or groups. And
every time he makes one of these changes he gets a new chemical
compound with characteristics good or bad of its own. The
atoms of ordinary gasoline are joined in a chain: the chemist
breaks up these molecules and rejoins the same atoms in a compact group and he has a different fuel called high octane gas of
much greater power. The linking of cellulose molecules together
in long chains, all lying parallel and strung out in the same direction, makes it possible to spin the resulting tiny threads into
strong and durable yarns.

Sir Lawrence Bragg has vividly compared this tinkering with
atoms to building with a Meccano set: "Now atoms are like the
standard parts in Meccano, while molecules are the structures
built from them. The nuts and bolts which fasten the pieces
together are the chemical bonds which fasten atom to atom in
a molecule." * And he adds that we occasionally need special bits,
such as gear wheels in Meccano or stray atoms of phosphorus or
chlorine in chemistry, to finish off the structure.

The simile is right enough as to the method of linking atoms
together, but it fails if we consider the end results. Anything
built with Meccano is still a recognizable Meccano structure when
you get through. But the results a chemist gets by changing the
proportion and arrangement of his pieces are unbelievably varied.
Starting with the molecules of cellulose (the wall substance of
all plants) as his Meccano set and throwing in various special
pieces, he can build structures as widely varied as your wife's
new rayon dress, the paint on your car, the explosives that leveled
Berlin, the bakelite case of your alarm clock and the wall board
with which you lined your attic. With the hydrocarbon molecules
of coal and petroleum as a base he ranges as wide, if not wider,

* *Science Digest*, February, 1944, p. 73.

to an assortment of compounds that makes the index of a Sears, Roebuck catalog look like a mere shopping list: as high octane gas they carried the plane to Berlin, as synthetic rubber they made its tires, as transparent lucite they shielded the pilot and gunners, as toluol they put the disruptive force in the explosive, as dyes they color the pilot's service ribbons, as sulfa drugs they healed the wounded with beneficent speed. For their dramatic value we cite these wartime applications, but every one of them and hundreds more have a service to render in the betterment of living throughout the longer years of peace.

7

It is this betterment of living that the chemist holds as his ultimate objective. He is engaged in repairing what are, judged by human standards, nature's faults and errors, making up her omissions and improving her workmanship. There is scarcely a material supplied to us by nature in the quality and uniformity we need, especially now that we have committed ourselves to mass production, which cannot operate without standard quality and uniformity of characteristics in its materials. So long as we relied on handicraft, in which variability is as acceptable as it is to nature, we could make out with wood, stone, and iron, sheep's wool, silkworm's thread, flax fibers, and animal leather. But now we want many kinds of steel made from iron and alloys, with exact and unvarying attributes, and we want other and lighter metals equally special. We want to banish rust, rot and, so far as possible, wear. We want wood or something like it which is stronger than the natural product, is absolutely uniform in grain, will not split or warp, shrink or expand with moisture; we want it tough and hard and incombustible, and it is very helpful to be able to mold it into any form we need. As for threads, we need to have them more uniform in strength and diameter and stronger than any made from hair of animals or fibers of plants. And we have vital need for a long list of materials, protectives, chemicals, and drugs which nature has not seen fit to provide.

It would be silly to say that, as yet, we can make all that we need. But we have made a substantial start in that direction and the change-over from natural to man-made materials is well under way. In the 21 years from 1920 to 1941, our use of synthetic fibers in the weaving of cloth rose from 10 million pounds to more than 580 million pounds, almost as much as our consumption of cotton and more than our consumption of wool. And at the same time our use of natural silk declined between 1929 and 1940 from 81 million pounds to less than 36 million pounds. In 1920 we used about 5 million pounds of synthetic plastics of all kinds. By 1941 we were using 450 million pounds. Since then war has accelerated the activities of the chemical industry enormously. It is not a matter of increased production alone, although this has been multiplied several times—new formulas have been discovered and new techniques and applications worked out.

Plastics especially have been pushed into new realms, taking over more and more ground from wood and metal until we begin to realize that there is almost no limit to their applicability. Already there are hundreds of types of syntheses from cellulose, phenol, formaldehyde, urea, the casein of sour milk, lignin which is the binder in wood, the hydrocarbons of coal and other inorganic compounds. They are solids, binders, fillers, preservative finishes, and threads. They vary from the stodgy but enormously useful bakelite through translucence and a full spectrum of colors to the ethereal lucite, so much more transparent than glass that you can read fine print through the length of a six-foot rod. They can be molded by heat and pressure or by injection, or spun into strands twice as strong as hemp, or extruded in rods, tubes or elaborate sections, or pressed into sheets of any desired thickness.

They are notably poor conductors of both heat and electricity, and they include both the thermoplastic types which soften at a relatively low temperature and thermosetting types which will char at very high temperatures but once molded cannot be softened again. Strength is continually being augmented until Dr. Stine's prediction that plastics may be made stronger than steel seems conservative.

The impregnation and bonding of thin layers of plywood, cloth or paper by means of waterproof plastics give a material that is light but approximates metallic strength and has more than metallic toughness and resistance to distortion. This development alone opens up a whole new field in the fabrication of light but strong shapes composed of compound curves, and its thorough wartime testing in the making of airplanes and boats is preliminary to countless peacetime applications.

All that we have done to date in this plastic field must be seen as mere experiment and exploration preliminary to full exploitation of its possibilities. In stating this viewpoint, Dr. William J. Hale a few years ago predicted that the real plastic age would begin in 1950.* Now we know that its beginning coincides with the war's end, or will come as soon after as we can get back into full peacetime production.

It was Dr. Hale's opinion that when this day comes metal alloys will yield their supremacy to plastics. This may not be true, but unquestionably plastics will supersede metals, wood, and porcelain in many applications. We shall have plastic automobile bodies lighter but tougher than steel, dent-proof and scratch-proof. We shall have plastic bathtubs, warm to the touch and light enough for the plumber's helper to carry in one hand; and plastic sinks and transparent plumbing pipes. All kinds of kitchen and laundry equipment and household appliances will be molded, and new plastic finishes incorporating the silica of glass will provide surfaces as hard and resistant to acids and wear as glass or porcelain but flexible and crack-proof. The structural parts of much of our furniture will be molded, cushions will be of synthetic rubber "foam," and extremely durable but beautiful synthetic fabrics will be universally used as coverings. Extruded plastic sections will replace wood in the trim of our houses, and eventually our entire prefabricated house will be made of molded plastic panels—fireproof, termite-proof and with a lower coefficient of heat transmission than any building material now in use; while our windows will be glazed with transparent plastic sheets which admit all the health-giving actinic rays of the sun as glass does not.

* This Chemical Age, p. 372.

8

Metals may yield territory to synthetic materials, but at the same time they are extending their own. The metallurgist today is as sure of himself as the chemist and physicist: he deals with known factors and is equipped with adequate tools. When he wants a specific alloy he no longer melts up combinations of metals in a crucible until he gets something that seems to be about right: he predetermines the combination of elements and the crystalline structure that will give him the characteristics desired, and proceeds confidently to synthesize them.

Components of an alloy can be analyzed exactly in the beautiful color-patterns of the spectroscope, and it can be done instantly by electronic heating of the samples to be studied. All stages of the alloying process can be observed and controlled by electronic spectrometers, which analyze the light given off by the molten compound to indicate its exact temperature and the proportion of elements in it. This is cooking with an accuracy that should turn a culinary chef green with envy. In addition the metallurgist has means of testing his products exactly for strength, toughness, fatigue, uniformity of structure, reaction to stresses and strains, resistance to corrosion and oxidation. All these tests are made by instruments which duplicate, in very brief intervals, long periods of use or exposure.

As a result, metals are being designed to fit specific needs with much the same precision the chemist attains in his syntheses, and old-line metals such as steel are acquiring a wide versatility. During the war our steel production was stepped up to the unheard-of total of 96 million tons a year and at the same time there was a rapid development of special steels which will prove immensely helpful when we have a chance to make full use of them in peacetime production. Tensile strength of 190,000 pounds has been achieved—amazing as compared with the 50,000 pounds of ordinary structural steel. It is impressive to contemplate a weight of 95 tons suspended from a bar of steel one inch square.

This very great strength reverses the role of steel and light metals in many applications, for where strength is essential it often happens that it can be obtained with less weight in steel than in aluminum or magnesium. We shall find that high tensile steel will be used instead of the light metals in many structural members of future airplanes, trains and automobiles, with a saving in weight.

But the light metals are set for great new careers of usefulness, as the flood of increased war production of aluminum and magnesium is diverted into consumer industries. When materials are abundant and cheap, we are extraordinarily fertile in finding new uses for them, and we can now produce aluminum at the rate of a million tons a year, more than seven times as much as we produced in pre-war years, and the price has dropped from 20 cents a pound to 15 cents. This price may easily go lower in the competitive postwar market. And magnesium, which is a third lighter than aluminum and a generation ago was more costly than gold and rarer than platinum, can now be produced at the rate of 100,000 tons a year and costs only 20.5 cents a pound. A thousand pounds of magnesium, on the average, went into every military plane we built, in castings, forgings, rolled and extruded shapes. At its present price it is cheaper by the cubic foot than aluminum.

If we had plenty of magnesium for critical wartime uses and enough for the saving of weight in all kinds of peacetime goods, we can thank the capitalism which Mr. Laski thinks—or says—is endemically hostile to invention. Ninety-five per cent of all the magnesium in the United States has been produced by the Dow Chemical Company. For more than forty years the first Dr. Dow and his son have doggedly pursued the objective of extracting magnesium from the lakes of concentrated brine that underlie much of Michigan, and from sea water. They have plowed back more than a third of their earnings into research, and have obtained many other results besides magnesium. From their brine they get chlorine, bromine, and bromides for sedatives, photographic chemicals, calcium chloride for laying dust. Their company has developed important plastics of the ethyl cellulose, polystyrene, and vinylidene chloride types, and it provides styrene for the synthetic rubber program.

As the demand for bromine exceeded the Michigan plant capacity, the Dows moved to the sea coast and began working with sea water. All this time the extraction of magnesium chloride was being studied, and methods perfected for isolating the metal from this salt by electrolysis. The work was pressed in the face of almost complete market and governmental indifference. But when our vast airplane building and bombing programs—magnesium burns with dangerous ease and is used for flares and incendiary bombs—were launched, Dow knew how to produce as much of the light metal as anybody wanted. Every day more than a half-billion gallons of sea water were forced through huge pumps and intricate apparatus to give up their minute magnesium and bromine content. Here we see surviving, in a modern large-scale organization, the vision and pertinacity of our pioneer inventors.

Sea water may be inexhaustible, but our supplies of bauxite from which we obtain aluminum are not. In fact our bauxite reserves in the United States are nearing exhaustion, and will last only for four or five years more. At present we ferry much of the ore we use across the Caribbean from Surinam. But every foot of earth contains aluminum, and there are enormous deposits of alunite clay which have an average alumina content of 27 per cent. It has not paid to process this clay, as compared with high-grade bauxite which is 50 per cent to 60 per cent alumina. But industrial corporations have worked out the processing problems, and in these low-grade alunite deposits lie our hopes of future aluminum supplies. There is no question but that when the pressure is great enough we shall have as much aluminum as we need for as long as we need it.

9

The chemists, metallurgists, physicists, and engineers are barely hitting their stride. They have bigger problems facing them than any they have solved. They must find out how to create sugars directly from sunlight, air, and water, as every plant does, and so free us from dependence on nature for our food supply. They need to be able to control plant and animal growth at will through the administration of enzymes and hormones, and they need to subjugate forever the harmful insect and fungoid worlds that might conceivably in time overcome the human race. (New insecticides such as DDT developed for the use of troops are extraordinarily lethal to insect life and may give us complete dominance over this very dangerous enemy.) They need to build machinery that will not generate frictional heat or need lubrication, and they need to transform the latent energy of fuels directly into electrical energy. They should be able to reduce or eliminate the transitional difficulties of adolescence, the illnesses we suffer and the deterioration of old age. There are any number of materials we could use which have not yet been created.

In short, human life on earth is still far from completely perfect—healthful, comfortable, carefree—and until it reaches that ideal state the work of the four technological professions will not be done. For all our present self-appreciation, the world fifty years from now should be able to look back at 1946 as a time of naive, well-intentioned, not unintelligent beginnings leading to really great achievements.

CHAPTER VIII

WE CAN MOVE AS WE PLEASE

VERY few men can live to themselves, and these only because somebody else puts within their reach the things they do not exert themselves to go after. We are critically dependent on each other, and in the past century and a half the circle of our dependence has expanded to the ends of the earth. To keep us decently in this modern world requires a busy shuttling to and fro of men and an uninterrupted exchange of goods. If all of us suddenly were forced to stay at home and stop shipping our wares, we should die like flies and most disagreeably. No plague would be as lethal.

Modes of transportation will do more than anything else to set the physical pattern of population in the future. If you doubt it, observe the effects of two major revolutions in transport in the recent past.

After ages of reliance on horse-drawn and water-borne vehicles, we discovered, about a century and a quarter ago, that two iron rails laid parallel made a road over which a steam engine could draw carriages with ease and speed. Railroads were built in a nation-wide grid which concentrated the population in an identical grid-like pattern: towns not on the railroad lines withered to hamlets, cities burgeoned at their intersections; farmers were mos' prosperous when they were within easy hauling distance of ship ping points. Away from the railroads, land travel was generall limited to an eight or ten mile radius of easy highway transpor and this was practical only for those prosperous enough to affoi horses. Factories must be on railroads, workers must live in tl shadow of factories or on the slag-heaps of mines, remote farm were lonely hermitages out of the stream of life. The result was an artificial congestion of people, industries, and trade in the ribbons and knots of an urban system grievously lacking in urbanity.

In the first quarter of this century the mass production of automobiles began to undermine all these arrangements, to launch a second, many-faceted revolution. It instigated a complete reconstruction of our highway system and an elaborate provision of ubiquitous service facilities. It caused a rise in wage-scales * and living standards and enabled many millions of families to afford automobiles although they could not have afforded to keep a horse in the horse-and-buggy days. Theoretically, and to a large extent practically, these families were given the range of the continent.

Many reasons for collecting along the railway grid were at once canceled, and while a mass movement of population is not accomplished overnight it was well under way before the war. People had already fled in great numbers from the hearts of the cities to their outskirts, leaving behind them everywhere the municipal problem of blighted areas. Existing city street systems proved to be exasperatingly ill-adapted to automotive traffic but could not be replanned and rebuilt as readily as the inter-city highway systems. Cities continued to grow because there was an enormous expansion of industry and trade, but decentralized shopping districts sprang up where parking could be had more conveniently than in the old centers, and suburbs flowed out over the countryside far and wide. Motor transport freed many factories from bondage to railway spurs, and workers no longer needed to live within walking distance of their work. Factory parking lots began to spread acre by acre, and electric trolley lines, which for a generation had been among the country's prime investments, began to wither and droop and their rails were taken up from thousands of streets.

Toward the end of the prewar period it became the ambition of innumerable city men to live on a farm in the country, and

---

* The average annual wage in the automobile industry rose abruptly between 1914 and 1919, from $802 to $1,431, largely as a result of Henry Ford's establishment of a five-dollar minimum daily wage in his own plant. The rest of the nation's industries followed suit.

thousands of old farms in the hills of Connecticut, New Jersey, and a dozen other states were modernized and put back into production at great cost and little profit but with much satisfaction. Thus we saw started in the luxury brackets—where many popular movements such as automobiling and private aviation have had their beginnings—a genuine movement back to the land and a kind of living that can now be earthy, elemental, and gratifying with all modern conveniences. This return to first principles of living without sacrifice of sophisticated comforts may very well become a general trend in the postwar era, and we shall take a later look at its implications.

While our population pattern was still in the early stages of adjusting itself to the automobile, the war began to scramble the country, as briefly sketched in the third chapter of this book. The rapid shifting of great masses of people to crowded industrial centers caused a fine crop of municipal headaches, and in addition we had a mushroom growth of wholly new industrial centers, especially in the West and South. This wholesale migration has been made possible, to a very large extent, by the fluidity which the automobile gives to a motorized population such as ours. A comparable shifting of population, with the adoption of new homes and new ways of living by millions, will continue in the postwar years as we take full advantage of the freedom of choice which easy land transport gives us. And in these years, we shall be adjusting ourselves to a third great transformation, as maturing aviation adds its novel factor to the influences shaping the pattern of modern living.

2

Outside its own orbit, aviation will have a profound influence on all forms of land transport and especially on the railroads, which had not completed their adjustment to the highway competition of automobiles when the war gave them a suddenly expanded sphere of usefulness. Trains and ships have no rival in one field, which is the carrying of great bulks of heavy goods and large numbers of men. Automobiles have greater mobility and planes have more speed, but neither shows any signs of competing with trains and ships for heavy duty. This country's railway system has been called upon to perform a gigantic task in the war —such mountains of goods and such armies of men have never before been moved to and fro over a continent in so short a time. Passenger traffic alone in 1945 was five times the total of 1939, and two and one-half times the previous record year of 1918, while freight transport reached many millions of tons a month. The railroads have performed magnificently and demonstrated a permanent value that some were beginning to doubt. So long as iron ore, structural steel, oil in tanks, cattle, heavy machinery and such commodities are to be moved overland in bulk, and armies of men are to be shifted in mass, it appears that it will be done most economically by the railroads.

How much else of their past functions will be retained by the railroads is a question not yet settled. Certainly they will be in a better position to meet competition than for a long time past. They emerge from the war in greatly improved financial health, having reduced to manageable size the debt that was loaded on them first in the old buccaneering days before the first Roosevelt and then unavoidably increased during the depression decade. The debt reduction has been estimated at three billion dollars, and ample cash resources have been accumulated besides. This state of solvency has been recovered none too soon, because the railroads have been operating with 30 per cent less equipment than in 1918. Much of this is obsolete, and replacement on a tremendous scale is long overdue. In 1943, 97 per cent of the locomotives in use were over ten years old and 35 per cent were over twenty years old.* Today they are not only technologically antiquated but they and at least 300,000 cars are worn out, ready for scrapping. During the first half of 1946, the railroads received 18,000 new cars but were forced to retire 29,000 that were falling to pieces.† Locomotives must be replaced with improved electric, diesel, steam-and-mercury turbine and gas turbine engines, and immense numbers of modern, light-weight freight and passenger cars must be built as fast as materials and men are available. This will be fine for the general

* Address by William C. Dickerman, Chairman of the American Locomotive Company, reported in *Wall Street Journal*, November 24, 1943.

† *Business Week*, Aug. 10, 1946, p. 10.

economy, and it will improve the railroads' service and lower its cost. But it is far from solving the whole problem of what the railroads are going to do to hold their own against airplanes and highway transport.

Railroad management, being intelligent, is aware of the difficulties ahead, and as one solution has endeavored to obtain leave to enter the aviation, bus, and marine fields. Whether the public interests will best be served by letting these naturally competitive means of transport come under one control is a serious question, one that falls within the cognizance of government. In an economy such as ours, the police powers of government should be exercised vigilantly to maintain fair and free functioning of all competitive activities. The railroads have shown a certain amount of imagination and progressive energy in the past decade, but not enough to make one yearn to entrust the future of aviation to their care.

But if the airlines capture most of the profitable passenger, express, and mail traffic, some steps must be taken by the railroads to cover the loss. For longer passenger hauls, more luxurious trains will help to hold a substantial share of public patronage. Although greatly outclassed as to speed, the railroads still have greater comfort—and for the present greater safety—to offer in competition with the airlines. The possibilities of comfort had been tentatively explored in a few crack prewar trains, but never fully developed or extended to all classes of travelers. Now we shall see very active building of luxury railroad equipment—not necessarily to be operated at luxury prices—and in these new trains it should be possible to obtain a freedom from vibration and noise, a degree of ease and attractiveness and an expertness of service which have never before been approached. Many travelers will accept these inducements for the good reason that not everyone is in a breathless hurry and many people really enjoy an interval of leisurely relaxation to mark the transition from one episode of their lives to another.

But luxury trains and fast freights will not enable the railroads to retain short-haul passenger and express traffic, which already was declining to a trickle before the war. Unquestionably the railroads' best chance of filling this threatened gap lies in a closer integration of their service with public highway traffic, and for this purpose they own one of the best assets imaginable: they already occupy the finest available highways.

The traction of flanged steel wheels running on steel rails is such that they cannot negotiate steep gradients, and hence when railroad lines were laid out they followed level routes with long and very gentle inclines if any. Also railway trains cannot turn sharp corners, so that curves in the rail highways are all plotted with very long radii. Since the railroads have determined the growth of cities, their routes today are usually the shortest lines between the most populous points. Grade crossings are infrequent and in many territories have been entirely eliminated. Compared with most of the public highways—crowded, twisting, with steep hills, right-angled turns and much cross traffic—the railroads' right of way represents a highway planner's dream.

Yet before the war a very large share of traffic, both passenger and freight, had been diverted to commercial bus and truck lines operating over the less efficient public highways. This had happened because of the greater convenience of door-to-door carriage of freight, involving only one handling; and the greater convenience of curbstone pickup of bus passengers, and their delivery at the very street corners of their destinations.

There is no God-given or man-made law restricting the railroads to flanged wheels on steel rails. Granted that this is the most economical method of hauling heavy freight, it is not the most economical or convenient method of hauling everything. A railway coach for about 80 passengers weighs 100,000 to 135,000 pounds. Coaches must be made up into trains and trains must each have a locomotive and tender, weighing 370,000 to 890,000 pounds. For long hauls with full loads, as between New York and Chicago or between San Francisco and Los Angeles, even these mammoth conveyances can be operated very cheaply. But the system is notably inflexible, incapable of ready adjustment to varying loads, and poorly adapted to short hauls. We frequently see trains weighing more than a million pounds carrying no more passengers than could be seated comfortably in a few motorbuses weighing altogether less than 50,000 pounds. As additional disadvantages we have the rigid routes of the steel rails, and the inconvenient fixed points of loading and discharging.

Railroad rights of way generally are wide and only partly used. In many cases, with minor adjustments, it would be possible to lay concrete pavements in place of or beside the tracks. On these private highways conventional buses and trucks could be operated under constant signal control and with no interference from other traffic. Speed and safety would both be greater than can be attained on the public highways, and these would be relieved of a part of their burden. Yet the public street systems could be utilized for pickup and delivery, and the railroads could achieve flexibility and convenience of service equal to present bus and truck lines. A system like this would give the railroads a decided advantage in competition with exclusively highway transport paralleling their routes and be very much in the public interest.

A step in this direction has already been taken in the development of equipment that will run both on steel rails and on paved highways, and this may bridge a transition period. It may in fact provide the ultimate answer, if too much efficiency is not sacrificed and too much weight added in making the vehicles so versatile.

Yet we should not shut our eyes to the possibility that steel rails and flanged wheels may become entirely obsolete within a generation. It should be possible to construct conduits in which torpedo-like vehicles will be neatly fitted and safely contained with a minimum of friction and complete automatic control. Practicable speeds on land today are limited by the rapidity of human nerve reactions, but with all necessity for internal direction eliminated our torpedoes can be shot through their grooves at speeds at least equal to prewar air speeds. Instead of dispatching a Twentieth Century Express on a 17-hour run to Chicago every 24 hours, a single carriage can be discharged every hour on a four-hour run.

A pair of these high-speed conduits can occupy the central portion of the railroad's right of way, and be paralleled by conventionally paved lanes for conventional motor transport. On these private highways, it would be possible to operate heavy duty trailer trains to take the place of present-day freight trains, giving to heavy freight traffic also a flexibility it does not possess today.

This scheme of high-speed grooves and flanking motor lanes presupposes the use of methods of construction and types of motive power now available. But Dr Irving Langmuir has gone much further * and envisioned a vacuum tube in which airtight vehicles are magnetically suspended in space while being propelled forward electronically at speeds of 2,000 or even 5,000 miles an hour, their operations at all times safely under electronic control. Such a tube built across the continent would bring San Francisco within one hour of New York. And Dr. Langmuir has proved conclusively by demonstration that bodies can be suspended in a vacuum and propelled in this way. The economic practicability of building the system and operating it profitably will be determined by events that are still on the laps of the gods: if enough people are in sufficiently urgent need to cross the continent in an hour, it will be done.

3

The maritime interests also must adjust their operations to an Age of Flight. We ended the war with a Navy more than twice as big as the world's biggest in 1941, and a Merchant Marine of at least 40 million tons, five times the prewar total and about as much as all the rest of the world possesses. But at least three-quarters of this merchant fleet is made up of slow vessels of the Liberty type, intended to be expendable, and only some 10 million tons are of fairly modern design with a speed of 17 or 18 knots. Shipbuilding must of course decline from its astronomical wartime levels, but if ships are to continue in service there will be an immediate need for vessels designed for fast and economical transport and not merely for fast construction.

And ships will remain in service. They are needed for the vast quantities of heavy freight to be shipped all over the world in the immediate postwar years. Certainly we should make whatever exertion is necessary to hold our present maritime leadership, and not lose it by default as we did after World War I. Shipowners are organized to that end and there is every reason to believe it

* Herald Tribune Forum, November 20, 1943.

will be accomplished. Our shipbuilders and sailors are paid much more than those under other flags, and we shall be forced to offset this competitive handicap by greater efficiency and more economical operation. During the war we raised shipbuilding to a peak of efficiency and economy, in spite of high unit costs, which other nations have never approached. We shall now have to apply the same ingenuity to the reduction of operating costs. Gas turbines will contribute to this objective not only by their low cost and easy maintenance but by the space they release for additional cargo. Light materials, improved methods of freight handling also offer opportunities for savings.

We shall be forced to apply to the Merchant Marine the practice that is standard in industry, namely, the replacement of equipment whenever better is available, no matter how far from worn out the discarded machines may be: this insistence on the utmost efficiency in operation has proved to be a thrifty policy in the long pull. Applied to the Merchant Marine it means that a large part of our emergency shipping must go to the scrap pile and the shipyards must be called on to build many new vessels and refit many still usable hulls.

Airplanes of course will take over much of the ships' former passenger traffic. No one in a hurry will take a five-day liner to Europe when the trip can be made overnight by plane. But the five-day trip still will have great allure for many travelers. The leisure, the calm, the wave-washed air of ocean voyages are pleasures that the human race would be worse than stupid to give up, and there is not much likelihood that it will do so. In fact, and in spite of the hundreds of thousands who will flit across the oceans by air, we may very well be doing much more traveling by sea than ever before, and many new liners are being planned to meet this probable need.

4

Of all existing modes of transport, the automobile will be least affected by the postwar spread of aviation. There are many reasons for this. We have been conditioned to automobiles so completely that they cannot be dislodged except by some other vehicle as universally adaptable and convenient, which airplanes certainly are not. Automobiles in fact are supplementary to planes rather than competitive, and will remain so for years to come. A completely roadable, dependable helicopter may in time largely supplant the automobile, but that is merely to say that when the automobile grows wings it will be more useful than ever.

The automobile industry had hoped to resume production with an annual output of about 4.5 million cars, equal to the industry's biggest previous record, which was in 1929. If industrial strife not only in the automobile industry but in steel, coal and suppliers' industries can be allayed for a few months, this mark will be reached and passed at once. The demand is great enough to absorb much more than this initial output, and total production should rise to six or eight million cars a year and we shall be on our way to the 60 million cars in use—twice the prewar total—that some prophets see crowding our highways in another ten years.

What the car of the future will be like is still a subject of debate. It has long been assumed by many that it will be a rear-engined, rear-drive model, with very spacious interior and greatly improved visibility. Undoubtedly cars of this type will appear as soon as they can be cleared through the engineering departments, test tracks, and tool rooms. The engine and drive will be built as a single unit mounted on the rear axle, and it will be possible to remove and replace this power plant with great ease. In the rare event of mechanical failure requiring servicing, you can drive into a garage and have a new power unit installed as quickly as you now get a new battery.

But in the Jeep the war produced a quite different type of car which has become instantly and immensely popular. Many people are fascinated by the idea of an all-purpose car which will carry its passengers into roadless wildernesses for hunting and fishing, and plow a farmer's fields or snake his logs out of the woods as easily as it carries his eggs to market.

The four-wheel drive has the combined advantages of the front-drive and the rear-drive, both of which are supported by earnest schools of thought among engineers. A pancake-type motor mounted centrally under the body would give practically perfect weight distribution, and such a car would be skidproof and stall-proof as nearly as makes no difference. Properly sprung with a light-weight aluminum or plastic body it would have as much comfort and as ample room as any car of equal wheelbase. We shall certainly see a great many utility cars of this type competing in the future with the sleeker, smarter models.

The plastic body is already a demonstrated possibility. Before 1942 Henry Ford had molded sample bodies of a tough preformed plastic in which the filler consisted of the long fibers of sisal, ramie, and hemp instead of wood pulp, and this material has an impact resistance ten times that of steel: hammering with an ax doesn't dent it, and since the finish is integral with the material it cannot be scratched off. Here are obvious advantages over lacquered sheet metal, and we may expect to see plastic models in wide use as soon as the equipment can be provided for making them and the techniques of preforming and molding such large parts are thoroughly mastered.

The lucite "blisters" of airplanes have inspired many predictions of transparent-topped automobiles, and they are a definite possibility. But all transparent plastics known today are soft compared to glass, easily scratched and abraded by sand and dust. This is not a great disadvantage in the clean upper reaches of the air, but it is a serious fault at ground level. The chemists are working to harden the surface of plastics and probably will succeed in the effort, but until they do we will forego use of a material which in service would retain its transparency for a disappointingly short time.

As to style, we can expect to see very simple forms adapted to airflow, but not streamlined to teardrop shapes. The latter sacrifice inside room and serve no purpose in vehicles where maximum benefit in reducing wind resistance is not obtained until illegal speeds are reached. The chief objectives in body design will be internal spaciousness and comfort and maximum visibility. Fenders will be absorbed in the body, polaroid screens will eliminate headlight glare. Air-conditioning will become universal, wireless telephones in cars will be as common as radios and when you are late for an engagement you can dial a number and explain that you are held up in a traffic jam. Simple radar equipment will give you warning of unseen obstacles when driving in darkness and fog, but most highways will be lighted automatically as you traverse them so that visibility will be almost as good by night as by day.

Better fuels and high compression engines of light weight but great power will give increased mileage—probably forty to the gallon. And when gas turbines are evolved for automotive use the cost of motoring will be cut to a mere fraction of its prewar level. This economy, with the greater comfort of the new cars, will encourage seasonal and occupational migrations which will raise serious problems but will not necessarily be objectionable.

5

Of one fact we can be sure—we shall have many more cars and become a much more mobile people than ever before. And to the cars, railroads, and ships that serve us will be added fleets of planes that will crowd the skies.

Perhaps it is just as well that the third revolutionary movement in transport will be upon us while we are still dealing with the second: we shall avoid a later uprooting by combining it with our accommodation to the automobile, and the new trends may actually simplify our problems by indicating solutions we might not otherwise perceive. Arrival at an orderly disposition of population will be hastened, and we may all the more quickly work out a pattern of life that will be stable while it is anything but static. In any case we cannot avoid the experience, because at the war's end we are passing abruptly into the Age of Flight.

We must realize that aviation has suddenly become adult during the few years of the war, and that little more than forty years after the first flight at Kittyhawk we have acquired the skills, the equipment and the personnel to effect another radical change in our transportation habits.

CHAPTER IX

INTO THE AIRWAYS

THE YEAR 1903 was not very long ago. Vincent Van Gogh, who is considered a "modern" painter, had been dead ten years; Henry Ford at forty was founding the Ford Motor Company which he still heads; the wartime Prime Minister of Great Britain and present leader of His Majesty's Loyal Opposition was already a celebrated veteran of the Boer War. At the end of 1903—December 17, to be exact—the first flight by man in a heavier-than-air machine was made. The man who made that flight died young, but he lived to see aviation introduced and practiced all over the world. His brother, who shares equally with him in credit for the initial achievement, is at this moment a distinguished elderly citizen of Dayton, Ohio.

So short is the history of aviation. Yet by 1944 this country was building airplanes at the rate of 100,000 a year, with the value of airplane production amounting to more than 16 billion dollars,* a sizable fraction of the war budget for the year. What this means can be grasped by comparing it with the 1941 production in the automobile industry, which amounted to 3.7 billion dollars. As the war drew to its close, huge all-American armadas of thousands of planes were filling the skies over Europe and Japan. There were three million men in the Army and Navy Air Forces, and about a half-million of these were fliers. Of the rest, all had some knowledge of flying and many had a firm intention of getting their pilot's licenses just as soon as circumstances should make it possible.

* $16,339,000,000. Figure supplied by Aeronautical Chamber of Commerce.

More important than the fighters and bombers, in their peace-time implications, were the great fleets of transports operating literally to all parts of the world. They were built, with capacities twice as great as those of the common prewar DC-3, at the rate of 15,000 a year, and they maintained regular services between the United States, India, and Australia via Hawaii and the islands of the Southern and Western Pacific; between the United States, Russia, Siberia, Asia Minor, Africa; they shuttled back and forth between America and Britain and France like daily flights of swallows; they supplied Chiang Kai-shek's armies across the Hima-layas from India, and served United States outposts in far-away isolated spots from Iceland on one side of the globe to Guadal-canal on the other. By the latter part of 1943, 150,000 miles of these regular transport routes were criss-crossing the globe, in addition to 110,000 miles being operated by commercial carriers.

Before the war we had less than 33,000 miles of lighted airways operating within the United States, with 359 planes in the com-bined fleets of all commercial airlines. During the war the devel-opment of civilian passenger planes was forbidden, except as mili-tary needs might be served, and their construction completely stopped. Now both have been resumed intensively, and orders for hundreds of such giant transports as never flew before are on the builders' books. Meanwhile many of the Army's C-54's, big brothers of the DC-3, have been converted to serve the airlines until the newer and still bigger models are ready. By the end of 1946 American airlines were operating at least a thousand planes, with greatly expanded services within the United States and regular schedules extended by many routes to Europe, Asia, and South America.

That first flight by the Wright brothers lasted only a few sec-onds and covered a few hundred yards, at a few feet above the sand. Forty-two years later a Boeing B-29 flew nonstop from Guam to Washington, and nonstop flights across this continent now attract no attention unless they succeed—as happens at fre-quent intervals—in lowering the time record. In future transport service, flying ranges of 10,000 miles can easily be exceeded, if necessary, but 10,000 miles is enough for all practical purposes since in the Northern Hemisphere no principal centers of population are more than that distance apart by the shortest route.

To cite an example of endurance and dependability: a nation-wide system of broadcasting television and frequency modulation from the stratosphere is planned by the Westinghouse Electric Corporation and the Glenn L. Martin Company; planes similar to the B-29 will work eight-hour shifts, in pairs, at a series of fixed stations 30,000 feet aloft, blanketing the country with relayed broadcasts which will be greatly improved and extended by this method.

For a time the ceiling on flying was kept at comparatively low altitudes by the decreasing oxygen content of the air—a motor unassisted loses more than half its power at 20,000 feet, a man without an artificial oxygen supply loses consciousness at 18,000 to 26,000 feet, and even with oxygen masks of the best type, men reach the limit of safe flying at about 37,000 feet. But super-charged engines and supercharged cabins, maintaining normal atmospheric pressures as well as oxygen supply, have changed all that. Our bombers often went on their missions at 40,000 feet. Much commercial long-distance flying will be done at 15,000 to 25,000 feet, but certain extended flights will be made, with the aid of jet propulsion which works better in rarefied air, in strata where weather does not exist and storms never happen.

As to speed, 200 miles an hour was normal for transport planes before the war, but this is being increased by another hundred or two as the more advanced postwar models are placed in service. Three types of propeller-driven fighter planes in this country's service were officially rated at speeds above 400 miles an hour, and in power dives speeds above 780 miles have been attained. At about 400 miles an hour the conventional propeller begins to reach its limit of "bite," and for sonic speeds and over we must look to jet propulsion.

But speeds immediately practicable will reduce the world to very small proportions. A landfall flight from Newfoundland to Ireland has been made in 6 hours and 12 minutes; from Burbank, California, to New York, 2,467 miles, in 5 hours and 28 minutes by a propeller-driven plane. We have all become familiar with a God's-eye view of the world from above the North Pole, and adjusted ourselves to the fact that the shortest distance from New York to Peiping is not across the Pacific but across the Arctic Ocean north of Alaska, and that from San Francisco to London a straight route will take us over the middle of Hudson Bay. By these direct lines and at present planned schedules, Washington will be only 12 to 14 hours from Paris or London, some 16 hours from Moscow, Rio de Janeiro or Istanbul, 8 hours from Panama, 36 hours from Sydney. A man will be able to spend a full day in his New York office on Monday, confer all of Tuesday with business associates in London, see a London show that evening and be back in his office at the usual hour on Wednesday morning. Week-ending in Paris will be as easy for New Yorkers as it used to be for Londoners. This continent will be crossed regularly in seven hours or less, Mexico City will be seven hours from New York. It is hardly reasonable that anyone should be in a greater hurry than that, but you never can tell.

2

In 43 years the Wright brothers' frail little contraption of poles and canvas has had monster offspring. Nature needs millions of years to work out anything like the same degree of evolutionary change that has taken place in airplanes in these four decades. That typical work horse of wartime transport, the Douglas C-54, has 4,400 horsepower in its four engines, a wingspread of 117 feet, a capacity of ten tons of freight or 50 passengers with baggage, mail and express. But it has been outclassed in size for several years by the veteran Martin flying boat Mars, with 12,000 horsepower, a wingspread of 200 feet and a weight when loaded of 82.5 tons. This largest plane in actual wartime service has shuttled steadily and almost without rest between San Francisco and Hawaii with 50 passengers and 30 tons of freight and fuel.

In the new postwar airline equipment we move into a new scale. The airlines are commissioning hundreds of startling giants: the Boeing Stratocruiser, a 65-ton ship for 100 passengers; the Douglas DC-6, of 40 tons and 50 passenger capacity; Consolidated Vultee's giant of 160 tons to carry 200 passengers.

In recent years the problem of weight versus lifting power, which once threatened to hold planes to modest sizes of 15 or 18 tons for all time, has been solved, and theoretically the only limit on size in the future will be the practicability of fabrication: whatever can be built, if properly designed and powered, will fly. The Mars is as big as a fifteen-room house, and its builder has said that there is no reason why an aerial Empire State Building should not be given wings. Planes of 400 passenger capacity and bigger have been designed and may be flown. The Jules Verneish quality in this forecast does not discredit it, but it may never come to pass for quite other reasons: planes may be held to a relatively small scale as compared to marine vessels, not by the impracticability of flying great weights, but by considerations of economy and convenience. When the Atlantic can be crossed in ten or twelve hours, why build a Normandie or Queen Mary of the air to do it? Why make 200 passengers wait while another 200 with all their baggage are gotten aboard? Loading, unloading and servicing oversize transports will take more time than their flights, and it will be sensible to schedule more frequent departures of smaller planes that can turn around faster.

Practical reasons call for a wide range of sizes, speeds, and capacities for various regular services. Non-stop flights of 3,000 miles or more will be made by the large, extremely fast luxury liners, whose pressurized cabins will enable them to cruise at very high altitudes. For intracontinental flights between centers of population and to and from the ports of the superliners, ships of intermediate size, still fast and accommodating perhaps 40 or 50 passengers, will be used. Twenty to 30 passenger planes will connect smaller towns with major airports; still smaller planes will serve outlying communities, and great fleets of helicopters will replace buses to transport passengers to and from the airports.

In 42 years the Wright brothers' kite has evolved into not one but dozens of well-developed species, from its own minnow size to huge leviathans. Whatever kind of flying machine we may need in the future for whatever purpose, you may be sure will be built. And the evolutionary process is still in its early stages.

3

Momentous changes are already impending as a result of the development of the gas turbine engine, the jet propulsion engine, and the controllable, liquid fuel rocket motor. All three of these power sources were advanced with revolutionary speed by war-inspired research, and it seems certain that they will be used increasingly, singly and in various combinations, to drive the planes of the future. As a result we shall attain higher speeds and altitudes, lighter weight, greater economy, and still more accurate specialization of plane design.

We have already discussed the gas turbine engine (Chapter IV), which will drive ships and trains and power plants as well as planes. In aviation its attractions are many. It will deliver more power from less weight and bulk, and it has a beautiful simplicity. By comparison with the thousands of things that can go wrong with present multicylinder reciprocating airplane engines, the gas turbine is about as simple as an old-fashioned mill wheel. Its trouble spots can be counted on one's fingers, and its maintenance should be as easy as inspecting railway journals for hot boxes. This will represent a major economy, and in addition its fuel will be much cheaper than high-octane gas.

This fuel saving will grow in importance as petroleum reserves diminish, since as long as reciprocating engines are used not even private fliers will be happy with less than high-octane gas. If the prediction of half a million fliers in the air by 1950 comes true, the drain on oil supplies may be greater than can be met. The gas turbine burns a fuel oil that is very low-grade by comparison, and it may very well prove to be as easy to synthesize from coal or carboniferous vegetable matter as high-octane gas from petroleum. When gas turbines are built for four-passenger planes, the cost of private flying will be less than the cost of driving a car at present.

Both gas turbines and jet motors have proved themselves to be magnificent power sources, and their potentialities are still unplumbed. But their ultimate development waits on finding a metal alloy or a ceramic much more heat resistant than any now available, to form the rotors that in both types of motor are driven by flaming gases. The search is on and the needed material will be found. Then both gas turbines and jet motors will move into new levels of power delivery, beyond anything yet achieved by man-made engines.

There is a close relationship between the principles of the gas turbine and jet motor, and both can and will be combined in the same engine—the exhaust gases from the turbine being utilized as a forward propelling jet. This hybrid will give a well-balanced performance, delivering maximum power at low altitudes and moderate speeds where the turbine-driven propeller is most efficient, and at high altitudes and maximum speeds where the jet comes into its own.

Jet propulsion is a special application of the same law that we see exemplified in every Fourth of July rocket—that for every action there must be an equal and opposite reaction. If you create a very high pressure in a cylinder and relieve that pressure through a small opening in one end, the unbalanced force will propel the cylinder in the opposite direction. High pressure is obtained in rockets by burning an explosive. Since any explosive contains within its own chemical formula the oxygen it needs for combustion, it burns with terrific speed and the gases it releases expand with equally terrific speed and therefore enormous force. Where the best conventional airplane engine develops one horsepower per pound, military rockets develop several hundred horsepower per pound. But only for a short time: the large and relatively slow-burning stick of black powder used in a five-inch military rocket gives up all its energy in about three-fifths of a second. In certain liquid fuel rockets, the components of the explosive are carried in separate compartments and fed together at a predetermined rate, in order to prolong their combustion.

But the fuel is still an explosive and its combustion an explosion, which obviously is not a carefree method of driving a vehicle in which human beings must ride. It would take a very large cargo of highly unstable fuel to power a flight of any great duration, and three-fourths of this cargo's weight would be oxygen. As there is ample oxygen in the air all around us, why carry it in

the fuel tanks? Why not use a more tractable oxygenless fuel—
kerosene, for instance—and draw on atmospheric oxygen for combustion? This is exactly what is done in jet propulsion motors,
and the term "jet propulsion" has come to signify the rocket
principle adapted to the use of oxygenless fuel, in distinction to
the true rocket method of propulsion by explosives.

In a jet propulsion motor, air is drawn in through a wide mouth
at the front, compressed in a turbine supercharger and passed into
a chamber where it unites with the fuel in combustion. A little
of the energy thus created is used to turn a rotor like that in a
gas turbine, and this rotor drives the air compressor. The rest of
the pressure is released through a carefully designed nozzle or
nozzles at the rear. The unbalanced forces thus set up—restrained
in one direction, relieved in the other—drive the plane forward.
There is of course no propeller, and no moving parts except those
involved in the air compressor. In basic principle the jet propulsion motor is thus supremely simple, and effects a very direct
transformation of energy into work.

Since a rocket carries its own oxygen supply and exerts no force
on anything outside itself, it would operate in a vacuum much
better than in air: the air only acts to retard its flight. It was
long ago recognized that a "rocket ship" would be a means of
navigating interplanetary space, and in our boyhood Jules Verne
took us on a voyage to the moon by this means. As a practical
exploit, navigation beyond the atmosphere is still barred by the
impossibility of carrying an adequate fuel supply, as one among
numerous difficulties. But it is equally true of a jet propulsion
motor that no force is exerted on anything outside itself, and a
plane so powered will fly best in the thin upper levels of the
atmosphere where an ordinary gasoline motor loses much of its
efficiency and propeller blades can no longer get a sufficient bite
in the air. The ceiling on jet propulsion efficiency is reached only
at the point where the supercharger can no longer compress the
rarefied air sufficiently to maintain the required pressure in the
combustion chamber.

Research into both rocket and jet propulsion had been carried
on for a number of years by a few persistent scientists who got
themselves classed with the lunatic fringe for their pains, but

after 1939 their work was organized officially and intensified both here and abroad. At that time a number of factors converged to make practicable what had been a mere alluring dream: knowledge of jet action derived from parallel research on military rockets, the perfection of high heat-resistant alloys, improvement of superchargers, the development of the gas turbine principle for operation of superchargers. Jet propelled planes were successfully developed and hundreds of them were flown in combat by the Allied armies and by the late Luftwaffe.

Having neither propeller nor reciprocating movements, the jet propulsion plane is vibrationless, and as the noise is directed out the rear the crew finds it remarkably quiet. Hence it imposes much less nervous strain on those aboard and creates less fatigue than normal flying. It can be flown without special training by any competent pilot. Since there is no big propeller to clear the ground it is built low and the landing gear greatly simplified. Kerosene being the fuel, the hazard of explosion is reduced as compared with high-octane gas. The motors are placed close to the fuselage, giving better balance and maneuverability. At speeds above 500 miles an hour and elevations of 40,000 to 60,000 feet, jet propulsion is at its best and has no rival.

A limit on the speed of jet propelled planes is not yet in sight, but as speed increases it opens up a whole series of new and formidable problems. Peculiar conditions are encountered when the speed of an object traveling through air approaches the speed of sound—763 miles an hour: the air ceases to flow past as a fluid and begins to act like a collection of solid particles too dense to get out of the way. A machine gun bullet moving at twice the speed of sound encounters terrific resistance, and photographs show that a pane of glass is shattered not by the bullet but by the air which the bullet pushes ahead of it, so that it passes through an opening already blasted out for it. Sonic speed thus presents the designer with various aerodynamic posers, since the form that best penetrates a fluid is not the form that best penetrates a solid. An additional complication is the apparently illogical fact that the critical speed is less in thin air than in dense air—at 50,000 feet sound is slowed down, and the air reacts to a speed of 666 miles in the same way it reacts to a speed of 763

miles in the denser lower levels. But solutions to these puzzles are
being worked out with great care and elaborate apparatus, and we
inch steadily forward.

On August 1, 1945, a jet propelled Lockheed Shooting Star flew
from Dayton to New York, 544 miles, at an elevation of 20,000
feet, in 62 minutes. On January 26, 1946, another P-80 flew from
California to New York in 4 hours and 13 minutes, 584 miles an
hour, with two sister ships only a few minutes behind. These
records will take their place among other worthy but crude pioneer achievements in the not so distant future, when air speeds
will be measured in thousands of miles instead of hundreds. It
is probable that within a few years 10,000 miles will be regularly
flown in 10 hours, and speeds up to 2,000 miles an hour are confidently predicted.

In August, 1946, two B-17's flew from Hawaii to California under
fully automatic controls, directed by radio, with no man aboard. In
the Pacific war the Navy made lethal use of a device which was a
logical advance along the lines of the German V-1 missile: both
were miniature jet-propelled planes carrying an explosive charge
and automatically stabilized in flight. But the German flying
bomb was discharged in the direction of its target and landed
where luck decreed, while the American weapon was guided accurately to its target by radar. So far this radar system is only
practicable for use in naval warfare, when an enemy ship or shore
installation is the target. But radio control, from point of take-off
and desired landing point, has immense peacetime possibilities.
We can see here significant implications as to the future of mail
and express transportation.

Robot cargo planes of any size can be powered by jet motors
and guided safely and accurately to their destination by radio control from the ground, with no crew whatever aboard. It is possible that intercity mail and express will be transported in these
automatic missiles as easily as if they had been shot through
pneumatic tubes, and much more swiftly. If we are stupid enough
to have another war in another generation, perfected machines
of this type carrying atomic bombs may work a destruction that
will be irreparable in the lifetime of the human race.

4

The rocket principle is still being explored, and the fact that the trajectory of the German V-2 missile—a true rocket—reached an elevation of 70 miles above the earth makes interplanetary navigation seem not such a completely irrational dream after all. But military research has found an immediate and practical application of the rocket principle, which will be as valuable in peacetime flying as in war: it is used to get heavy planes off the ground in a fraction of the normal take-off runs.

If a many-tonned airliner can cut in a battery of rockets at the moment of take-off, it will find itself in the air with startling celerity. It is even feasible to use an explosive for this purpose, because the entire charge is consumed in a fraction of a second and its handling prior to firing can be amply safeguarded. The technique has been worked out for the Air Force, and "jet-assisted take-off" has been regularly practiced by military planes.

Such an aid to take-off can cut the length of runways by 40 per cent to 50 per cent, and the size of airfields can be reduced proportionately. Any complete coverage of the country by air transport will require a system of ubiquitous airfields, and it is disturbing to think of the acreage these fields will withdraw from other uses. Besides, enormous, flat, empty tracts of land on the Idlewild scale—6,000 acres or so—are not easy to come by in the neighborhood of great cities, and anything that will reduce the need for such outsizes will be a godsend. Jet-assisted take-off may do just that, most effectively.

During the war we built airports with frantic speed. At its outset we had only 76 airports with runways of 3,500 feet or longer, but by the end of 1943 we had almost 900 of this class and, of these, 600 had 4,500-foot runways or longer. In addition we had more than 2,000 smaller fields. Now at the end of the war we have some 4,000 fields of all classes. Some of these have only military value, but many will pass into local control to serve the needs of commercial and private flying.

Still we are far short of the needs of a peacetime age of flight, and many municipalities are busy with plans for the necessary postwar extension and improvements. The Civil Aeronautics Administration estimates that we shall need 6,000 civilian fields, if our aerial conversion is to be complete. As there are 6,669 towns in the country with a population of 1,000 or more, CAA is probably right if we count all the fields from simple crossed strips for small communities to the huge international and transcontinental ports such as New York and San Francisco will need.

The experience of New York is an example of the inconvenient speed with which aviation outgrows its clothes. La Guardia airport was built at a cost of 40 million dollars to replace the outgrown Newark airport, and it was opened in 1939. In two years it was serving annually a million arriving and departing passengers and its facilities were greatly overtaxed. Now New York is spending another 200 million dollars to build an airport more than eight times the size of the La Guardia airport, to be the world's biggest, on marshy wastes at Idlewild on Jamaica Bay. It will have thirteen miles of runways up to 10,000 feet long, a great seaplane landing basin and marine hangars, a large helicopter parking lot and all the facilities for servicing men and equipment such a port requires. It is projected as an ambitious forecast of future needs, with a long program of future expansions. Thirty thousand passengers will use it daily, 40,000 people will be permanently employed in its operation, and it is estimated that its international passengers alone will number 600,000 a year. In addition, it is also proposed at this writing to enlarge and improve the Newark Airport at a cost of 76 million dollars. New York's experience is not exceptional: most of the big cities of the country are making plans, relatively as ample, to handle their share of our huge air transport.

Excluding short-haul traffic, our airlines in a reasonable time and at rates well below present Pullman fares may be expected to transport 70 per cent of prewar Pullman traffic, or some 20 million passengers a year.* And at the end of a decade, at least as large a share of our present express traffic and practically all our

* "The Air Traffic of the Future," by William A. M. Burden, Special Aviation Assistant to the Secretary of Commerce, New York Times Magazine, February 20, 1944.

mail will be carried by air. And the Special Aviation Assistant to the Secretary of Commerce says, "We may do much better."

We certainly may, since these estimates are based on prewar volumes and take no account of the enormously increased traffic which air transport itself will create. We have never been a static people, and were on the move even when shank's mare, canal boats, and covered wagons were our conveyances. The habit has grown with time. With universal air transport, cheap and safe, cutting travel time down to a maximum of $3\frac{1}{3}$ hours per thousand miles, our nomadism will accelerate. It is quite possible that in ten years of peace—if it is prosperous peace, of course—the airlines will be carrying ten times the Pullman passenger and express traffic of prewar years. Such a volume would far exceed the capacity of any airport system now contemplated. But if in one generation we could rebuild our entire highway system at a cost of many billions of dollars to accommodate the automobile, we undoubtedly will manage to take care of all the planes it seems advisable to fly.

All this great increase in volume is predicated on a progressive reduction in cost, which will come about with increase in volume, more economical operation and servicing of planes, and lighter and less costly construction. All these economies are in process of being achieved, and in a free competitive society the traveling public will get the benefit.

We have seen that our American transatlantic airlines already can afford to carry passengers to Britain for $100 less than the British government will allow them to accept. Here we see a collectivist state at its usual practice of preventing competition from taking its normal course. Transatlantic traffic will suffer and with it international trade and good will, the people of Britain and the people of America, but so long as governments undertake to guarantee the prosperity of nationally controlled enterprises we may expect to see this kind of obstruction of progress. It is the cartel-conditioned mind at work.

But within our own borders, at least, aerial travel and transport will decline in cost as they expand to the immense volume this decline itself will stimulate.

5

To talk about commercial and military flying without discussing private flying of the future would be like discussing motor trucks without mentioning passenger automobiles. No matter how much expansion there may be in the professional fields, more than four-fifths of the predicted half-million planes a few years hence will be privately owned and flown: and this number may be greatly exceeded with the successful marketing of roadable planes and helicopters.

It is an accepted estimate that four-passenger planes with full automatic controls will be produced at $1,500 to $2,000, and if the national income is maintained and distributed as it should be these prices will bring flying within the financial range of millions of people. But planes present more than financial obstacles to ownership: there are the questions of where to land and take off, and where to keep the thing between flights. Not everybody will live on the edge of an airport, or be able to pay for commercial hangar service. Here are the reasons for new types of planes adapted to overcome just these difficulties, and the roadable plane and the helicopter give promise of being the answer.

Already carrier-based naval planes fold their wings for storage, and there is no reason why the same principle will not work in small private planes. Experimental models already have been built and tested. The result may not be both an ideal plane and an ideal automobile: but it is probable that as a plane it will be good enough for the amateur Sunday flyer, and as an automobile it will meet the need for limited land transport; and in both phases of its double life it can be improved with experience.

Many spectacular demonstrations of helicopters have convinced us that almost at once we shall all be commuting by air from our front lawns to the roofs of our office buildings. This is largely wishful thinking. Less optimistic engineers point out that the helicopter is a long way from complete development and that our hopes of large-scale, immediate postwar production is ill-founded. Probably the optimism and pessimism are both excessive: it may take a little time to adapt the helicopter to a mass market, but its principle is so sound that within a few years we shall have designs which will meet all requirements of the hedge-hopper and the commuter.

By their nature, helicopters are barred from competing with airplanes as to speed, elevation or range. But they are the safest of all aircraft because even with a stalled motor they will not fall but can be brought safely to earth. In gales they are more stable than conventional planes. For taking off and landing they need no more room than an automobile occupies, and some models will be made roadable to a practicable degree. They probably will be limited by law to a ceiling of, say, a thousand feet, so as not to interfere with the course of faster planes, and their speed at 100 miles an hour is adequate for short-range travel. In air travel they may be expected to become as universally acceptable as the automobile is on land, and we should live to see millions of them in use.

We shall need to have careful classification and regulation of planes, pilots, and traffic, because multitudinous flyers without a thorough knowledge of meteorology and aerial navigation cannot be trusted to fly at will except under specified conditions; and yet automatic stabilizers and automatic pilots, electronic steering and radar protection devices, all operating under simple push-button controls, will bring regulated, fair-weather flying down to the intelligence level of driving a car. And with the universal use of two-way radio telephones the skyways can be adequately policed. Occasions will arise when the sky-police will order all Class Two, Three, and Four flyers to the ground, and we shall see them settling down grumbling but acquiescent, like a flock of ill-tempered crows alighting in a pasture lot. At all times, these planes must keep to definite lanes and altitudes for travel in specified directions, and the police will be assisted by the fact that failure to observe the traffic rules may bring a calamity much worse than a dented fender or a five-dollar fine.

6

One of the major hazards of flying will be removed by the universal use of radar, probably the war's greatest gift to all types of navigation. As late as 1942, a list of much-needed inventions contained this item: "A means of dispelling fog over airports." But the Royal Air Force had been using from the beginning of the war this device which in its ultimate developments will make fog over airports a matter of indifference. Radar had a great deal to do with the winning of the Battle of Britain and the critical Battle of Midway and might have made the attack on Pearl Harbor abortive if its warning had been heeded. It helped to save Leningrad, Moscow, Stalingrad, and Malta, and it made it possible to send our convoys across the oceans through darkness and fog at top speed, in perfect formation without fear of collisions.

Radar is an electronic means of seeing through distance, darkness, fogs and clouds. Like vision by light rays it cannot bend around the curvature of the earth nor penetrate earth or water, but it can dodge these obstacles by means of that mysterious ceiling in the sky known as the ionosphere, which acts as a mirror to bend its rays. Radar is better than eyesight in that it measures accurately the distance to the object seen and will also tell exactly the speed and direction of a moving object. With a cathode ray device a picture of a specified field can be seen on a translucent screen.

Radar reports the approach of planes long before they can be detected by any other means. It reports the exact location of ships at sea, and any obstacle in their course. No ship equipped with radar would collide with an iceberg, as the *Titanic* did, or run down another ship, or strike rocks that project above the waves. Radar gives an air pilot an exact measurement of his altitude, and warns him of mountains or other planes in his path. It will guide a plane accurately into a landing strip which the pilot cannot see. When we recall how many fatal accidents have resulted from just this lack of exact information as to what lay in the pilot's course, we realize that radar will give protection against a very large percentage of past types of casualties.

7

But in spite of all safeguards, all the automatic controls and the ease of fair-weather flying, aviation in its expert phases will remain a highly technical art. The pilot of a high-speed, high-altitude plane who flies under any and all conditions must be the product of long and arduous training, and he must have special aptitudes, exactly as today.

Unquestionably the groundwork will be provided by our general educational system. A basic knowledge of flying will be as universally necessary in the future as a knowledge of languages, physics, electronics, and chemistry. Our new schooling refurbished and addressed to the keen interests which are also the practical requirements of modern life will supply this foundation of working knowledge and at the same time reveal special aptitudes which can receive intensive development. Before the war, tens of thousands of boys and some girls were being taught to fly as part of their high school and college courses, and these will be succeeded by millions in the postwar generations. Aviation, meteorology, navigation may be followed as a profession or may be merely the supplementary equipment of all literate men: no one should be wholly ignorant of these or any other vital science. From this educational priming and sorting will come a steady flow of expert flyers, recruits and replacements for the great body of trained men with whom we start the postwar era, the hundreds of thousands who are coming back from the armed forces.

We are seeing, of course, an immediate and severe contraction of wartime volumes of airplane building. Certainly we cannot support a 20 billion dollar industry in normal times, when 3.7 billion dollars' worth of production supplied us with a normal year's output of automobiles. But this curtailment is nothing like a total cessation and will in all probability leave airplane building as one of the major industries of the country.

We face a long and troublesome period of world stabilization during which our good intentions must be implemented by powerful aerial and naval fleets. An air force and a navy today are technological marvels, and they depend for success on technical superiority even more than on quantitative superiority. The Battle of Britain and therefore ultimately the war were lost by Hitler because in 1940 the Royal Air Force possessed two technical advantages over the much bigger Luftwaffe: it had radar, and the Spitfire plane had greater firepower than any plane Goering could send against it. These seemingly minor advantages, plus of course the incandescent courage with which they were exploited, were enough to decide the issue at the most crucial moment in modern history. On the other side of the world, the *Prince of Wales* and the *Repulse* were lost because they were not technically equipped to meet air attack as our battleships were later equipped.

So if we are capable of learning from experience, we will maintain the technological superiority of our Air Force and Navy as long as we have need for them—which will be until the world's habits of thought and behavior are firmly fixed in patterns of which we can see inadequate signs at present. This means that we must continue to experiment and test without relaxation, and we must be ruthless in supplanting obsolete equipment with better equipment whenever the better is available.

Engineering research in the field of military aviation will not be wasted even if, as we hope, we never have to send a plane into combat again. Much of it will be directly applicable to civilian aviation, as it has been in the past. In the civilian field also there will be rapid replacement of equipment, to keep pace with technical developments. A continued program of military construction, plus the swift expansion of commercial and private flying, should maintain the airplane building industry at a level close to that of the automotive industry, if not above it.

The actual size of an industry gives little indication of its influence on the economy as a whole. It has been calculated that the automobile industry, for every two men it employs directly, provides employment outside its own ranks for five other men before production and five more afterwards. This dissemination of employment will be as true of the new aviation industry as of any other. Aside from the building of planes and the actual operation of airlines, there will be the usual sequences carried back through the processing of materials and mining, the immense requirements in plastics and textiles, the preparation and distribution of fuels. Then there will be the building of airfields and marking of airways, and a great system of merchandising and servicing planes. Back of it all will be the organization of research, maintaining the advancement of the art.

Thus it is obvious that with aviation as one of our four principal means of transport and perhaps the leading one, it will provide livelihoods for millions of men. Practically none of this work will be menial, or mere routine physical exertion: practically all will require some degree of expertise, and much of it a very high degree indeed. Transport through the air is an application of sciences more abstruse and intricate than transport on land or water, and it will make correspondingly greater demands on the gray matter of the men involved in it. It is already one of the most stimulating of human activities and will continue to provide exceedingly valuable mental gymnastics for an increasing section of the population through many generations to come.

8

Whatever augments the individual's freedom to plan his life as he wants it to be, and enables him to move at will without bondage to material circumstances, is a good thing. It marks a step forward in the emancipation of the race. But like any other freedom it calls for an adjustment of self-assumed disciplines to cover the enlarged field of action. Whether facile transport by air, land and sea turns us into a nation of shiftless nomads or more productive free men will be decided in other compartments of society: by adequate education, a lively social consciousness, a broad prevalence of material well-being. Certainly the new facilities will not be withheld until people are proven qualified to make the best use of them. They will be issued when ready and the consequences will be on our heads without delay.

A further radical change in the pattern of living is inevitable, and the next half-century will be a period of shifting population and the crystallization of new types of community structure. There will be nothing to compel the congestion that has characterized urban and industrial building in the past, and the influence of the railroads in concentrating population along their lines will be steadily reduced. Airplanes and helicopters will give wider range to a movement already started by the automobile, and the utility of the automobile will be further extended by the completion of a nation-wide network of superhighways and parkways connecting our thousands of airfields. It will be possible for most men to live at a considerable distance from their work, so that the population can spread more evenly over the face of the country.* One's domicile will be located according to the surroundings one prefers, and not determined by necessity to anything like the past or present degree. Domestic life should be enhanced in charm, salubrity, and peace.

The world as a whole will be drawn into a single community by constant intercourse, and the mutual dependence of nations increased until the thought of war eventually will be rejected not so much because of war's horrors—men have always been ready to suffer and die if the cause seemed good enough—but because the world structure will have no aperture at which war can be admitted.

Surveying the scene today, one would have to be a completely hopeless pessimist not to perceive that these changes can be immensely for the better. They do in fact hold potentialities for general betterment of living so great as to be in fair proportion to the technological advances that make them possible.

* See Chapter XII.

CHAPTER X

WE CAN PROVIDE MILLIONS OF HOUSES

WE DO a great deal of smug back-patting about the "American standard of living." We are very conscious that we have more automobiles, more supermarkets, more bathrooms, more modern kitchens, more central heating, more electric service than any other people in the world. We live better than the rest of the world, without a doubt. Our shops are stocked with more kinds of food, we take better care of our teeth, we buy more clothes, we wash more thoroughly—a small-town movie audience in this country does not smell like a small-town movie audience in, say, France. In fact it may not smell at all. We are pretty complacent about our way of life.

Our complacency is remarkable, because we usually aren't satisfied with a worse-than-mediocre performance in any field. And in this matter of living conditions, if we will forget about foreign comparisons and judge ourselves by our *own* standards, we shall stop boasting and hang our heads in shame. In this country we have accepted, by general agreement, certain appurtenances as indispensable to decent living, and adopted a certain type of well-equipped domestic machine as the standard frame of American family life. And let's face the shameful truth: more than half our families have never enjoyed that kind of home. A nation that is perfectly capable of providing proper housing for everybody—if its productive system were functioning in an expanding economy of abundance—has not made even a fifty-fifty job of doing so.

Between the first World War and 1929, this country made commendable progress in raising its housing toward the accepted standard. To do this requires a great deal of reconstruction and replacement. During the decade of the 1920's we averaged 700,000 new dwellings a year, reaching an all-time high of 937,000 in 1925. This was not enough for a rapid change-over but it did mean that every year of this decade we were providing at least 200,000 new and undoubtedly better replacements, in addition to another half-million required to accommodate the new families annually adding themselves to the population. This went considerably beyond mere maintenance of the *status quo* in shelter.*

But for the past seventeen years, since 1929, we have not even held our own. Instead we have deteriorated at an alarming, even tragic, rate. From 1930 to 1939 inclusive we did not build enough even to take care of the much smaller annual crop of new families, with no replacements at all for the 45,000 units † normally demolished, from one cause or another, every year. The number of annual new families shrank to 290,000, but we built an average of only 273,000 dwelling units each year, and in 1933 the number actually shrank to 93,000. In those ten years we fell behind the previous decade by more than four million units, with existing houses ten years older and going to pot by the hundred thousand.

After the low point of 1933 the amount of new building increased each year and the curve continued to rise through 1941, when it reached 715,000, still far below the 1925 record. But the average for the four years 1940-1943 is only 541,000 units,‡ and since 1941 this quota has been maintained mainly by the slapping together of several hundred thousand "minimum" war dwellings. These government-built collections of bleak hutments are scattered in the neighborhood of our overgrown industrial centers, and unless they are demolished as soon as possible they will certainly and swiftly degenerate into appalling slums.

From 1929 we slid downhill so rapidly that ten years later it

* The number of new families in the decade 1920-1929 is stated by the Economic Almanac, 1942-1943, as just under five millions; for the following decade it was 2.9 millions, showing the effect of the depression on marriages.

† Testimony of Dr. Isadore Lubin, Commissioner of Labor Statistics, before the Temporary National Economic Committee, June 27, 1939, Part II, Page 4966.

‡ Statistics on annual building from Bulletin 713, U. S. Department of Labor, "Building Construction 1941."

was possible for Dr. Isadore Lubin to announce that four millions of the houses occupied in this country, judged by the minimum possible standards, were unfit for human habitation and should be demolished in the interest of health and decency.* The Census of 1940 reported that 18 per cent, or almost seven millions, of the houses in America were in need of major repairs—and that meant really *major* repairs, without which the houses are in some danger of tumbling down around the occupants' ears. The National Housing Agency estimates that the number of houses unfit for human habitation, calling for complete demolition, has risen during the war to eight millions, while another 4.6 millions can be made habitable only if they receive the major repairs they urgently need. Here we see swift deterioration in progress.

Dr. Lubin went on to say that more than half our houses were then over 25 years of age and one-fourth were over 50 years old.† The F. W. Dodge Corporation had previously calculated that the turnover of housing in this country, at the rate of construction prevailing between 1921 and 1933, years of prosperity and years of depression, was once in 142 years. Age alone does not necessarily condemn a house, provided it was well planned and soundly built in the first place, has been kept in good repair and has been equipped with modern technological improvements. But only a minute percentage of the 25- and 50-year-old houses meet all or any of these conditions. A little later we shall see how largely they lack the conveniences with which even a very old house can be made livable. The decline in new building has been paralleled by a decline in upkeep and modernization, and nothing deteriorates more dismally than a poorly built and subsequently neglected house.

After 1940 workers flocked by the millions to industrial centers that were already crowded, and lived wherever they could find a place to sleep—in close-packed tenements, trailers, shacks, tents, even sharing the same beds in shifts. Government emergency

* Testimony previously cited.
† Confirmed by the Census of 1940. Statistics as to conditions and equipment of dwelling units are to be found in *Housing*, Volume 2, General Characteristics, 16th Census, 1940, U. S. Department of Commerce.

housing provided a little, but not much, relief—and that of such minimal character that workers in a number of instances declined to occupy it. Life that used to pass in sunlit somnolence in San Diego or dignified placidity in Portland, Maine, became sheer feverish hell for many thousands of people in both places, and in scores of similar centers of production. A Pittsburgh paper in 1941 could say of the prosperous boom town of Duquesne, Pennsylvania, that it "is 50 per cent slums. . . . New automobiles galore in the streets, savings bank deposits skyrocketed, and spending money jangling in nearly every pocket . . . But behind the surface manifestations of well-being were row upon row of dilapidated, unsanitary, overcrowded, broken-down houses, the homes of about 10,000 of Duquesne's 20,000 residents." You can put dozens of other names in place of Duquesne, and change the figures a little, and the description will still be accurate.

2

This shortage in construction is no reflection on the homemaking proclivities of the American people. We are at least as ardent nest builders as any, and in the past we did better than most. Certainly we devour more magazines and books on the subject, and flock in great crowds to centers where information on the improvement of the home is dispensed. But there is something very wrong with the way our housing needs are supplied: this phase of production and distribution is out of line with others less essential. Contrast our performance in housing with our record in transportation: before the war we had an automobile for every four people in the country, or an average of one per family, which, statistically at least, made it unanimous. Not all of these were good cars, but they could not have been in need of "major repairs" or they simply wouldn't have run. If we had done as well in housing, the majority of dwellings would be less than a dozen years old, every one would have some kind of a bathroom and a sanitary indoor water closet, would have a tight roof and would be properly warmed in winter. Instead, you shall see our worse than 50 per cent achievement in these respects. And yet as a nation we spend one-fourth of our income on shelter and only one-fifteenth of it on automobiles.

The contrast between these two spheres of provenance is due to a time lag in the construction industry. The automobile industry is the lustiest, most typical child of the Industrial Revolution, it produces its wares by the most efficient methods of mass production and distributes them by the most direct methods of mass marketing. By contrast, the building trades in the housing field linger in another age. The domestic construction industry as such is only now experiencing the Industrial Revolution, and not until later postwar years will it be dragged, kicking and screaming, from medievalism into modernity.

Some of us whose memory goes back to the turn of the century have watched the Industrial Revolution operating on transportation, from scratch, before our eyes; and, with greater astonishment, have seen it pass by domestic construction almost without leaving a trace. We have seen a whole complex of businesses having to do with the horse—livery stables, blacksmith shops, harness makers, carriage painters, carriage and wagon dealers—disappear from the little communities where we grew up. They were swept away by the big wind that rose in Detroit, and in their place today we find a much bigger complex of garages, service stations, automobile dealers and suppliers. But we find that houses are built today in these countless home towns by the same methods we used to watch with such keen interest as small boys. There is the same succession of masons, carpenters, plumbers, plasterers, and painters engaged in the same minute divisions of labor, there is the same piecemeal buying from many sources, the same cutting and fitting and nailing at the site, the same great lapse of time between start and finish.

The Brookings Institution says that between 1900 and 1929 the average increase in productivity per man-hour in American industry was 60 per cent. Another average increase of 40 per cent was achieved between 1929 and 1940. These increases were due to the greater use of machine and mass-production methods. These methods have been applied to many of the materials and parts that enter into construction, and great suppliers like Weyerhauser, Johns-Manville and the like have effected economies equal to any in comparable industries. But in dwelling house construction itself there has been no gain whatever in man-hour output, and some authorities assert that there has been an actual decline.

The efficient use of machine methods requires a concentration of capital adequate to swing a long-range operation; it means large-scale purchasing, the most advanced equipment, constant research to improve quality and lower costs. A survey made in 1938 by the Bureau of Labor Statistics showed that in 72 cities 86 per cent of the houses built were the work of contractors who built less than five houses a year, and only 6 per cent were constructed by contractors who built ten or more houses a year. What chance here for large-scale buying, mass-production economies, endowed research?

By contrast, in 1941 there were only nineteen brands of automobiles in the United States of sufficient importance to be listed in the weekly sales reports of *Automobile Topics:* and these were made by only nine companies, but with a total volume of domestic sales of passenger cars and trucks, in 1941, amounting to 3.7 billion dollars. Of course, the stockholders who own these nine companies and divide their profits are much more numerous than the contractors in the building field; but they have pooled their resources so that manufacturing can be concentrated, and all the advantages of mass production obtained.

An ordinary low-priced car, if built by the kind of handwork methods used in building houses, would cost about $17,500 for labor alone, and wouldn't be anything like as good a car as comes off the assembly line. As a matter of fact, a Ford car in 1941 cost less than half as much as it cost in 1904 and was a far superior car. A house in 1941 cost *twice* as much as it cost in 1904, and structurally was little if any better. This in spite of the mass-produced parts supplied to the builder ready for installation.

3

It has been blandly assumed that a family should pay two to three times its annual income for a house, but it's my opinion that a family with an income of only $2,000 a year can't afford to pay $4,000 for a house, either in purchase or rental. If such a family can dig up the $550 needed for down payments, and get a 5-per cent 25-year mortgage, it is committed to $32 a month for the next quarter-century for interest, amortization, insurance and taxes, and will have paid more than $10,000 before it can have a clear title—not to mention repairs and upkeep. The average duration of ownership under these conditions is only five to seven years—by which time the original purchaser is glad to pass his obligations and his used house on to someone else.

Yet, of all the houses built in 1938, only 20 per cent were in the $4,000 class that three-quarters of the population, who were then in the $2,000 family income bracket, could even consider; while 48 per cent of the houses built—practically half—were in the $6,000 class and up, available to only one-twelfth of the population.* In other words, high costs forced builders to concentrate on the small upper-income markets and by-pass the vastly bigger low-income masses where the great need and the yearning desire exist. This majority of the population had to make do with old, worn-out, discarded dwellings of the more prosperous, which, being a permanent condition, explains the great age and sad disrepair of millions of American houses. As someone has said, it is as if only Rolls-Royces and Cadillacs were ever built, and only discarded cars of these models were available to men of low incomes.

It is obvious that the incomes of much too many families are much too low. The whole argument of this book is that, in the coming years, we should and can accomplish the increase in production-consumption which is the only means of remedying this evil. But even generally diffused prosperity will not make good houses available to everyone until popular-priced models are built to supplement the Rolls-Royce and Cadillac variety. In 1944 we had full employment at high wages, and incomes were at the highest levels ever: but still only 42 per cent of families and individuals enjoyed, for the time being, an income which if permanent would justify the purchase or rental of a new $6,000 house; and owing to a rise in all living costs, the millions whose incomes were still below the $2,000 mark were less promising pros-

* Dr. Isadore Lubin, testimony previously cited.

pects for the realtor than ever. It is clear that, even with full employment at high wages, good housing will not be available to all while building costs remain at their present old-fashioned levels.

Even large-scale operations will not bring these costs down so long as archaic construction methods persist. This is proved by the record of the United States Housing Administration, which up to March, 1942, had contracted for about 185,000 dwelling units, mostly of the multiple-dwelling, slum-replacement type, at a total expenditure, federal and local, of something more than 850 million dollars. The projects were all solidly built by conventional methods. The program was conscientiously and intelligently administered, care was exercised to cut costs and raise standards, purchasing as far as possibe was on a large scale, all economies permitted by the building trades-unions were employed. Yet the simple arithmetic of dividing total costs by total results shows that the dwellings built cost over $4,600 apiece.

In spite of spreading its amortization, so-called, over the absurd period of 60 years—consider the present slum state of any tenement built in 1887—the government must still pay a subsidy equivalent to $180 per family per year so that the low-income tenants for whom these dwellings are intended can afford to live in them. In other words, taxpayers in general are paying $180 a year toward the rent of each of 185,000 favored families. The best that can be said for these USHA projects—and it is a lot—is that they have provided examples of rationally planned and humanized apartment communities for the inspiration of many cities and towns. But they made no advance toward what should be our ultimate objective, which is to *produce modern houses at actual costs so low that people can afford to buy or rent them when new without public aid*. And in fact there is no evidence that any of the public agencies involved in housing ever thought of the problem in these terms or considered any solution except subsidies of one kind or another.

Traditionally built houses not only cost too much, more than most people can afford to pay, but they are too hard to buy; contrast the elaborate and fearsome mortgage rigmarole, itself a survival of a handicraft age, with the simple installment-plan purchase of an automobile. And a third great drawback is that our houses are inflexible, too hard to change or move, they last too long. Their solid fabrics are permanently congealed just as they were two centuries ago in more static times, when a man could be expected to live comfortably and contentedly in his grandfather's unaltered house. But we now have a mobile, shifting population, rapidly changing living habits, swiftly advancing technologies. A house today is obsolete after ten or a dozen years, but it still stands and some family must put up with it.

4

There are complex reasons for this unique survival of antique customs in an age of machine and mass production.* The most fundamental of all is this: that it has never been possible, and is not now possible, to make a clean break with the past and change over abruptly to a wholly novel and superior type of shelter necessitating wholly new and different production and marketing methods. When we switched from horses to automobiles such a break was not only possible but unavoidable: we could not breed automobiles as we had bred horses. A comparable switch might have occurred in shelter if we had suddenly changed from living in caves to living in prefabricated houses. But we have lived in houses for a long time, and there is no such radical contrast between our grandfather's house and our most modern house. Both *can* be built by exactly the same methods, and the native conservatism of the human race being what it is, most of them are. They will continue to be built so at certain economic levels for a very long time.

So long as people can afford to build houses according to their own plans and tastes, of stone, brick, or wood, to fit a specific site

---

* "The picture is one of barriers built up from every side—from our land system, from methods of taxation, from builder organizations, labor, real estate operators, mortgage lenders, and even from government itself—against the maturing of house-building to the stature of an industry capable of producing and distributing in sufficiently large quantities and at sufficiently low costs to meet the vast housing need the country faces."—Miles L. Colean, *American Housing*, Twentieth Century Fund, 1944, p. 9. This book is the best study of the housing problem yet to appear.

and to exemplify the owner's individual conception of what his home should be, houses will continue to be built this handicraft way. Admittedly it is an expensive way to build, and we are surrounded by a nation-full of proof that the great majority of houses so built cease to be satisfactory long before they cease to be inhabited. But thrift is not the sole consideration involved, and whatever part of each generation has the necessary funds will seek this form of self-expression. A romantic attitude toward the domestic machine is understandable and defensible. We are not ants or bees, thank God, and we have every right to gratify our whims and make our own mistakes. But more than half the nation will not be housed as well as it should be until some attractive alternative is offered it—some means of satisfying the buyer's romantic as well as practical needs in the way a bright new car satisfies them, and not as a poor imitation of a Tudor cottage satisfies them; and at a price that families in the lower half of our income scale can afford to pay.

What our vast, shifting, wage-earning population needs if it is to be well housed is a bright, shining, handsome, completely equipped, up-to-date machine for living, costing between $1,000 and $2,500; a house a man can alter or enlarge by buying spare parts; a sturdy but light-weight house he can disassemble and take with him, if he wants to, when he shifts his job, and turn in on a new model in ten or a dozen years when it becomes obsolete; a house he can buy on the installment plan and pay for in two or three years without a lot of red tape. That's the kind of merchandise, that's the kind of buying he's used to in other markets. And that, incidentally, is why at least 300,000 families, even before the war, had submitted to the discomforts of life in trailers.

Such a house must, of course, be mass-produced on an assembly line, and in quantities big enough to realize the economies possible through mass production. It will be offered first at the very low price levels where conventional building cannot compete. But the intensive research which is a necessary corollary of mass production will be brought to bear on it, and this with volume production and experience will bring about a rapid improvement of the product. In time it will leave very little reason for resorting to conventional building at all—just as low-cost cars have improved so much in the past ten years that there is little reason for buying the big, expensive vehicles that the well-to-do once considered essential expressions of their dignity. More and more prefabricated parts will enter into conventional building, and the handicrafts will retire to an aristocratic vestigial level; as horses are still kept for riding and racing long after they have ceased to play any part in practical transportation.

5

There are no economic or technological reasons why such a house cannot be produced today in the $2,000 bracket. But there are strong opposing forces, in addition to our habitual romanticism and conservatism in this matter of nest building: union opposition, for one thing, is a bugaboo that haunts the dreams of all prefabricators. The building trades-unions even have prevented the introduction of economies in conventional building, such as spray-gun painting and preassembled wiring and plumbing. In spite of these efforts to hold their own, the building crafts are notoriously ill-paid among skilled workers, if judged not by their high hourly rates but by their annual income over a period of years: their practices contribute to their own defeat by retarding the prosperity of their industry.

The realtors with their vested interests have taken an equally shortsighted attitude, and city building codes have been drawn either to protect the unions and realtors or to enforce requirements that ceased long ago to have any validity. This intrenched opposition, coupled with doubt as to public acceptance, has sidetracked many would-be prefabricators into a type of semi-prefabrication which has few of the economies of mass production and few of the virtues of conventional techniques.

The problem cannot be solved timidly. You cannot have a little mass production—it must be whole-hog or nothing. On the other hand, you cannot maintain mass production without a mass market, and it may not be surprising that no one, in the past decade of repressed enterprise, with change in housing preferences so slow to assert itself, has yet had the nerve and resources to venture on a big scale in this field. No one has been willing to set up to produce the parts for thousands of houses a month without being reasonably sure that he could sell that number of houses, and such assurance must have been, in the nature of things, a matter of inner conviction rather than demonstrated fact.

It seemed, in the early days of the war effort, that this hurdle could be surmounted, and mass production of housing established as a going operation in the course of providing emergency war housing. The government even made a good beginning at giving it this impetus, and then muffed what was not, after all, a government responsibility but merely an opportunity. If the policy of encouraging the infant prefabrication industry had been continued, the sheep quickly could have distinguished themselves from the goats and uniform high quality could have been achieved with experience. Union and realtor opposition might have been by-passed in the emergency, and public acceptance established through familiarity. War housing would have been of a more practical type, and the end of the emergency would have seen at least a few well-organized, well-equipped companies all set to supply modern homes to the half of our population who are now shut out of the market. But a shift was made to favoring local design sources and local construction facilities and again a government housing program was carried out without making any contribution to a solution of the national housing problem.

As restrictions on materials and building types closed tighter as a war necessity, prefabrication has not had a chance to develop on its own as might have been expected in a period of such urgent demand. And there has been a vigorous effort to prove its impracticability, inspired mostly by interests which might lose by its success. But actually, prefabrication has never yet been tried— that is, *the assembly line production of a small number of standardized and interchangeable parts designed for combination in a wide variety of plans without craftwork at the point of erecting.*

It is possible to divide a house into a small number of essential panels, and set up an assembly line to produce each type of panel, all accurately dimensioned, held to high standards of quality and fabricated by swift machine methods. Houses assembled from these interchangeable parts can have a sturdiness and rigidity far beyond conventional construction, and their walls, though not more than four inches thick, can have a coefficient of heat transmission as low as that of a 16-inch masonry wall. By this method of construction the weight of a four-room house, 24 feet by 32 feet, can be cut from the 46 tons * it weighs today to ten or twelve tons, at the same time that its strength is more than doubled. Although the principal material at first will be plywood, quite soon it will be possible to mold entire panels in one piece of synthetic material, with finished surfaces and integral insulation.

These units will be devised for assembly as the buyer's needs dictate, in arrangements that can be altered or expanded at will. Additional varieties of panels will serve special preferences—for plate glass walls, sliding or folding partitions, outdoor terraces, fireplaces—yes, the open fire and the vine-covered trellis satisfy legitimate cravings and will be forthcoming. The monotony which some people fear in prefabrication will be rarer here than in conventional construction, since no arrangement will be fixed and unchangeable and variety can be had even from season to season. The maximum efficiency in housekeeping operation can be combined with esthetic values, charm and comfort of a kind the low-cost home owner has not been able to afford in the past and the more well-to-do often has not known how to obtain.

Throughout this period of retardation there has been a general converging of thought and experiment toward a system of prefabrication such as I have outlined, and a general agreement as to the characteristics of the standardized parts. At the same time, public receptivity has grown to an active demand. Whenever there is intelligent public discussion of prefabrication, a tidal wave of correspondence surprisingly discriminating in its understanding of the problems involved rolls in from all parts of the country. Anyone who has been submerged by this response can have no doubt of the eagerness of the waiting market. The unnatural arrest of development in this field has accumulated a tremendous force behind it, and the dam will burst.

* Detailed estimate prepared by the Technical Division, Federal Housing Administration. See pp. 352-53, *American Housing*, previously cited. This is a house without a basement.

In spite of any arguments that can be advanced against it, the factory production of shelter on a large scale is as certain as anything in the future can be. Inexorable logic compels it: one industry cannot hold out against the universal trend of the times and its habits of trade. In this way, and in no other way, high quality in housing, utmost convenience and full enjoyment of technological advances can be made available to the whole range of our self-supporting population at prices they can afford to pay. It will be accomplished, but probably by forces not previously active in housing: it is not a problem in architecture or construction but in mass production, and the great pioneer successes are most likely to be achieved by men who have mastered the art of mass production in such fields as airplanes and shipbuilding and other large-scale operations. Automobiles were successfully evolved, but not in livery stables.

6

Even leaving prefabrication out of the reckoning, we are due for a huge building boom in the next decade. Its impetus will come from the acute housing shortage that alarms every community in the country. A number of surveys have shown that a large part—as much as a quarter or a third—of the accumulated savings of the war period is earmarked for the purchase of new houses as soon as they can be built. Thus funds are in hand already to finance the purchase of ten to twelve million dwellings which can cost, on the average, $5,000 each. The National Housing Agency estimates that the building industry as now constituted might, if it exerted itself to the utmost, succeed in producing about twelve million units in the next ten years. This would be a creditable achievement, and would mean that at least families in the upper income brackets would be reasonably well housed. But this is not enough.

Twelve million houses in ten years will no more than take up the slack of the past fifteen years, and 3.5 million substandard units will still be occupied. The National Housing Agency estimates that we must have more than sixteen million new dwellings by 1955 if all the nation's families are to be decently housed. We cannot count on present production sources and methods for any such number, and certainly for nothing to supply the millions who cannot afford to spend more than $2,500. Fortunately, the chances are that present sources and methods will cease to be our sole reliance before 1955 is in sight.

If prefabrication breaks the dams that restrain it, and the building industry is industrialized as it must be, we shall see low-cost industrial production rise to supply the needed extra millions of homes. It may very well pass conventional building in volume before the end of the decade. Factory techniques can be applied not only to single family dwellings but to multiple dwellings as well, so that substandard housing replacement can be made the profitable enterprise it should be in city, suburb, and country alike. This is our sole hope for seeing all our needs fulfilled, with a resulting lift of living standards throughout all economic levels of the population, and we should be satisfied with nothing less.

The ideal of an entire nation well housed is probably unattainable until we have a uniformly high-grade human being to house. But as the objective of a practical program it is not in the least extravagant. So far I have discussed only one phase of such a program—the creation of an adequate supply of new and proper houses. I am well aware that there are other essential requirements. One is the furnishing and equipment of all houses in conformity with our American standard of domestic decency, and their maintenance at that standard which is not fixed but constantly advancing. Another is the reconstruction of the communities in which new housing must take its place.

CHAPTER XI

AND FURNISH THEM DECENTLY

As ONE whose powers of observation, such as they are, began to function in the horse-and-buggy age, I have no patience with that familiar lament over the decline of the American home. We are told that the automobile and the movies have destroyed its close-knit solidarity. What they have destroyed, if anything, is the colossal boredom of close confinement. The automobile has given millions a freedom of action that some have not known how to use, but these would have been no better men sitting at home; and the option of change and escape has been more salutary than if nobody had ever had a chance to prove himself equal to its new responsibilities. The movies provide variety of vicarious experience and emotional exercise, and even Grade-B pictures are an intellectual cut above the rocking chair gossip or mere vacuous thumb-twiddling of a less privileged age. The home itself has acquired in radio what is on the whole a great cultural agent: the upper registers of its fare are the best the world has to offer, and there are plenty of listeners whose horizons are broadened even by soap operas and the Korn Kobblers. The fact that so much time is now spent outside the home does not prove that the home has declined: it may prove that the home was just never good enough, and still isn't.

Poverty of physical equipment may not be an insurmountable obstacle to a happy home life, but it certainly is a formidable one. Give a person a drab setting and a dull routine and he will feel a healthy urge to get the hell out of there, and this will still be true when the setting is called home and the routine makes up what is called home life. Housework in the past has been a round of unbelievable dullness: the price of order and decency has been the slavish subjugation of women to tasks only a masochist could enjoy. The fact that so many of them could still be dispensers of sweetness and light really excuses all the sentimental twaddle that has been written on the subject. These conditions still persist in far too many homes: they are shabby and backbreaking hangovers from another age.

By contrast, George Spelvin and his family can step out to an automobile or the movies, where they find many of the most spectacular achievements of science and engineering and often a very high order of art placed lavishly at their service. This is good for their egos, generating a healthy sense of mastery and opulence, in fact of fulfillment. They *could* find the same satisfactions in their homes, provided they possessed a domestic machine of equal quality. Modern technology has devised the component parts of such a machine, and in combination they could eliminate all the grimmer aspects of housekeeping. Manual drudgery could be replaced by skillful semiprofessional activities, swiftly performed with gratifying results, in a setting of beauty and comfort. If homes were engineered to take full advantage of existing technological and esthetic opportunities, they could meet their outside competition on an even basis. General success along this line probably would pay social dividends in excess of any achievement we can imagine, comparable only to the drastic lifting of health standards and educational standards which could be accomplished at the same time.

2

Many of the parts that will be co-ordinated in the domestic machine of the future have been available for some years in more or less well-developed versions. They entered the scene as luxuries, but by 1929 their distribution was hitting its stride and they had been accepted among the necessities that go to make up the American standard of living. All of them are supplied by our mass-production system and after the general paralysis of 1933 their distribution resumed a progress which stands out favorably in comparison with many lines of activity. Certainly it has far surpassed the record of new dwelling construction. You don't have to build a new house, necessarily, in order to have central heating or a bathroom, and it is still easier to install an electric refrigerator or a telephone. So you might suppose that even if houses were going to pieces, the movable equipment in them would be more commendable than the structures. But here again, in this field of utilities, the Census of 1940 shows that more than half the job is still to be done.

American plumbing is almost as much of a national symbol as the American eagle, and our shiny bathrooms are unquestionably among our indigenous masterpieces. But almost two-fifths of the homes in America—39 per cent or more than 14 millions—have no bathroom of any kind, shiny or otherwise. We are also the land of central heating, accused by Europeans of maintaining indecently high indoor temperatures. But almost three out of five of our homes—58 per cent or more than 21 millions—are warmed if at all by some more primitive means. And lest you think that the deep South alone pulls this percentage down, two out of every five homes in wintry New England still depend on the base burner and the kitchen range to keep them warm.

Electric light is the most commonly enjoyed of all modern conveniences—except for radio—but one-fifth of our dwellings, or about 7.5 millions, have none. And more than seventeen homes out of every hundred have no radio. We make the best mechanical refrigerators in the world and the most of them, but 56 per cent of our houses, or 21 millions, get along without them. The South, where food preservation is most essential, has the least equipment for that purpose; Mississippi has mechanical refrigerators in less than fifteen homes in every hundred; Arkansas in seventeen; in most of the Southern states the proportion of homes equipped varies between a quarter and a third. The national average is pulled up by richer states like New York, New Jersey and Connecticut, where 60 to 62 per cent of the homes are able to keep their food supplies cool by mechanical refrigeration.

The "party-line" may seem to have tied even the remotest farm house to every other home in the nation, but not at all: 61 per cent of all residences, 22.5 millions or three out of five, have no telephones.

If we look at farm homes alone—and in 1940 there were 7.6 million farm homes in this country—we find that in rural districts the "American standard of living" has been ignored to a disconcerting extent. Many a sturdy rural family has been raised with no bathing facilities except the Saturday night washtub or the old swimming hole, and even at Mount Vernon and Monticello every drop of water used in the house was carried in by hand. But there is no reason why this should be true today. The farm home is much more of a working organism than the city home, and deserves better equipment rather than worse. But actually three-quarters of the farm houses are more than 25 years old, a third are in need of major repairs, and the Department of Agriculture considers that two millions of them are unfit for human habitation. Only twelve out of every hundred have a bathroom and only eighteen have running water in the house. Less than a third are served with electric current. Nine out of ten have no indoor toilets and 9 per cent have no toilet facilities whatever! This last appalling state of affairs may be related to the fact that in five Southern states the *average* value of farm dwellings is less than $500.

We know that as production hits its stride, there will be a rush to make up the shortage of modern equipment in millions of homes. By midyear of 1943,* families had set aside funds for the purchase of 1.75 million mechanical refrigerators, 1.5 million kitchen ranges, more than a million each of vacuum cleaners and electric irons, a half-million sewing machines and almost as many kitchen mixers. These quantities undoubtedly will be much bigger by the time the goods are available, and the number of purchases may easily be doubled by those who aren't making prior arrangements to satisfy their wants but will do so when the opportunity offers. Thus we see a prospect of high prosperity for important industries and improvement in the depressing conditions revealed by the 1940 Census. This is all to the good. So long as millions of homes survive from another era, they should be supplied as quickly as possible with all the devices that make for labor-saving and more gracious living.

* U. S. Chamber of Commerce survey.

But the typical home of the future will not be equipped in this haphazard and piecemeal way. It will be engineered as a unified mechanism, for maximum efficiency, convenience and charm, as has never yet been done. It will gain immensely in livability by this coherent treatment.

3

Such an organization of the domestic machine, integrating both structure and equipment, will be developed most effectively in the process of prefabrication. Only mass production can continuously afford the highest engineering and design talent, backed by intensive research and thorough testing, and only mass production can reduce the cost of the resulting product to the dimensions of the average pocketbook. Also, the rigidity of conventional construction makes no allowance for advancing technologies, and houses so built can represent only the possibilities existent at the time of their completion. A momentary adequacy is not enough: a house should be a flexible and growing organism, keeping pace with progress and ready at any time to adjust itself to technological advance. Prefabrication, with the demountability which is its corollary, will make this swift adaptation possible. It also assumes that the structure is not ultimate, to outlast the ages, but is an expedient which can be superseded as soon as something basically superior is available.

This is not to say that conventional design will not be influenced in the same direction. It also will strive to produce an integrated domestic machine, and there will be successful individual achievements along this line in the more costly structures. Already tentative experiments have been made in the design of unit kitchens and unit baths, and they have attracted a great deal of attention wherever they have been shown. So far they are definitely in the luxury class, like a great many innovations that have later become common necessities. They will be available in various forms in the next few years, and we shall see a great many dwellings built in a conscious effort to take advantage of these and all other technological advances. We shall learn a great deal from these efforts, and we can be glad that there are people who can afford to experiment and have the initiative to do so.

But it is never so important that a few people should have Rolls-Royces and Cadillacs as that everybody should have Fords, Chevrolets, or Plymouths. Through prefabrication a complete, basic, domestic machine will be made available at a popular cost, just as the low-cost cars provided basic transportation. The first offerings may not be much more impressive than the first Model T, but if they meet the popular need as well—and there is no reason why they shouldn't—their acceptance will be as enthusiastic. Also their successors will show the same progressive improvement and ultimately reach an admirable quality.

The early prefabricated houses to win popularity will be assembled around a simple, compact and very convenient service unit, containing kitchen, bath and heating plant. The kitchen and bath will be placed back to back, with a highly simplified plumbing system in the dividing wall. To meet all the requirements of low cost, space saving, labor saving and light weight— this latter a factor of great importance and, revolutionary import—the service unit will be an arrangement of new types of appliances devised for the purpose. A minimum of heavy metals will be used. Sinks and bathroom fixtures will be molded of thin but tough synthetic compounds, probably with a paper or plywood base. Similar synthetic sheets will form bath stalls, partitions, cupboards, and closets. Plumbing pipes will be of plastic tubing which can be bent and joined without threaded fittings. Metal will be used only where temperatures require it, and then it will be used sparingly with great reliance on highly efficient insulation, such as the new "plastic foam" which weighs only ten ounces a cubic foot and yet transmits less heat than any other known insulating material.

Ranges and refrigerators no longer will be self-contained rectangular cabinets in which all the elements necessary for cooking or food preservation are crowded together without regard to convenience. In fact they will no longer be identifiable as separate appliances. The refrigerator will become a set of compartments or drawers, rather like a filing cabinet, in which different temperatures will be maintained ranging from zero for frozen foods to 45° for milk and vegetables. The B.T.U.'s extracted in refrigeration will be used for heating water. Ranges will be broken up into their component parts of cooking top, oven, and broiler, with a pressure cooker added, and these will be disposed where they are most accessible.

A radical change in cooking technique and equipment will come about with the early introduction of infra-red rays as a source of heat. Power for this purpose can be transmitted by electronic tubes without wires, so that the apparatus will be portable and consist of little more than an assortment of lamps, tubes, and containers. The results in cooking will be quicker and more even, with less loss of essential vitamins in the food.

The use of infra-red will be a step toward cooking by high-frequency induction, which, if successfully developed, will simplify the equipment still further and render the operation of cooking—once the food is prepared—practically instantaneous. In fact it may just as well be done at the dinner table, in the dishes from which the food is to be served: they need not even be heated in the process. And many foods will be delivered to the home, frozen or pre-prepared, ready to be put into the cooking dish.

Ceramic dishes will survive as heirlooms and *objets d'art*. The majority of our dishes, forks, and spoons will be molded of unbreakable synthetics, cheap, colorful, and beautiful in design. After use they will be dumped into a hopper where they will be thoroughly cleaned, sterilized and dried, not to be touched until they are needed again. Many of these utensils will be disposable; after being used once they will go into a macerator, along with the garbage and other waste, to be ground to a pulp and flushed down the drain.

4

The heating plant in the early prefabricated houses will provide winter air-conditioning: that is, air will be filtered, warmed, humidified, and circulated through ducts to all the rooms, from which cooler air will be withdrawn from near the floor and re-circulated. The apparatus necessary to do this will be surprisingly small, as the efficiency of heat-producing equipment burning oil or gas has been greatly increased in the course of our war developments. Very soon summer air-conditioning will be added by the inclusion of condenser coils in the system, to be operated in place of the heating unit. But the trend of postwar development will be away from this primitive method of keeping ourselves warm by submersion in a bath of warm air. It will lead to a separation of the functions of warming and ventilating.

The human body has its own heating system, set to maintain a temperature of 98.8° F. To do this it must give off every hour about 400 heat units of its own manufacture, no more and no less. Any marked variation in this radiation of heat from the body will cause discomfort and may even endanger health. Surrounding air temperature is only one influence on the rate of the body's radiation, and others can be made to counteract the air's effect entirely. A skier on a sunlit snow field in clear mountain air may be quite comfortable in bathing trunks, even though a thermometer in the shade may show that the air temperature is far below freezing: the air takes some heat from the body by convection, but this loss is more than counteracted by the radiant heat received directly from the sun and reflected from the snow, and by the fact that the snow reflects back some of the body's own radiated heat.* Applying these principles to the home, we shall have a source of radiant heat embedded in the walls, floor or ceiling of our rooms; these walls, floor, and ceiling will be so thoroughly insulated that the heat loss to the outside will be negligible, and so treated with aluminum foil or a silica finish that they *reflect* radiant heat and do not absorb it. In these conditions we can forget about the temperature of the air, and the body can be maintained at its normal comfortable temperature with a minimum expenditure of fuel energy.

Ventilation thus becomes a separate operation. Fresh air, without warming or change in its moisture content, can be introduced and recirculated through a precipitron, which will remove from it practically all dust and pollen particles by charging them electronically and collecting them on a metal plate. This is a far more effective method of cleaning air than any mechanical filter

* Dr. Clarence Mills, *Science Digest*, March, 1944, p. 44.

and does not impede its flow. At the same time the air can be passed through the rays of a battery of ultraviolet lights which will kill all but a negligible percentage of the bacteria that may be floating in it. Tests of these lights in schoolrooms, under conditions not as propitious as such a recirculating system would provide, have proved that they greatly reduce the transmission of colds and other communicable diseases.

Dr. Mills proposes that cooling in summer be obtained by placing in each room an area of extremely low temperature—say, a ceiling plate chilled to 150° below zero—which would absorb the body's heat radiations. It is a question whether it would not be cheaper and simpler, for some time at least, to continue the practice of cooling and dehumidifying the circulated air, since we seldom need to lower the air temperature more than 10° or 15° to obtain comfort. By contrast, if warmed air is the only source of body comfort in winter, we may need to raise its temperature by as much as 70° to 90°. Thus we may find it advisable to cool air in summer for a long time after we have ceased to heat it in winter.

Possibly we may make much more general use of the sun's rays for heating our homes. Large areas of plate glass, with a space of dehydrated air sealed between, make very effective heat traps, since the direct radiation of the sun readily passes through them while the lower-frequency radiations from within the room do not. These transparent areas can be made to pass all the healthful, ultraviolet bands of the sun's spectrum, or exclude them if we do not want our fabrics faded. The latter drawback will disappear as all dyes are made sunfast. There are certain other objections to this use of solar heat, however, since it is of course exceedingly intermittent and must always be supplemented by some other heat source: so far it has been difficult to synchronize the furnace and the sun so that an even temperature is maintained at all times. Also the glare of full sunlight filling a room may be trying on the eyes, especially when there is snow on the ground outside, and in summer we have the problem of excluding the rays that we welcome in winter. So we may find it more convenient to place no direct dependence on nature in this as in so many other instances.

5

Lighting in the home until now has been left to chance and the crude improvisations of the householder, with great harm to the nation's eyesight. In the future, lighting will have its place in the engineered scheme, and illumination will be maintained at correct optical levels throughout the house. In prefabrication this can be done by providing ceiling panels and certain other panels each with its own light source, thus guaranteeing an adequate number of lumens for a given area. A similar dispersion of sources will be arranged in conventional buildings as well. The objective will be an evenly diffused light, not shadowless but without sharp contrasts, with sources concealed. These sources, needless to say, will be fluorescent tubes, generating little heat and consuming less current than our present crude lamps. They will be turned on automatically, by means of photronic tubes, whenever the daylight falls below a specified level, just as heat in modern systems is now turned on by a thermostat.

A further advance, not at all improbable, consists in the more general and direct utilization of phosphors as a light source. Phosphors are the luminous element in fluorescent light tubes and in the screens on which television pictures are seen: they are tiny crystals which fluoresce, or give off light, under the influence of electronic rays which themselves are beyond the range of human vision. Walls and ceilings coated with phosphor crystals will become luminous in the ultraviolet rays from concealed tubes, and thus we can obtain a much more generally diffused and higher illumination than by our present somewhat crude and wasteful method of reflecting visible light rays.

These phosphors have another valuable characteristic, in that they can be made to "store" light and will continue to give it off long after the primary source is no longer active. This emission of stored light may continue for hours and even days, and since daylight is a powerful activating influence we may be able to trap enough light during the daylight hours to illuminate our living rooms throughout the evening.

Phosphors are by far the most efficient known method of converting electric power into visible light, and since this light can be either white or colored it will be possible to combine illumination with an interesting variety of decorative effects: we can change the color scheme or the mural decorations of a room by flipping a switch. This will satisfy that urge for change which inspires so many housewives to push the furniture around into new arrangements and has made the fortunes of wallpaper manufacturers. And stored fluorescent light will free us forever from the hazard of stumbling over chairs in the dark, just as it will mark our highways, private driveways, and the landing strips of airports, and take the place of parking lights on cars.

6

In mass production, the esthetic qualities of the output can receive the same expert attention as the functional characteristics. The most able designers can exercise their talents on the product to give it fitting form, color, textures, and arrangement, with results in beauty and harmony that only the wealthy have been able to buy in unit production. Much of the furniture will be designed especially for the houses that will hold it, so as to make the best use of space and insure that the ensemble will be entirely satisfactory from the standpoint of charm as well as utility. This furniture too will be light—comfort isn't measured by the pound, and an "easy" chair that needs two strong men to lift it is an anachronism. Skillfully developed contours in our chairs and couches, the use of synthetic "foam rubber" cushions, molded synthetics and plywood for structure, washable synthetic fabrics for coverings, will create an authentic new "style" in furniture, to be carried out in all the conveniences that make up the equipment of homes rationally planned for human ease.

It isn't desirable that home life should be made entirely effortless, even if that were possible. We've no desire to develop into a race of queen bees, fed and tended by mechanical slaves. Cooking can be made an exciting art, and is being so practiced by an increasing number of people. Making things for one's own home, by needlework or at the home work bench, is a highly gratifying form of self-expression when it can be indulged as such and is not an enforced drudgery. Child care can be satisfying and greatly rewarding, if it isn't one more harassment among the many that now crowd a housewife's days. All these are natural human occupations, enriching home life. But the home should benefit from the same trend that alleviates so many modern activities: the progressive elimination of mere muscular effort—weight lifting and pushing—and the progressive enlargement of the sphere of intelligence, knowledge, and skill. The home we shall develop will be clean with a minimum of cleaning, it will be healthier because of its own aseptic characteristics as well as because of the general improvement in health. It will be free of drudgery while it stimulates the exercise of arts that yield pleasure and gratification. With developed television, perfect world-wide radio reception, perfect magnetic recordings—a whole symphony in a volume no bigger than a spool of thread—universal home movies, the home can be a complete microcosm with tentacles drawing into itself whatever is interesting or exhilarating or inspiring throughout the world. Family life can have a well-rounded satisfactoriness that puts a strain on our present inexperienced imaginations. And this home itself, as it evolves, will be a powerful influence and probably the most powerful influence in developing human beings capable of exploiting its full possibilities.

CHAPTER XII

IN GRACIOUS COMMUNITIES

No MATTER how admirable the home itself may become, it still must be a unit within a society. Our gregarious instincts can't all be satisfied by electronic radiations, no matter how vivid or various they may become. We shall still feel the desire for companionship and that spiritual support which many people derive from mere proximity to other people: the asocial attitude of a Daniel Boone or a Davy Crockett is rare.

Our need goes beyond the bounds of family and intimate friendship: we crave the comradeship of like-thinking men sharing a community of beliefs, principles, loyalties, and interests. Very few of us have the strength to stand alone, even in a good cause, and if that kind of isolation is forced on us it may be splendid but only a very peculiar temperament could find it enjoyable. The interdependence of individuals is not only social and moral; it is the essential factor in the democratic process, without which a free way of life is not possible.

De Tocqueville realized a hundred years ago that the "mature and calm feeling" of self-sufficiency, the outgrowth of a consciousness of equality, which he found so characteristic of Americans, might easily prove to be a socially disintegrative force. But he also saw that this "individualism" had its corrective in an extraordinary tendency to group coalescence: "The political associations that exist in the United States are only a single feature in the midst of the immense assemblage of associations in that country. Americans of all ages, all conditions, and all dispositions constantly form associations. . . . Wherever at the head of some new undertaking you see the government in France, or a man of rank in England, in the United States you will be sure to find an association."

This was many decades before Rotary, Kiwanis, Chambers of Commerce, and a thousand others had given us the name of a nation of "joiners," but Tocqueville saw even then that these associations, both official and unofficial, were an indispensable part of the democratic mechanism, by which an immense number of socially necessary functions are performed. And he wisely concluded: "Among the laws that rule human society there is one which seems to be more precise and clear than all others. If men are to remain civilized or to become so, the art of associating together must grow and improve in the same ratio in which the equality of conditions is increased." *

The tendency to group coalescence would induce us to build our homes in clusters even if there were no practical reasons for doing so. But in a civilization such as ours we are completely dependent on the exchange of labor, goods, thought, and diversions which can only take place at certain focal points of population, themselves interdependent and linked together in a national network of exchange. The concentrated resources and group activities which these communities can provide are just as essential to the good life, on farms or in cities, as a happy domestic atmosphere: unless they serve it adequately the home itself is defeated. How well they do their job is probably the most crucial test of our skill in "the art of associating together." By that test, using the towns and cities of the United States as a measuring rod, our skill in association would appear to be very meager indeed in spite of all the exercise we have given it.

We still have a few old and small communities which have not outgrown their original patterns, as fixed by well-recognized practical necessities of more static times than ours. These unspoiled survivals display an authentic order and a beautiful logic. Unfortunately it is the logic of the seventeenth and eighteenth centuries, rich in nostalgic charm but without present-day relevance.

Such relics are rare. The great majority of our towns and cities have not been shaped by any such compulsion and the only order

* Alexis de Tocqueville, *Democracy in America*, Knopf, 1945, Vol. II, pp. 106-10.

they reveal is that of the drafting board and T-square, having
(nothing to do with vital activities either past or present.)Their
plans never suited the convenience of anybody but the draftsman,
the surveyor, and the real estate broker, and now that we have
developed very special needs in transportation and higher standards of living these arbitrary patterns are positively nerve-racking
in their obstructive inefficiency. Times have changed so swiftly
that even the best community plans made more than a generation ago are not suited to the needs of today; and if the plan was
not good to start with, and if the community has grown to city
(proportions, the amount of exasperation and frustration it causes
is appalling.

Our towns are not only poorly planned, they are apt to be
poorly built; they are structurally shoddy, forlorn and depressing.
(As we go up the scale in size, squalor is multiplied, population is
jammed together in shocking circumstances, large sections have
deteriorated owing to the shift of population toward the periph-
ery, the avoidable blight spread around itself by unmodernized
industry is increasingly stultifying to human life; and as operating
mechanisms the bigger cities grind and jolt erratically like worn-
out machines that threaten at any moment to stall completely.

A nation-wide condition such as this is a national indictment.
But it would not be fair to judge our associative skill by this physical evidence; it is no measure of our present understanding of
communal requirements. Towns and cities are stubborn and persistent, and it isn't possible to shift them like stage sets as the
scene changes; especially when the drama itself is still being written and we aren't sure just what the next act will be. During the
past century our moods have changed so swiftly that no builder
could keep pace with them, even if he had been inspired and had
had a free hand. So it is not surprising or entirely discreditable
(that we find ourselves living in ill-fitting, outgrown shells that
cramp our lives and frustrate our aspirations. But it will be unforgivable if we do not now, as one of the first tasks of peace,
attack this problem.

We are ready for the undertaking because the major outlines of
our future pattern of living are now more clearly defined and we
understand, in a general way, how to adapt to that pattern the

physical structure of our communities. The task of revision and reconstruction will be enormous, the biggest we face, and it will take a long time, but it will prove to be one of those fertile, self-rewarding labors that make us richer and happier as we spend ourselves on them. If it is done wisely, we shall find that we are eliminating many of the most nerve-racking complexities of modern life, and restoring to it a measure of simplicity, peace and charm. We have a chance to practice "the art of associating together" with a competence never before attainable, since no epoch heretofore ever needed such a wholesale renovation or had the knowledge and means to accomplish it.

2

In the first place, we now are ready to repair the ravages of the Industrial Revolution. Smoke, dirt, and disorder are no longer unavoidable by-products of industry: they are in fact symptoms of waste and inefficiency, and while they still persist like any bad habit they are not only remediable but intolerable. The scars burned by industry across the land, in and around thousands of communities, can now be healed. Order and cleanliness can be restored, the blackened hulks of factories can be replaced by bright crystal palaces that enhance the welfare of their workers and are no blight on their neighborhoods. Many of them can be detached from the railroads, and the habit of building factories side by side, until great areas of land contain nothing else, can be discarded. Powerful influences will work on the side of decentralization.

One of the two important discoveries about the functional design of buildings, made in modern times, is that structures to house large-scale industrial production should be extended horizontally, so that raw materials can enter at one end and progress as nearly as possible in a straight line, without lost motion or change of level, until they issue at the other end as finished products. This represents the ideal of efficiency and to it modern factory design is approximated as closely as circumstances permit. Single-story, horizontal construction of this kind is economical of everything but land, and this fact is one of the most powerful incentives to lift industry out of urban congestion and relocate it where space is more available.

In the process of relocation, increasing consideration is being given to living facilities for workers, and in future this will certainly influence selection of sites at least as much as the older considerations of transportation and availability of materials and markets. The radius of employee settlement of course is steadily expanding, and in a suburban or rural region the workers in any factory can pick their dwelling places from a much broader range of choice. When factories are deliberately located in salubrious, not overcrowded areas, it will be possible for increasing numbers of workers to bring up their families in as pleasant and healthful surroundings as any peasant of a preindustrial age—but with all the advantages of an opulent civilization which those peasants never knew.

In the second place, we are now ready to undertake the task of adapting our cities to the needs of modern living and the opportunities created by modern building techniques.

Some defeated theorists have concluded that the very idea of cities is evil, and that we should abandon them all and move out into the country. It is possible that a day may come when comparatively few people will have their dwellings in cities, but that will only be because improved transportation will make it possible to get into and out of urban centers with great ease. So far as we can see now it will always be necessary for many people to spend a part of their waking hours together in large groups—for certain kinds of production, for administration, for the transaction of business, for education, for all kinds of group activities from prize fights to symphony concerts—and simply because people like a crowd. Great cities are no products of modern conditions—some of the largest ever built flourished and disappeared before the dawn of history. The human race is addicted to cities. They are here to stay, and we might as well accept the fact and face the problem of making them not only endurable but pleasant and efficient.

The most acute urban irritation at present is caused by transportation difficulties and these in turn are aggravated by two

modern inventions: the automobile and vertical building. Both
have great advantages and neither will be discarded. We must
find ways of living with them without discomfort.

To take vertical building first, it is the second great discovery
in functional planning made by this age: we have found that
where large numbers of people are to be sheltered under one
roof, either for domesticity or work other than large-scale manufacturing, vertical multistory structures are most economical and
convenient. This is because the basic problem in any populous
human warren is the circulation of people, as the transport of
materials and sequence of operations are the basic problems of
factory design. We have solved the latter by the invention of the
moving assembly line, but we have never devised any satisfactory
means of transporting people in a horizontal plane indoors. For
that we have found nothing better than our own two legs. We
have, however, devised a highly effective means of transporting
people *vertically* indoors. The high-speed elevator is an extraordinarily efficient device, economical of space and time, convenient,
safe. It has made the tall building an efficient arrangement of
enclosed space and will keep it popular, in spite of some of our
lugubrious pundits who look on it as the root of most modern
civic evils.

The height of buildings in the future will be limited not by
prejudice or structural practicability but solely by the percentage
of floor space required for elevator shafts. To be convinced that
tall buildings will continue to be built, we need only compare the
time- and temper-wasting horizontal labyrinth known as the Pen-
tagon Building in Washington with such smoothly functioning
vertical structures as, say, the Rockefeller Center Building in New
York.

The trouble with skyscrapers is that they have been misused to
crowd more and more people into already congested areas, while
their great potentiality for good has been neglected: in time we
shall see that their proper usage is to free the ground for other
purposes than building.

Close juxtaposition of skyscrapers greatly aggravates a problem
which the automobile has made acute even in towns that have
no skyscrapers. Scarcely any street in this country was planned

for more than one per cent of the traffic it is now forced to accommodate: if we suffer appalling waste of time, strain on nerves and general disorder now, it is dismaying to think what will happen when the number of automobiles in the country doubles as it probably will do within a decade. We lost no time in rebuilding our intercity highway systems to meet the new demands on them, and this unfinished process of adaptation will be continued. But the rigid structures of cities have so far resisted any but the most tentative experiments in relief; and up to the outbreak of this war we continued to let multistory buildings be built as closely as they could be packed in the centers of the cities, and continued to license more and more automobiles to use the streets. If we allow this expansion within unexpanded limits to be resumed after the war, a not very gradual paralysis of city life is sure to occur. All communities will suffer proportionally, and all national life will be affected by the failure of its nerve centers to function.

3

Present-day traffic conditions are a universal irritant, a burr under every man's shirt. As such they have distracted our attention from other urban inadequacies and other objectives in reconstruction, affecting the conditions under which people live at home as well as those under which they circulate.

It is true that we are moderately conscious of the necessity of slum clearance. The elimination of these substandard, stultifying areas has been piously acknowledged as a major responsibility, but with an insufficient sense of urgency. And so far we have contented ourselves with spotty and small-scale replacements. We have not attacked the conditions which have made slums common and in fact inevitable, or revitalized the sluggish system of policing which has tolerated them.

Slums continue to exist because of the high cost of replacement. It has not been profitable, as it should be, to demolish outmoded dwellings and build new, modern shelters to be rented at or near the same rates as the old. Thus it has not been feasible for public authority to carry out widespread condemnation programs, although it could easily do so in the ordinary exercise of its police powers, for the simple reason that it had no practicable alternative to offer the occupants of condemned areas. In no case, by public or private financing, has it been possible to replace sub-standard tenements with modern housing at equal rents, except where the difference between a practicable cost and the actual cost has been made up out of public funds.

This procedure, whereby an archaic system of provenance is publicly subsidized, is unsound to the point of absurdity. Even if we were willing to ignore the social implications of undertaking to house the national population properly at public expense, the problem could not be solved that way: this democracy would ruin itself either financially or politically before the job could be half done. And the paternalistic consequences are not attractive. Municipalities are shrewdly reluctant to become the permanent landlords of their citizens. They have done so in the drop-in-the-bucket USHA program only under lavish bribing by federal agencies who do not have to stay on the hot spot after the enterprise is launched.

City slums are an aggravated product of the same causes responsible for the deplorable state of housing in general: time lags in the evolution of methods whereby dwellings are constructed, financed, marketed, paid for, taxed, and regulated. This does not mean that venal landlords would not exploit their tenants even if other alternatives were practicable. But if cost of replacement should be reduced until the operation became feasible without penalizing the occupants by raising their cost of living, venal landlords could and would be more summarily dealt with.

Industrial mass production with its economies can be extended in the multiple-dwelling field as advantageously as in the single-dwelling field, but to induce this progress we need to remove a number of obstacles. Labor unions will have to realize that their opposition to technological advances which cut costs is short-sighted and self-defeating; building codes will have to be revised to encourage all economies which do not jeopardize the tenants' or the public welfare; taxes will have to be realistically levied so that they do not actually favor substandard properties as is often the case today; financing must be made as easy and economical as in, say, the electric appliance field; contractors, suppliers and realtors will have to be more adequately policed to prevent collusion and other unfair and antisocial practices. Above all, long-range city plans must be developed in a way that will allow new dwelling construction to take its allotted place in a system of organic neighborhood groups: in this way its soundness as an investment and its attractiveness to tenants will be enhanced, and building thereby stimulated.

Slums will vanish when it is more profitable for everybody concerned—owners, tenants, and municipalities—to replace them with proper housing. It has never been necessary for government to subsidize the manufacture and sale of automobiles; it is just as unsound for government to assume that it must subsidize housing. Because of the healthy state of automobile production and distribution, government finds it practicable to require that motor-cars be kept up to rigid standards of performance, that unsafe cars be ruled off the highways, that drivers pass tests of competence, that traffic conform to strict regulation. All this is a normal and democratic exercise of police powers which could be applied as effectively to the maintenance of housing standards if the production and supply of housing were as economically sound and popular. Here is the root of the trouble and it should be the point of attack. A successful campaign to change it will be long and difficult, admittedly, but there is no other hope that housing of this democratic nation can become as admirable as its means of transportation.

4

We are just beginning to appreciate generally the varied benefits that would flow from the reorganization of our municipal residential areas in a system of neighborhood units: * the regrouping of population and services in a series of more or less self-sufficient communities, as islands around which the major streams of traffic will flow, and within which the daily round of living—marketing, education, recreation, entertainment, commu-

* See Clarence Arthur Perry, *Housing for the Machine Age*, Russell Sage Foundation, 1939. A pioneer work on the subject of neighborhood planning.

nal and social activities—can be carried on in an atmosphere more tranquil, more propitious for both children and adults, than is now possible amid the indiscriminate confusion of present-day cities. In this way the stability of neighborhoods will not only be enhanced, but something of the desirable intimacy and fellowship of the small town can be restored to city life and some of the cities' devastating loneliness eliminated.

The most intellectually productive communities of the past have always been of a size that allowed personality to rub against personality in mutual support and stimulation, and knowledge of men to be acquired through familiarity with many. We have no way of knowing how many human potentialities have failed to develop in the social desert of modern urban life: we do know that neighborhood organization of municipalities will go far to restore normal living conditions within their boundaries, and perhaps retain in the cities some of the population that now seems destined to seek its home life elsewhere. In these self-contained communities of not more than 5,000 people, with their own shops, churches, schools, theaters, and recreation centers, people can get to know each other, children can play in safety and go to school without crossing thoroughfares, youths and girls can pick their mates from circles in which they have grown to maturity. And still the greater city will supply employment and those major resources that only a great city can support.

In satisfying the social urge in this way, other related needs can be met. Cities have been built too exclusively as work centers, with too little provision for health-building play, both youthful and adult; for quiet relaxation in the sun or shade, where the eyes can rest on green grass and bright flowers; for sheer tranquil enjoyment of the passing hour in unhurried ease. And too little consideration has been shown our esthetic sensibilities: the squalid disorder of the modern city is an offense to the human spirit. In their reorganization our cities should and can acquire a man-made, harmonious order that will soothe the nerves and satisfy our craving for that evident rightness we call beauty.

This kind of bodily and spiritual refreshment has been resigned to the country, but it need not be. If we build vertically, and space residential towers liberally, and direct our main streams of traffic around islands of relative quiet, it will be possible to have as great a concentration of population as should ever exist and at the same time allow space for the country to flow into and through the city as Spring came to town in Dunsany's story.

Taking New York as an example, there are sections of the city where people are crowded together in far too great congestion, much more than should ever be permitted to live within any equal acreage. And these sections are not only the ancient slums but also the better apartment house districts built within the last half-century and regarded as acceptable. But there are still larger areas, even on Manhattan Island, where the land is wasted appallingly on walk-up tenements, one- or two-story shops, mysterious, untenanted warehouses; and in the outlying boroughs there are great seas of tiny, crowded, single-family homes covering the ground to nobody's satisfaction, and other huge tracts waiting to be similarly despoiled. A thriftier use of the city's surface, a more uniform distribution of the city's population, would allow all its people to be housed in high towers with ample green acres between and around them.

This is no idle dream. The population density of New York City, certainly one of the most congested areas on the continent, was only 39 people to the acre in 1940.* If half the acreage is allocated to streets and commercial and industrial usage, an excessive allowance, the density in the rest would be only 78 people, or 17 families to the acre. This is a figure more than acceptable to the most exacting sociologist or city planner. In one cross-shaped tower of twenty stories, 170 families easily could be housed in complete privacy, with windows open to the sun and air—and more than nine acres of lawns, gardens and playgrounds for their enjoyment around them. Much less than this would be good enough, and the remoter reaches of Richmond and Queens could be left until we need them.

To accomplish anything like this sparse distribution, we shall have to apply to building much more rigid restrictions than we have had. We may very probably decide that no dwelling house

* The 1940 Census Report gives the population of the five boroughs as 7,454,995. The World Almanac of 1945 gives their area of dry land as 299 square miles or 191,360 acres.

less than twenty stories high shall ever again be built within certain areas of New York City, and that no such building shall occupy more than a fourth, or a fifth, or a tenth, of a given plot. We shall also have to be far less prodigal of the area devoted to streets. At present we are incredibly wasteful of pavement according to the rules of a day when every little plot 20 by 100 feet was entitled to have a broad highway in front of it. We can decide that in time this uniform grid-work of streets is to be replaced by a system of main arteries, few in number but amply designed without intersections to carry the great floods of traffic of the future. And, from these, feeders can penetrate to the neighborhood focal points as required. A scientifically engineered system of this kind would reduce the amount of pavement to a fraction of its present extent but allow a smooth and uninterrupted circulation not possible in the existing rigid pattern.

Such drastic reallocation of the city's land obviously calls for an equally drastic reorganization of the municipal tax structure, but this should be easier to accomplish than the physical changes and certainly could keep pace with them. Substantial economies in the provision of city services, including police and fire protection, could be effected in the new plan; and forms of revenue raising other than the taxing of real estate on the basis of its improved valuation are long overdue. The present system has acted as a brake on change and improvement, and at the same time it has brought most municipalities to a deplorable state of financial insecurity. It should not be beyond our ingenuity to make taxation both a stimulus to advancement and the basis of sound financing.

We shall see certain changes in transportation habits occurring in the normal course of events, facilitating our planning. It is probable that, in the not too distant future, city thoroughfares will be used almost exclusively for intramural, short-haul passenger traffic: extramural arrivals and departures will be almost entirely by helicopter, and so will longer trips within the city limits. When this type of transportation is practicable, silent and safe, with landing stages atop of many buildings, and adequate air traffic regulations in effect, the saving of time and nervous strain will be immense and the relief of surface congestion substantial.

Further relief will come from the requirement that all new buildings provide adequate indoor parking for occupants and visitors. This will not be unreasonable in the widely spaced construction of the future, as the pattern has been set by San Francisco in its huge new municipal parking lot built beneath a downtown park. It is also probable that the transport of freight will be entirely eliminated from the streets and restricted to a system of underground conduits.

By these measures we can avoid that favorite expedient of modern civic theorists, the multilevel street. After seeing the difference in Sixth Avenue, New York, made by the removal of the relatively open grillwork of its elevated railway, we will never again resort to the dank and depressing superimposition of street levels. Certain utilities can go underground, yes, and certain types of traffic into the air; but streets in the smokeless cities of the future should be thought of as sunny, unshadowed, unobstructed, and not overburdened lanes. Underground will do for freight and passenger subways and for parking; men will live and walk in the sun.

5

It is easy to plan thus, in theory. Given a clean sheet of paper, ink, and a facile imagination and any intelligent engineer can lay out a better city than any that exists. But a city, big or little, is an obstinate mass of masonry accumulated over many years, with land and buildings owned in small parcels by people properly jealous of rights as authentic as any human rights. This ponderous construction is woven through with an intricate, costly, and vitally necessary network of services for supplying water, gas, electricity, power, sewage disposal, telephones, fire and police protection, in some cases heat and underground transportation, all very difficult to alter by any sweeping gesture. And the whole complex is overlaid by tradition, sanctioned by habit and custom, hallowed by surprising loyalties. Grand Street in New York a generation ago probably would have been deplored by any sociologist, but the "Grand Street Boys" of today, many of them eminent citizens, annually meet to celebrate their nostalgic affection for their birthplace. People can and do love their cities, like their mothers, just as they are.

Thus the problem of city reconstruction presents two opposing aspects: ease of theoretical solution, and extreme difficulty of doing anything drastic about it.

This impact of urgency on inertia explodes in a clash between authoritarian and democratic tendencies. Ardent city reformers resolve the dilemma in favor of arbitrary action. This is not surprising. When people are professionally dedicated to doing good to others, they often develop a terrifying ruthlessness: in conscious rectitude, come hell or high water, good shall be done, no matter who suffers or what fundamental rights go down in the process. Fortunately this type is seldom elected to office—it does not appeal to voters. But it often lands in office by appointment, by mere gravitation of power toward hands eager to grasp it. And it is practically always vocal, not to say vociferous.

The National Resources Planning Board concludes that in order to rebuild urban America, "enlarged powers and programs of action will be necessary at all levels of government." The Uthwaite Commission in England looks longingly at the "nationalization of all land," and foregoes it only because it is not at the moment practicable, not because it would be basically undesirable to make all people tenants and government the only landlord. The public ownership of all municipal land dances alluringly before the eyes of innumerable planners—it would make reconstruction so very easy.

Rexford Guy Tugwell carries the tendencies of many of these impatient benefactors to a logical extreme: he would go wholehog and create a planning authority of life tenure, universal cognizance, and unrestrained authority; and he adds, unnecessarily, that we should need "an enlarged and nationalized police power for enforcement." * Doubtless it would be called USPP, rather than GPU or Gestapo.

Thus for well-planned cities we are asked to trade a full complement of rights we have come to value highly. We have seen

---

* Quoted by Robert Moses in a devastating article entitled "Mr. Moses Dissects the 'Long-Haired Planners,'" New York *Times* Magazine, June 25, 1944.

that the people of England, who were not under authoritarian control, were willing to see their cities blown to bits rather than yield a single item of their rights. It will be ironic if they now pay these rights as the price of correcting mere municipal imperfections. As between continuing to live in inefficient cities and accepting a government with powers enlarged to become the mentor and manager of its citizens' private lives, I should choose the former and I should be in a huge majority of Americans.

There is also a strong probability that arbitrary revision would be abortive even if it were acceptable. A city is a living organism which must grow in conformity to its own inner spirit as well as its physical needs. Not even these material needs, to say nothing of those less tangible, are always evident to the finite mind that must draw its conclusions from maps, statistics and aerial photographs. Le Corbusier has given us proof of the limitations of sheer intellect in the face of so complex a problem. He has a mind as brilliant and creative as any active today in the field of architecture and civic planning, and in his *La Ville Radieuse* * he has proposed new plans for several of the world's great cities: for all his ingenuity, it is hard to believe that the same treatment would be equally satisfactory if applied to Algiers and Nemours as Le Corbusier proposes.

More power is not the only answer, nor any answer. We need "enlarged programs," yes; "enlarged powers," no. Programs, so long as they remain such and do not become a Procrustean bed, are indispensable in crystallizing opinion and guiding the direction of movement. Their supreme virtue is that they are always subject to revision in conformity to new needs, expanding knowledge, and keener perception. Cities will always be a lap or two behind an ideal concept of what they should be, and this is much better than if they were committed to arbitrary errors almost impossible to correct.

Community planning has always been a public function. All communities are planned, after a fashion, and it requires no more authority to plan a community well than to plan it stupidly. It does require more intelligence and more breadth of vision, cer-

* *La Ville Radieuse*, Editions de L'Architecture d'Aujourd'hui, Boulogne.

tainly. City planning is a means of setting up conscious and clearly defined objectives, which become easier to attain as they become more vivid, more generally accepted, more enthusiastically desired. No situation is hopeless when people know what should be done about it and want it done. There is nothing which cannot be changed: buildings can be demolished in any numbers, streets can be widened and relocated to direct the streams of traffic where we want them to flow (New York has made a beginning with its two express highways along the outer edges of Manhattan Island, Chicago with its Outer Drive); the rules governing building can be revised and a pattern of neighborhoods laid down to guide future construction. These are rights communities have always possessed. A man is not allowed to play a cornet all night or keep pigs in a city back yard merely because he does it on his own property. With equal ease he can be required to respect his neighbors' values and refrain from antisocial exploitation of his own. He can even be restrained from offending his neighbors' optical sensibilities, as the cornet player is restrained from exacerbating the neighborhood aural sensibilities. Existing police powers are adequate for any control of the use of land or the characteristics of buildings that is in the agreed public interest.

6

Municipal improvement, like all other phases of advance, depends on putting the creative energies of the country to work at the job. The necessary abilities, concepts, technologies, capital, all exist in ample quantities. Yes, capital, too—what need is there for public subsidizing if we have all those unemployed billions on which the "mature economists" based their bleak conclusions? Show capital a profit and it will go to work, just as men will do. If we can bring to bear on this problem of proper living conditions that greatest force in the world—intelligent self-interest—we can provide decent housing and gracious communities by exactly the same processes that have revolutionized transportation, communications, and power distribution and are at work on the other fundamental needs of diet, recreation, and education. It is only necessary to get self-interest working on the right side, which can be done by requiring it to work within the framework of a publicly accepted plan that will give it both scope and direction.

Already many municipalities, large and small, are preparing long-range plans for their own reconstruction, and this movement will expand by geometrical progression as the results begin to show. Emulation is as strong an influence in the civic as in any other sphere: in a period of general civic vigor, progress is contagious. Mistakes will be made in both planning and execution, but so long as these mistakes do not include the sacrifice of any fundamental rights they are not irreparable.

It is quite possible that in the course of the next half-century the communities of the country may develop into gracious, urbane, and peaceful dwelling places: it is also possible that with practically universal air transport, the commercial, amusement and cultural foci of cities may cease entirely to be dwelling places. The population which they serve may spread thinly over the neighboring country, to occupy isolated groups of tall towers which leave the major part of the land undisturbed around them. Urbanity may be rusticated.

A period of drastic change obviously lies ahead of us. And the immense job of civic reconstruction which this change entails, together with a vast expansion of private housing construction, will make the biggest single contribution to the high level of prosperity which this country must maintain. It will supply tens of billions of dollars to workers for many years to come—there is in fact no end to the work in sight, other than the ever-present possibility of stupidly induced disaster: these are activities as interminably cyclic as the planting and reaping of crops.

Such sustained and intensive effort will help greatly in pushing up the general income level of the American people, as it pushes down the cost of shelter until the two bridge the great gap that separates them today. Only as products are produced and consumed in greater and greater quantities do their prices go down while both their quality and the wages of their producers go up. We have seen this happen to great numbers of mass-produced commodities and the workers who make them during the past generation. As it happens to shelter, the commodity which influences the people's welfare most profoundly, and bulks largest in the people's budget, we shall see our rising national prosperity more universally distributed and more unshakably established. Thus better housing and better communities will be the most powerful economic factors in making possible that higher standard of living for which they are also the most essential items of material equipment.

CHAPTER XIII

WE CAN BUILD A BETTER PEOPLE

A PRINCIPAL reason for the dim view of this country's future taken by "mature economists" is the decline in the rate of growth of the population: since there are not enough new people to supply, there can be no further incentive for economic expansion, and insufficient opportunities for the investment of private savings; the economy grinds slowly to a stop, and government must take over the distribution of whatever static supply of loaves and fishes may exist. There are other facets to the "mature economy" argument, but none of them shines with any more luster than this.

As to the decline in the rate of population growth, we have had it with us a very long time—since 1850, in fact. It was 35.9 per cent from 1840 to 1850, and only 16 per cent from 1920 to 1930. But during the eighteen-forties we added only six million people to our population, while in the nineteen-twenties we added seventeen millions. The depressed nineteen-thirties limited family increases still further, but the nineteen-forties are certain to show that our breeding propensities have revived with the economy. If the rate of the eighteen-forties had been maintained, we should have had about 190 million people here in 1920, well over 340 millions in 1940, and could look forward to 465 millions in 1950, a prospect which might disconcert even the "mature economists." Thank God we do not exhibit this particular guinea pig characteristic.

Mere population growth is not a decisive factor in economic expansion, as relatively static nations have proved. Sweden enlarged its production 300 per cent between 1900 and 1930, with a population increase of only 20 per cent. Between 1900 and 1930 we ourselves increased our production 120 per cent, while our population rose only 60 per cent.* During this time, the average daily hours of labor declined sharply, so that the higher output was obtained by a smaller expenditure of individual time and energy.

To put it another way, during those three decades we added much more than a third (38 per cent) to the average amount of goods provided each year for every man, woman, and child in the country, a too meager but far from discreditable achievement. This is the kind of expansion on which our ambitions should be set—to provide better living for the people who dwell in this country, regardless of how many they may be. There is no other way in which the material welfare of the nation can be advanced.

Instead of alarming ourselves about the quantity of our population—we have enough to make a mighty nation and certainly a crowded land is nothing to be desired—we should focus our attention on the way the population lives, and its physical and mental quality. Here we shall find that we have immense continents of achievement lying open to us and crying to be occupied. The world's greatest market waits here within our own borders, among the under-privileged and under-supplied millions of our own people, whose unfilled needs are at once our greatest national discredit and our greatest opportunity for advancement.

Until at least half the population is provided with at least twice the quantity of goods it now consumes, and another quarter receives a substantial increase, we cannot assume that production has reached even decent proportions. When this volume is attained, it should be possible to supply the basic necessities of life to all the people, but at least half of them will still be missing some or all of the desirable superfluities we like to think of as the American birthright. These "superfluities" are in reality only less urgent necessities, and include such moderate blessings as a liberal, balanced diet, adequate medical and dental care, amuse-

---

* *America's Capacity to Consume*, Brookings Institution, 1934, pp. 16-17. The percentage of production increase is adjusted to the decline in the purchasing power of the dollar, the actual increase in total national income from all sources, in dollar volume, having been 480 per cent (p. 152).

ment and healthy recreation, modern bathroom and kitchen conveniences, comfortable and attractive home furnishings, clothing that satisfies one's self-respect, all the education the individual can profitably assimilate. The ultimate goal of a production program should be to supply all of these accessories to comfortable living—and many others as time adds them to the list—to all the people in the land.

If a higher standard of living resulted only in greater enjoyment of life, it still would be greatly desirable. But a given standard of living is directly correlated to the physical stamina, mental stature, and moral health of the people who pass their lives at that level. Deficiencies in living conditions produce deficiencies in health, mentality, and morals, and these in turn reduce ability to contribute to the national welfare. Thus a vicious circle of cause and effect is closed. For this reason the various standards of living in this country—for there are many—become a matter of acute practical concern to all of us, and the elevation of the lower levels our Number One national imperative.

2

Since in any exchange economy—ours or the Russian's—people can only have what they can afford to buy, family income becomes a revealing yardstick with which to gauge living standards. The year 1929 was a prosperous year in this country, and the last in which our economy was functioning under what up to that time we had regarded as normal conditions. At the prices prevailing then, "a family income of $2,000 may perhaps be considered as sufficient to supply only basic necessities. However accurate this generalization may be, it is significant to note that more than 16 million families, or practically 60 per cent of the total number, were below this standard of expenditures." * The median family in this year had an income of $1,700: that is, half the families in the nation had less than that, half had more. But "the greatest concentration of families was between the $1,000 and $1,500 level, the most frequent income being about $1,300."

* Op. cit., p. 56.

Relating these facts to living standards, the Brookings Institution found that in this boom year of 1929, 42 per cent of the population—families with incomes under $1,500 and unattached individuals with incomes under $750—lived in a state of "subsistence and poverty," while another 36 per cent—with family incomes of $1,500 to $3,000 and individual incomes of $750 to $1,500—lived in a state of "minimum comfort." In the next bracket were 14 per cent in "moderate circumstances," while a mere 8 per cent above $5,000 were rated as "comfortable" or better.*

These figures need some adjustment, as it is obvious that a family of two can be comfortable on an income which would mean privation for a family of seven, and a family living on a debt-free farm flowing with milk and honey can do nicely with much less cash than a tenant family in the city. But no matter how we juggle the facts, it is plain that in 1929 a majority of Americans were living on much less than we like to think. They may have bought radios and jallopies and gone to the movies, but if so they pinched still further on necessities to make up for these pardonable extravagances.

One of the items on which they saved was food. The Bureau of Home Economics of the Department of Agriculture prepared a series of food budgets for a family of five in 1931-32, ranging from a minimum diet on which life could be supported temporarily at $350 per year to a "liberal" bill of fare at $950. The Brookings Institution concludes that in 1929 there were 16 million non-farm families, or 74 per cent, who could not afford to eat "moderately well" at $800, while only 10 per cent were able to enjoy the "liberal" diet at $950.†

Let's look at the distribution of food from another angle. Of all the provisions sold in 1929, only 27 per cent went to feed the 42 per cent of the population who were in the subsistence and poverty group.‡ Few of the more fortunate 58 per cent were gluttons, and most of them ate no more than they needed, if that, as we have seen. But a little figuring with paper and pencil will

* Op. cit., p. 87.
† Op. cit., pp. 122-123.
‡ Op. cit., pp. 88-89.

show you that the millions among the 42 per cent ate almost exactly half as much per person (in dollar value) as those among the 58 per cent. A great many Americans must have been seriously undernourished in 1929.

In addition to food, a family requires some kind of a roof over its head; it must have clothing, it must occasionally have doctors, amusements, and gasoline; it usually pays taxes. We have already canvassed briefly the state of American housing and found it shamefully below par. As to clothing, it took 1.8 billion dollars in 1929 to dress the 930,000 families and individuals who had $10,000 or more a year to spend, while almost the same value in clothes—1.9 billion dollars—had to be spread thinly over the back of the 14 million families and individuals in the subsistence and poverty group.* This is not to say that the well-to-do always had more clothing than they should have had—probably very few of them, by actual count, were in the peacock class. But it indicates that millions of Americans were dressed too poorly for health, comfort, and a decent self-respect. As to doctors and dentists, we shall see, a few pages further along, the effect of an undersupply of their services.

Nineteen hundred and twenty-nine was the last year of prosperity until 1941, and in the interval incomes and living standards sagged tragically. In 1935-36, which was not the low point of the depression by any means, the median line of incomes stood at $1,160, the number of families in the subsistence and poverty groups had received a heavy increase, and those with more than $3,000 a year—able to afford that safe but moderate diet—had shrunk from 22 per cent of the total in 1929 to a mere 8 per cent.† The sheer physical privation during this period may not have equaled what the Chinese have commonly suffered for centuries, or what the war-devastated countries of Europe are enduring now, but it was much too much for our national honor to take without flinching, or our national health to take without impairment.

As wartime prosperity swept over the land, we registered a sharp

* Op. cit., pp. 87 and 88.
† Consumer Incomes in the United States, National Resources Committee, 1937.

rise in incomes. In 1941 the median line rose to $1,900; in 1944 it was $2,700, even after taxes. About 42 per cent of city families and single persons had incomes above $3,000 after taxes in 1944, the number having more than doubled since 1941.* It is true that the greater prosperity of the people could not be translated at once into better living conditions, which instead actually declined in many instances due to the wartime crowding of industrial centers and the shortages of needed consumer goods. But if this level of incomes can be maintained as the production of goods, food, and housing rises to equal the demand, with prices held down by competitive exploitation of technological economies and expanded volume, we shall see many of the dismal deficiencies of the past made good.

In these strictures on our record we are condemning ourselves not because we have lagged behind other nations, but because we have not done as well as we should and can do. Lest you think our system has proved its inferiority as a creator of well-being, we should hasten to say that its record at its worst far surpasses that of any other system. Even if there should still be a substantial percentage of our people in the "subsistence and poverty" level of $1,500 or less per family per year, we can set that against the fact that the bottom third in Europe and Latin America, and the bottom two-thirds in Asia and Africa—48 per cent of mankind—must live on the equivalent of 14 cents down to 4 cents per day per person. And the families in this country who have $17 to $35 a week to spend are as well off as the most prosperous third of the peoples of Europe, Russia, Japan, North Africa, and Latin America; while the man who makes $75 a week is among the wealthiest 3 per cent of the entire world's population.†

It all depends on what standard you judge us by, and we should use only the standard of our own potentialities. This leads us to the conviction that, as we have means to create vastly more wealth than we have yet done, we urgently need to do so.

* Statement of the Bureau of Labor Statistics, Department of Labor, reported in the New York Times, December 9, 1945.
† Science Digest, December, 1943, p. 18.

3

When we called up our young men and women for war, we had
a chance to assess the effects of inadequate living on their generation, and the result was a shock. The facts are baldly stated in the
opening sentences of a Senate report on the subject:

"The Nation has been deeply impressed by the fact that approximately 4.5 million young men in the prime of life have been
found unfit for military service because of physical and mental
defects. In addition, more than a million men have been discharged from service because of defects other than those sustained
in battle. One and one-half million men in uniform were rendered
fit for service only through medical and dental care given after
they were inducted.

"In all, it is estimated that at least 40 per cent of the 22 million men of military age—between 8 and 9 million men—are unfit
for military duty." *

These shocking facts are no reflection on the youths themselves,
and do not indicate that by and large they are not as sound as
the youths of any other country. Many of the 4-F's rendered indispensable services in other phases of war work, and defects that
barred them from the armed forces will not necessarily handicap
them in civilian life: a hunchbacked Steinmetz, a deaf Edison,
or a paralyzed Roosevelt would not have been looked at twice by
a Selective Service Board. And we need not conclude that the
health of the nation has actually deteriorated—quite the contrary
is true.

The same young men had added an inch to their average stature since World War I,† and their life expectancy had expanded
by several years. Between 1900 and 1940 the death rate in this

* Interim Report Number 3, Subcommittee on Wartime Health and Education to the Committee on Education and Labor, United States Senate,
January, 1945.

† American youth has grown taller and slimmer since World War I. The
Quartermaster Corps reports the soldiers of this war required an inch longer
trouser-leg, a size larger shoe, a larger hat, a size smaller collar; their chest
measurement dropped from 37 inches to 36 inches.

country fell from 17.2 per 1,000 people to 10.8 per 1,000, and the death rate from what were once the dread diseases of typhoid and paratyphoid fevers, diphtheria, diarrhea, and enteritis had declined close to the vanishing point. There have been spectacular declines in the incidence of many germ diseases such as smallpox, scarlet fever, and pulmonary tuberculosis.

But with all these and many other prideful facts in mind, it is still humiliating to realize that 40 per cent of our young men do not measure up to the physical standards of the military forces: humiliating because it is so very largely a preventable and remediable condition.

That the picture can be changed is proven by the services' own performance in rehabilitating that million-and-a-half who came to them unfit, and in caring for those whom it accepted. Many more cases could have been remedied by longer-term, more patient treatment than the harried services could give in wartime, and many more need never have existed at all if the youths had grown up on a proper diet, been protected from venereal disease, had adequate dental and ocular care, gone to school, and lived in a community which possessed a competent public health service.

First of all in a health-building program is the requirement of an ample supply of varied, balanced foodstuffs. Millions of youths encountered leafy green and yellow vegetables for the first time at the army mess, and viewed them with acute distaste until army exercise opened their minds and mouths to anything edible. The country as a whole consumes less than half as much of these important vitamin-bearing foods as it should, and only a little more than half the proper amount of milk and milk products.* When twelve million young people were suddenly put on a really ample diet by the armed services, we civilians found to our surprise that the country was not producing enough meat, butter, vegetables, and fats to supply the customary quotas for the rest of us.

But in the light of recent research, the influence of diet on health has taken on new dimensions. We are beginning to be-

* National Resources Planning Board study of March, 1942, quoted by Stuart Chase in *Goals for America*, The Twentieth Century Fund, 1942, p. 40.

lieve that although a man may eat all the meat, fruit, and vegetables he wants, he will suffer most unpleasant consequences if
these foods are grown on soils deficient in certain imperceptible
minerals and chemicals. Among these are calcium, phosphorus,
iron, iodine, and minute quantities of what are known as "trace
minerals." There is strong but still largely circumstantial evidence
that a shortage of these essential ingredients in the diet produces
the degenerative diseases such as tooth decay and associated
troubles of the jaw and gums, deformities and diseases of the
skeleton, hardening of the arteries, heart ailments and cancer.*

The soils in various sections of the country differ widely in
mineral content, and areas of deficiency everywhere have been
spreading during the past century, owing to wasteful methods of
farming which exhaust the soil's fertility. And it is a disturbing
corollary that even while medical science has been conquering the
germ diseases so successfully, the degenerative diseases have been
increasing at an alarming rate.

The greatest number of rejections by Selective Service were for
muscular and skeletal defects, a large part traceable to dietary
causes. Of the men rendered fit for service after induction, more
than two-thirds were made so by major dental repairs. Even beyond this group, the dental services rendered by the armed forces
were staggering in quantity—14.6 million cases among 12 million
inductees, with 53 million sittings and a use of dental supplies in
two years equal to 3.5 times the entire output of the United
States in any one year. For a nation which prides itself, and with
some reason, on its addiction to tooth brushes and its superior
dentists, it is sobering to learn that its youth needed these arrears
of dental care.

Caries, or tooth decay, is almost unknown to the natives of
certain areas, such as Deaf Smith County, Texas, where the water
contains about one part per million of fluoride, and the soil is
rich in calcium and phosphorus which find their way into flour,
milk, meat, and vegetables. An experiment is being carefully conducted in Newburgh, New York, where the city water is being
fluorinated, and near-by Kingston where it is not, to discover the
effects of this treatment on caries in school children. Circumstan-

* Dr. Weston A. Price, *Nutrition and Physical Degeneration*, Harper, 1939.

tial evidence gives reason to believe that it may be possible, in the near future, to produce a generation of Americans whose teeth are as shining, white, even and sound as those that gleam at us from practically every advertising page. Again a national standard may really be attained.

If caries proves to be controllable in such an easy and painless way, there is no reason why many other degenerative diseases cannot be conquered by replenishing the mineral content of agricultural lands. Already a great deal of work is being done along this line, as farmers have learned that an ample supply of lime, phosphorus, and trace minerals pays dividends in better crops and cattle. If mineral deficiencies in diet can be made up, this advance coupled with increasing knowledge of vitamins and their ample synthesis, and the impending nation-wide distribution of frozen foods which will make a balanced diet available in practically every community throughout the year, should make this a really well-fed country for the first time in its history.

4

Death from disease in our armed forces was reduced to less than one per thousand, as compared with more than 14 per thousand in World War I, which shows what medical science can accomplish today with sound, well-fed adults to work on. Its armory includes amazing new drugs such as the well-publicized sulfonamides in their many variations, penicillin, and others less well known but equally potent in their special ways; amazing advances in blood plasma and whole blood transfusion; knowledge of the potency of sex hormones in treating disturbances of sexual and reproductive functions; new and swifter treatments of syphilis, that prime scourge to which much insanity and heart disease, ocular defects and untold suffering are due; chemical control of disease-carrying insects and rodents; the electron microscope's revelation of the structure of living and non-living matter, and especially that "in-between" matter known as viruses by which so many dread diseases are caused; new controls of psychiatric disorders (by which 20 per cent of Selective Service rejectees were disqualified) due to the electroencephalograph, "psychosomatic" medicine and advancing psychiatry.

Along all these lines of scientific advance, the war provided an enormous amount of concentrated laboratory experience—one million neuropsychiatric cases alone were treated in Army hospitals. The catalog of health-building and health-restoring resources is growing daily, and all the war's medical conquests and all the swift scientific achievements of these crowded years are at the service of the nation to build a stronger, more vigorous, and more competent population than we ever dreamed the world would produce. The waste of disease, impairment, and untimely death can be cut to a mere fraction of the terrible drainage we have suffered since the race began.

Can be, yes. But 40 per cent of the counties in this country have no public health service and no hospitals: they may be thinly populated, but 15 million people live in them. Sixty-five hundred communities need new or better water supplies; 7,700 communities need new sewage systems; five million rural homes need better water supplies and more sanitary toilet facilities. There are only 3,000 qualified psychiatrists in the country to care for millions needing expert neuropsychiatric treatment. Medical personnel is too few and unevenly distributed, with almost all rural districts inadequately served. The Senate Subcommittee whose Report No. 2 I have drawn on for these facts concludes that 417,000 new hospital beds are needed.

In a national health-building program, the government, at community, state, and national levels, should discharge many responsibilities which cannot be assumed by citizen enterprise: public health services should be extended to complete coverage, and their facilities improved; guidance in soil replenishment should be available to all raisers of food; government should initiate the needed expansion of hospital service and an extension of medical education; competent medical, surgical, dental, and psychiatric treatment should be made available to all people who need them whether or not they can afford to pay for them; school children should be consistently examined to see that deficiencies are detected and made good and defects promptly repaired. All these are precautions which the nation owes to itself by any common-sense standard.

But all these responsibilities can be discharged without putting the vigorous medical profession, which has registered so swift and impressive an advance, under the dead hand of bureaucratic control in any system of socialized medicine. The national welfare will not be served by an attempt to institutionalize the population and turn the doctors and surgeons into listless time-servers dealing out standardized rations of medical treatment. Even some lack of uniformity or occasionally sketchy coverage would be preferable to any such metering of the stream of professional progress.

Much more important, fundamentally, than the State's part in a health-building program is the economic status of the population itself. A proper discharge of the State's functions must be meshed with a progressive diffusion of prosperity, if we are to become a nation of people sound in wind and limb, with clear eyes and perfect teeth, virile to the end of a long life-span. No amount of state aid to the indigent can possibly be as constructive as the elimination of indigence: and that is something which can only be accomplished by the huge increase in wealth production and wealth dissemination of which we are perfectly capable.

5

The connection between poverty and moral delinquency, as between poverty and physical disability, is no modern discovery. Crime occurs at all economic levels, and crimes among the wealthy or in that contemporary half-world known as "café society" attract much more attention than no more dull and sordid felonies among the poor. But anyone who surveys the inmates of penal institutions, especially the "reformatories" for the young of both sexes, will discover that while a very small percentage of the inmates come from comfortable or well-to-do homes, the great majority of these unfortunates have had socially, if not physically, starved and unhappy backgrounds. They come in hordes from the ranks of the under-privileged, many of them with no basically criminal instincts whatever: they have merely been born into circumstances with which they have no capacity to deal, and become embroiled at cross-purposes with a society which has shown them no generosity or kindliness. Transferred to a household where they find comfort, good fellowship, and friendly understanding, and a chance to build self-respect through the demonstration of competence, it is amazing to see how often they change from suppressed and wary animals to expansive, able citizens who will carry their own weight in the world. This, of course, is merely what should have happened to them in the households where they were born, and the reasons it didn't were almost always, directly and indirectly, economic.

The nation at this moment is troubled by a wave of juvenile delinquency of alarming proportions. An intensive study of 1,000 juvenile delinquents, made by Sheldon and Eleanor T. Glueck of the Harvard Law School,* explodes the popular fallacy that this is all due to the wartime disruption of homes or a general decline in domestic morals. Wartime conditions of living and the prevailing wartime mood of nervous excitement may have released an exceptional wave of delinquency, but this survey reveals an incontestable link between moral deficiencies and domestic deficiencies, existing prior to and independently of any wartime phenomena.

The evidence is overwhelming: 76 per cent of the youngsters come from "poverty-stricken" families and 85 per cent live in overcrowded slum areas. Since the *average* size of their families is seven, these circumstances are aggravated to the worst possible degree. Poverty and genetic deterioration react on each other as both cause and effect, in a vicious, mutually stimulative cycle. The result is indicated by the fact that, out of every hundred young delinquents, 56 have personalities that are classed as abnormal, only five are of superior and only 37 of normal mentality, while 58 are graded down from dull to feeble-minded. Eighty-five of each hundred show anti-social behavior in school—and from their experience of society what can you expect?—and only 17 ever enter the high schools which the State makes available to all of

* Quoted at length in Report Number 2 from the Subcommittee on Wartime Health and Education to the Committee on Education and Labor, United States Senate, September, 1944.

them; while at home half their parents have had no schooling,
75 of each hundred children have had no guidance in their
leisure-time activities, and 85 of their families have other delin-
quent members. In short, the great majority have lived not only
in poverty and a depressing physical environment, but in an atmosphere of ignorance and chronic anti-social revolt.

The swift elimination of all overcrowded, sub-standard slums,
urban and rural, and their replacement by amply spaced, modern,
clean, and attractive dwellings is, of course, an urgent national
imperative. It is moreover a job which will take years of the most
intensive building to accomplish, no matter how energetically we
attack it, and before it is finished many of the replacements will
have become slums by the advancing standards of decades hence.
Any such urban program, too, will be ineffective unless it includes
an adequate provision of supervised playgrounds for the young
and recreational facilities for adults. But no matter how well we
build and rebuild, decent living conditions for all our people can
only be established by the progressive elimination of the poverty
which creates and supports slums and which slums augment.

6

Domestic circumstances are one side of the coin, sterling or
counterfeit, in which society pays its debt to the young: the other
side is the school. Schools may be supposed to deal primarily with
the mentality of their charges, but they cannot help but spread
their influence for better or worse into the moral and physical
realms. And when the home fails the child, school offers society
its best chance to make up the deficit. Unfortunately, the schools
fall down about as often as the homes.

This country long ago committed itself to supplying a measure
of education without direct charge—that is, out of the general
tax fund—to all its young. And from making it available we have
progressed, in most sections of the country, to making a certain
amount of schooling compulsory. Fortunately the public school
system is supported and controlled by the states and communities
and not by the federal government, so that it does not offer the

strong temptation to ideological shaping of the youthful mind which scheming executives might be unable to resist in a national system. But this characteristic safeguard of our liberties is responsible for wide variations in school facilities, coverage and quality. There are large areas where public education is even poorer than the people, and even in the same community the training offered slum children is often inferior to that provided in prosperous suburbs. School facilities frequently are inadequate and overcrowded, and, while some educational plants are superior to the product they dispense, it is a sobering fact that more than half the school houses of the country are still of the one-room variety. And when we reflect that the number of college graduates in the country does not greatly exceed the number of total illiterates, while twice as many children never advance beyond the fourth grade,* we realize that our educational record is not much better than our record in housing and health.

In this field, plant is less important than personnel, but here too we fall far below a decent standard. What should be one of the best paid and most highly skilled professions is notoriously underpaid and too often poorly trained. As a result the teaching staff is more than half a million short of its proper quota, and many of those now employed are ill-equipped amateurs without any vocation for their work. This statement does not controvert the fact that we are blessed with many wise, noble, and skillful teachers: it merely stresses the point that while all should aspire to that classification, a great many do not.

Pedagogical methods generally are deplorably antiquated and resistant to change. They still rely on the printed and spoken word as the accepted means of communicating knowledge, in disregard of the fact that what a child sees and does makes a more lasting impression than what he reads or hears.

When the armed services faced the necessity of instilling much specialized knowledge into many men in record time, they utilized every likely device to speed the task: they used sound films, both still and movie, graphic charts, experimental apparatus and prac-

---

* U. S. Census, 1940. 3.4 millions have had four years or more of college, 2.8 millions have had no schooling at all, 7.3 millions have had only four years or less of grade school.

tical exercises, and after a week's concentrated assault on all his five senses a student emerged with the equivalent of, say, a first year's college course in basic hydraulics. Some antagonistic educators have claimed that their own deliberate, sleepy techniques are more thorough: as a matter of fact, the services' visual training was intensive, supercharged, exciting, and the student had actually seen and handled the facts he knew. Sheer inertia alone resists the adoption of these dramatic methods in academic training, but they will prevail in time.

Curricula will change with methods, and also take on new life. Today countless teachers attack a blank wall of disinterest in their pupils' minds, although these same minds seethe with the activities and facts of an exciting extracurricular world. The child's absorptions may have to do only with outwitting the cop on the beat, or collecting data on the unprivate lives of movie stars; or they may be concentrated on the engineering analysis of an eight-cylinder motor or a B-29: but they are always concerned with an existent, active world and not a shadowy, academic realm. More often than not, the child's interests are acutely vital. The amount of scientific knowledge gratuitously absorbed by school children today, with no help from school, is stupendous: there are many thousands of fifteen-year-old engineers who have taught themselves more about their favorite subject than any man alive knew fifty years ago. Many a young man had evaded higher mathematics until he found that he would need it to make the Air Corps, whereupon he briskly raced through calculus and trigonometry. We learn the things we are interested in learning.

This is no plea for the "progressive" methods that have produced so many unbearable little hellions of tender years: education which is not a discipline is no education at all. But education today should parallel the interests of today, and not linger in the preoccupations of long-dead generations which had never heard of airplanes, electronics, jet propulsion, or the atomic bomb. All science and all culture can be grouped around the vital interests of these times and made to come alive to the young, and the tools of training can be not only books but recordings, movies, television, aviation, the radio, and a countless array of devices that exemplify not only mechanical but mathematical laws, the laws of logic and the beautiful necessities of nature. Children can be taught practical versions of algebra, geometry, physics, chemistry, biology, geography, history, and art before they can read and write, and the arts of communication will come easily to these eager minds who have so much to learn and to transmit. Young hunters can be encouraged to race ahead into the, for them, unexplored jungles of knowledge, acquiring a well-rounded culture from sheer curiosity about the many-faceted world they live in.

New curricula, new methods, a generation of teachers and pupils touched by a divine fire, but also a greatly expanded plant and wholly new equipment: it is a program of expansion equal to the decent housing and adequate feeding of the nation. But to be successful it too requires that children and their homes be freed from the bitter, searing corrosion of poverty, in which few minds can ever know the joyous freedom of intellectual adventure.

7

It is true that there are many—a great majority—of honest and worthy citizens among the extremely poor, and there are those who are cultivated, competent, and physically fit. It is also true that if we all lived in good homes on sufficient incomes many citizens would still be fools and numbskulls, weak and disabled; and every crime in the calendar would still be committed every day. But poverty and its stultifying circumstances make inroads on self-respect which only the stoutest or the humblest hearts can withstand; and smarting with injuries both old and young almost inevitably find themselves at war with society and its standards, in emotional if not active revolt. A great many are destroyed in the struggle. The waste of human potentials through poverty is incalculable, and its cost to society fabulous. Poverty is such an expensive indulgence that no nation in the world can afford it.

And in our nation, at least, it should be almost disconcertingly easy to diminish poverty toward the vanishing point. It cannot be eliminated until all men are in sound physical, mental, and moral health, which will not come true tomorrow. But with the deleterious reaction of poverty steadily reduced through better living standards and broader opportunities for those who do not have them now, the fresh supply of defectives will diminish. Recovery, like disintegration, will prove to be a cyclic action, and the ascending spiral will carry racial quality upward abreast of economic expansion.

The determining factor is the more abundant creation of wealth, for which all the necessary conditions are present; and its broader dissemination, which we should be able to find ways of accomplishing naturally without resort to any self-defeating system of arbitrary partition.

PART THREE

DECISIONS

CHAPTER XIV

WAYS TO FELICITY

At the opening door where we stand, with this dazzling prospect before us, we need to seek the most flexible and effective means of giving the human spirit its head, putting the inexhaustible streams of human energy to work in a common effort. The thing to be avoided is any kind of finality, either of theory or practice, which would freeze or canalize our creative forces.

We are forced to make a decisive choice of methods—between our own and others'. The Political and Industrial Revolutions, after vitalizing the Western World for a century and three-quarters, are up for review. Large sections of this Western World have reverted to the thinking of a much older past, to make quite other commitments. We have to decide for ourselves whether we will get ahead faster if we stick to the still new plan of freeing all individuals to do the best job of work they can, or whether we should revert to the primitive practice of letting our thinking and planning be done for us by a few men at the head of the State. Should we go on trying to make it possible for every man to work out his own ideas and find his own way to happiness and fulfillment, or should we agree to do as we're told and God help us if we don't? A great many peoples are trying the latter method, although the choice was not put to them in exactly these terms.

Actually we have made our choice. The great majority of the people in this country are instinctively loyal to their own system, and wary of halters and nooses in whatever new form they are offered. But we face the fact that our system is on trial before a fanatically hostile opposition and is far from impregnable to criticism. It needs to be rectified, expanded, revitalized, if it is to prove itself by its works and justify our loyalty in the critical years ahead. The stakes that hang on our skill in steering this chosen course are the highest imaginable.

Time passes, men forget, minds are distracted and confused, the truth gets overlaid. We may think we understand the principles we have lived by and now must revivify or ultimately abandon, but the chances are we don't—at least not with any crystal clarity. Here is where we need to sharpen our perceptions and key up our wills. Conquering armies are not the only means of destroying a nation: it can be ruined just as completely by its own vague inattention or dim unawareness. It would be tragic if we were accessory, dull wittedly, to the termination of processes incipient and unperfected but infinitely expansible and incalculably productive of good.

2

Our pair of Western evolutionary movements—revolutionary only in their effects—are very young, originating in a mere yesterday of human history. They owed their inception to the Eighteenth Century's sudden addiction to reason. It is true that Eighteenth Century rational processes were never marked by the lucid precision once attained in a very small Hellenic society, but the Eighteenth Century world was anything but small, compact, well integrated: by comparison it was a huge, sprawling, bumbling, chaotic world, alive with a blundering vitality, rotten with a thousand sores and ready to try anything once in its search for the truth. But also the Eighteenth Century lacked the rather finicky preciosity of the Hellenic Golden Age—it did not mind dirtying its hands and tiring its muscles at hard labor. For these very reasons, in spite of its excesses and errors, Eighteenth Century rationality had a great deal more salutary influence on human welfare than the Greeks for all their genius managed to exert.

The most typical minds of the Eighteenth Century were animated by a shrewd skepticism and an imaginative curiosity—the most fertile combination in all human thought processes. They poked and pried tirelessly, rejecting assumptions and authority, seeking the truth with the enthusiasm of explorers in new-found, pragmatic worlds of thought. This was the spirit of countless otherwise diverse men—the pusillanimous, powerful, neurotic Rousseau, the meticulously rational Encyclopaedists, the acidly realistic and impish Voltaire. It is beautifully characteristic of the times that both Voltaire and his mistress, Mme. du Châtelet, shut themselves up in their separate laboratories every day for several hours of experimental scientific research, and that both made creditable contributions to physical science while carrying on a program of intellectual, political, artistic, social, and amorous activities that surely would have satisfied any less avid beings. They were exceptional only in that one of them was a very great genius: what they did, thousands of others tried, all caught up in a hungry urge to inquiry that found the mysteries of nature and the mysteries of human society equally fascinating. Science was a fad, but it was also an interest fresh and deep enough to make a scientific approach to the solution of any problem a current habit. This was notably evident in that extraordinary Revolutionary generation in America, of which two of the most influential, Franklin and Jefferson, were amateur scientists of no mean achievement and a dozen others were equally skillful in the practice of orderly thinking.

When this century of rational inquirers had taken apart the social structure of their times, they found that the whole fabric was reduced to a pile of bricks: when the arbitrary design had been subtracted there was nothing left but the individual building blocks which had been laid up and compressed in its forms. But these were not bricks, they were sentient beings who suffered, enjoyed, and possessed unpredictable capacities for growth. Reason perceived no object in combining them into a social pattern except that they must live together by some sort of agreement to practice mutual consideration and render mutual aid. And this led to the logical conclusion that social designs should exist for the benefit of their components, and not *vice versa*.

It was clear to these fresh visions that all past social and political systems, no matter how hallowed, had been highly ineffective in promoting the welfare of humanity, and that the average human being for this and other reasons was a deplorably defective creature. It was also clear that it should be possible for rational beings to work out an organization of society which would better serve man's social and private interests and that a rise in the level of human quality might thereby be effected.

From this point two schools of thought diverged.

3

One type of mind made the assumption that it was equal to the genius of the race; that it was within its own single capacity to define the ultimate in social systems, thus anticipating the slow unfolding of human destiny. And with the absolute revealed, why waste time working up to it? Appropriate action should be able to leap the gap, inducting mankind into felicity by a *coup d'état*.

A man who held these convictions and had experienced this illumination was elect. He was in duty bound to take whatever steps were necessary for the immediate accomplishment of his mission, even if this meant purging any recalcitrant elements of the population and enslaving the rest, at least until they appreciated what good was being done to them. Thus to accomplish his revolutionary aim he reverted instantly to the technique of absolute subjugation of the individual by the State, against which the revolution had been directed.

Rousseau took the lead in making the immediate perfectibility of man a plausible project. Rousseau was not a man of action, but this could not be said of Danton, Robespierre, St. Just. Like all egocentrics of this type before and since, they made a quick identification of the interests of humanity with their own will and were quite ready to exterminate all opposition. But, exasperatingly enough, humanity did not respond with the proper joyful acquiescence and they themselves were swept away in the river of blood they poured out of French veins.

Napoleon took over the ruins they left and continued the enterprise from a new angle, with tongue in cheek but with much more skill. Although he too failed to make Europe noticeably happier, he became the pattern for a succession of self-appointed saviors of the world, from his own nephew to William II and Hitler.

Karl Marx gave the Rousseauan dream an Early Victorian rendition, fitted to what he thought were the implications of the Industrial Age then just revealing its nascent outlines—implications which he complétely misinterpreted. He was a frustrated, bilious, and malicious little man, suffering like Rousseau from an inferiority complex—it is extraordinary, as H. G. Wells once remarked, that so many of the great lovers of humanity should have been such singularly unattractive persons—and his theories were inevitably marked by many of his own characteristics. But their content of venom doubtless has been one of their chief sources of appeal in a world admittedly sore with injustices and maladjustments. So, in spite of contradictions in logic, the weight of unfolding historical evidence, and a presentation which even his most ardent disciples admit is frequently incomprehensible, Marxism was and is a powerful influence in the world.

On the credit side, Marx saw that the production of goods and services—"the immediately requisite material means of subsistence," as Lenin put it—has first place in human concerns, and he appreciated the productive power and inevitability of the Industrial Revolution as many more amiable observers in his day did not. He also saw its critical fault in the disparity between the status of owners and the status of workers, an inherited feudal cleavage which the Industrial Revolution had done nothing to heal and if anything had exaggerated. But being German and anti-individualist he could not define this problem in terms of the Western civilization in which it must be solved.

Marx was an intellectual and spiritual alien to the society he undertook to reform. He was incapable of the direct, pragmatic processes of Western thought and he could not comprehend the individualist ideals which had produced both the Industrial Revolution and the political climate in which it flourished—ideals to which the conditions he deprecated were a glaring contradiction and an offense. Instead of seeking a solution of the problem in conformity with these ideals, Marx plunged into a swamp of Hegelian-metaphysical dialectics, and came out, muddy but transfigured, waving the prototype of all apocalyptic, totalitarian, absolutist creeds.

Marxism is Germanic in its origin,* its characteristics and its ideals, the most complete formulation of a great countermovement from the East against the tide of human liberty rising in the Western nations. In all later Communist and Fascist phases of this movement we see the same innate intellectual tendency to consider humanity in the lump as classes, masses, and races, and not as individuals; the same predilection for pseudo-philosophic rationalizations; the same rejection of a skeptical approach to truth through experimental trial and error in favor of revealed absolutes, "historic necessities," and manifest destinies; the same acceptance of hate and conflict as necessary constructive forces in human history. This habit of mind is essentially Eastern and metaphysical as distinguished from the realistic motivation of Western thought. When Hitler in his tirades habitually began with the Creation and worked down through all history to the inevitability of whatever project he had in mind he was not consciously imitating Marx's method: it was merely that they were both Germanic and thought alike.

4

Marx like Rousseau was no man of action and in fact showed a skittish distaste for practical details or concrete programs. But at long last his theories found a much abler Robespierre in Lenin, who undertook to apply them not in an advanced industrial society as Marxist logic stipulated but in the most primitive and completely agrarian of all great European nations. This was no accident of revolutionary opportunity, "for only in an early industrial or pre-industrial society does Marxism make sense." † When Marx put together his ideology he knew and could know

* The historical antecedents of the Marx-Engels dogmas, especially in the Hegelian metaphysic, are brilliantly traced in Jerome Frank's *Fate and Freedom*, Simon & Schuster, 1945, especially in Appendix One.

† Peter Drucker, *The Future of Industrial Man*, John Day, 1942, p. 206. This and the author's preceding volume, *The End of Economic Man*, are wise and truly liberal analyses of the problems existing in our industrial civilization.

only the characteristics of an early industrial system since nothing more mature existed.

It would have taken a much shrewder man than Marx to perceive that the structure and motivation of the industrial system as he saw it was not permanent—must in fact change radically if it were to continue its expansion. At that time there was nothing visible on the industrial landscape but two groups, Capital and Labor, owners and workers, having hostile interests with the workers getting a very dirty deal indeed. The standard industrial wage, used constantly by Marx as the basis of his calculations of values,* was then 75 cents for a 12-hour day. According to Marx, this just equaled the minimum cost of subsistence per family, and on it 11 millions out of a total English population of 18 millions were forced to live. In this deplorable state of affairs it is plain that the products of industry could find a market only within the seven millions of the upper crust, and not all of them. Industry produced in one large stratum of society for consumption in another much smaller stratum. Self-interest would tempt an owner to improve his competitive position by squeezing his wages down as low as possible and sweating the last ounce of effort out of his help, and there was nothing except whatever humanitarian instincts he might possess to restrain him. This was a situation worthy even of Marx's quite ample powers of hatred.

But it should have been clear to a really discerning student of the technological possibilities of industry that this condition must change: industrial production could not be restricted to the service of a mere 40 per cent of the population. Inevitably the workers too must become consumers—customers—or industrial development must stop. In time mass production grew out of machine production to bring a tardy realization that mass production demands a mass market of which labor itself must necessarily constitute by far the biggest part. The interests of all the elements in industry must converge. The prosperity of the entire population, providing a steadily increasing consumption of goods and services at steadily rising standards of living, must become the chief concern of industry as it is the chief concern of society as a whole.

* *Capital*, Chapters VI and VII.

This access of vision has coincided with the rise of a third great class in industry, a class not yet detectable in Marx's day, men who are employed but are neither owners nor manual workers and have an objective viewpoint toward the system in which they have become by far the most influential element. This is the class of managers, engineers, technologists, research scientists and specialists in the many phases of production and distribution. For a long time they have been rising in influence, abstracting control from capital and absorbing an increasing proportion of whatever talent reveals itself in the ranks of labor. If all capital and labor were suddenly withdrawn from industry and its plant destroyed, they could reconstruct it from scratch. They would have to accumulate new capital and recruit new forces of labor as they proceeded but they and they alone could do the job. As the industrial mechanism exists today they have created it, and their interest fundamentally is in its expansion and improvement. As a class—there are exceptions among them, of course—they see it for what it essentially is, a means of producing more at less cost. But they see too that less cost must be achieved by technological economies and large volume and not by low pay to industry's best market: as more of the industrial income is distributed in labor earnings with only an equally just wage paid to capital and the management-specialist group, the system as a whole will prosper accordingly. Undoubtedly this group will take the lead in accomplishing the final coalescence of the system, as labor too acquires an autonomous proprietorship equal to its share in the enterprise.

A momentous corner in industrial history was turned a quarter of a century ago, when Henry Ford, a capitalist who thought and acted as a manager and a technologist, startled the world by establishing a minimum wage of five dollars a day and instituting a 40-hour week in his plants. Mr. Ford merely had the common sense to realize, somewhat in advance of his fellows, that unless the American working man made at least five dollars a day he could not afford to own a car, and unless he had leisure to drive he would not have an incentive to buy one. As a result of this naively practical initiative, industrial wages were almost doubled in America within an interval of two or three years, with a drastic rise in general standards of living; and Mr. Ford, incidentally, was enabled to sell more than 30 million cars. This was a much more dramatic example of how the profit motive can be made to serve the common good than any of the many that Mr. Stalin has given us in Russia. It was a step leading certainly to another more drastic step which is still to be taken.

Marx can be forgiven for seeing only what was before his eyes, for not foreseeing the rise of the great intermediate and mediatory group in industry, and the convergence of the interests of all classes. What we cannot forgive him is the bile and Germanic perversity with which he sanctified the class struggle he saw around him as an inescapable "historic necessity." His theory of inevitably intensifying conflict leading to that verbal absurdity, the "dictator-ship of the proletariat" and, inexplicably, to a classless society, has impressed by its sheer turgid mass and its thermal fury. For a hundred years it has been a hogshead of gasoline dribbling on a fire that should never have been burning in the first place. That old Tory, H. G. Wells, has said that "from first to last the influ-ence of Marx has been an unqualified drag upon the progressive reorganization of human society." And he adds, uncharitably, that "we should be far nearer a sanely organized world system if Karl Marx had never been born." *

Marx's theories could have been valid only if the industrial system had remained static as of his day; and it "makes sense" only in a society which has not progressed beyond the stage which he observed. So we find Marxism making its strongest appeal in backward nations such as Spain, Mexico, Southeastern Europe, even China; and being given its great tryout in Russia.

5

Lenin's St. Just—a shrewder, better balanced, completely realistic but equally ruthless version of the original—survived and succeeded him in the person of Stalin. This symbolically named man of steel has hammered Russia into the first phases of industrializa-tion, bearing little resemblance either to Marxian blueprints or to

* *Experiment in Autobiography*, Macmillan, 1934, p. 215.

societies where industrialism has normally developed. Stalin has continued to pay lip service to Marxism but he has taken whatever measures he considered effective in the swift transfer of his people from an agrarian to an industrial basis. With no nonsense he interpreted the amorphous "dictatorship of the proletariat" as the very practical dictatorship of Joseph Stalin.

His methods have become so conspicuously heretical that it has been thought necessary for ten leading Soviet economists to prepare an official text reconciling current Soviet practices with the sacred scriptures.* This latter phrase is used advisedly, because the reverence shown the works of Marx and Engels by the writers of this apology is distinctly religious. One cannot imagine any free thinker being so abject before any human document: no matter how much it might be respected, the possibility of error would always be consciously present. Not so the Soviet economists: they must prove that Soviet usages in the matters of the profit motive, unequal compensation for unequal effort regardless of needs—"distribution according to the quantity of work"—prices based on *use* values as well as labor values, and the recognition and capitalization of *surplus* values are exactly what Marx and Engels intended all the time. It is too bad they didn't know it.

There is no question that Stalin's methods have been immensely effective in accomplishing what he set out to do. The ten economists say that they enabled the Soviet Union "to wipe out centuries of economic and technical backwardness at a tempo something like ten times that of the development of the most important capitalist countries." This is an exaggeration, as the Industrial Revolution is not yet ten times as old as the Soviet Union and the latter is still far below the development stage of the "most important capitalist countries." But the shift was made with great speed because industrial techniques had been developed in capitalist countries and could be taken over bodily, equipment and all, as fast as capitalist specialists could transmit them to the Russians.

As a result the Russian industrial effort in the war, like its military effort, has been mighty and creditable in spite of all its

* Translated as "Political Economy in the Soviet Union" in the quarterly *Science and Society*, Spring, 1944.

handicaps. The ten economists say it "would have been completely unrealizable under private ownership of the means of production." This may be true as to Russia, but we can smile tolerantly as we think of the prodigious output of capitalist Britain and America and the astronomical count of planes, guns, trucks, tanks, jeeps, and machine tools that flowed from their citizen-owned means of production to equip the gallant Russian armies.

We can recognize this disparity in ability to produce and at the same time recognize the superb efficiency of the Soviet system in converting a poor and industrially backward but energetic and profoundly patriotic people to total war. The secret of its success is revealed when the ten economists state the basic preoccupation of their system: *"How shall the Soviet government exercise the strictest accounting and control over the measure of labor and consumption of each member of society?"* So long as people are willing to accept this slave status a great deal can be done with and to them.

6

The Soviet "republics" are the first and least objectionable of the practical applications of collectivism—least objectionable principally because they can conceivably take a democratic turn in their future development—but it must not be forgotten that the Fascist and Nazi experiments are also true socializations of rights and property, and offshoots of Marxism. There are ideological differences and organizational differences, and divergences of announced objectives, and the Nazi doctrine particularly is unbelievably brutal and brutalizing. But they all deal, like revealed religions, in their own varieties of absolutes; they demand the surrender of the individual will and the individual faculty of criticism, and the complete submersion of the individual in the collective whole, which is the State. In exchange for the individual's freedom they offer emotional compensations in a fervor of devotion and the orgasm of self-immolation. The Nazi youth who rejoiced in his "freedom from freedom" was enjoying a primitive ecstasy: he was free from the necessity of making decisions, and free from responsibility for decisions he was not required to make. He had submerged himself in his deity. Here is dramatized the profound difference between the negative "freedom from" and the positive "freedom of."

All these forms of totalitarian collectivism, because of their essentially religious rather than rational nature, are necessarily built upon the leader principle—the embodiment of the will of God in one illuminated and predestined personage, a less amiable and more exaggerated exponent of divine right. And these leaders have acquired frightening effectiveness through modern technological aids to evangelism: no leaders in the past ever had such potent media or complete coverage in appealing to the fundamental human weaknesses of timidity, discouragement, nostalgia, and credulity. The same means serve equally well to support an authority once obtained and in all these experiments we observe a common pattern of a single orthodox party, organized propaganda, the persecution of heresy, secret police, summary "justice," firing squads, purges and concentration camps for dissenters. As a result we have seen power of unprecedented completeness concentrated in the incredible figures of Mussolini, Hitler, Franco, and a number of minor Balkan accidents. The antagonism most of these modern dictators display toward established religion is entirely comprehensible; they do not relish the competition of God.

In the British Commonwealth and the United States, where the people have an aversion to fire and blood and would resent them, the formulas for felicity are offered in the gentler guise of "planned economies." The most vocal exponents of controls have included such personally inoffensive citizens as Harold Laski in England and Lewis Mumford * in this country, who cannot be imagined manning a guillotine or commanding an elimination camp; but then neither could Rousseau or Marx. And they and

---

* In *Technics and Civilization* (Harcourt, Brace, 1934) Mr. Mumford sees the final or "neo-technic" phase of machine civilization, which is our phase, requiring state regulation of production and consumption—"rationed production . . . communized consumption . . . compulsory labor" (p. 405). This urge to set things right by force is expressed frequently in Mr. Mumford's writings, but recent events appear to have unsettled his assurance somewhat, as has happened to so many other eager evangelists. Not, however, to Mr. Laski.

all their fellow planners accept the inescapable conclusion that over-all formulas can only be applied by over-all authority. They assume this authority to be just, wise, and benevolent, but as to how that kind of despots are to be found and kept that way, not one of them has yet betrayed the ghost of an idea. And they have offered no practicable method of dealing without violence with the dissent which the natural cussedness of humanity will certainly produce, although it is plain to them as to anyone else that the suppression of dissent is essential to total authority.

The advocates of "planned economies" will indignantly deny that their systems would develop the administrative characteristics of other collectivist systems, because these characteristics are not mentioned in the planners' prospectuses. But they are implicit in any system of complete controls, and they begin to appear the instant any such plan is reduced even tentatively to a workable program. The human race has never yet conformed without compulsion, and compulsion becomes an ugly and bloody business in exact proportion to its inclusive extent. If we submit to having our lives and affairs—our "labor and consumption"—run from a central source, we may obtain the kind of "security" other prisoners enjoy but we must reconcile ourselves to the same absence of freedom and a great deal of collateral discomfort.

CHAPTER XV

THE WAY OF FREEDOM

So FOR more than a century and a half a certain school of thought has undertaken to accomplish the regeneration of society and man by various *tours de force*, operating on the basis of Rousseau's *contrat social*, Napoleonic imperialism (an old expedient with revolutionary decorations), Marxian Communism, its Russian variant, Nazi and Fascist corporate socialism, and "planned economies." Most of the tragic bloodshed during this interval has been caused by these ideologically inspired efforts to capture felicity quite literally as an army takes a fortress. But throughout the same period another school of thought, also crystallized in the Eighteenth Century, has been operative in the affairs of the world with far greater continuity and vastly more substantial achievement.

The founders of this school were the tough-minded men who brought to bear on political, economic, and social problems the same critical processes of thought they would have applied to any problem in physical science. They were not given to self-delusion, they were skeptical of absolutes, they were quite ready to write "Not proved" across the face of many beautifully complete and symmetrical assumptions, both the ancient hallowed ones and those newly advanced with glad acclaim. They knew their race well, and respected it without illusions—respected it too much, in fact, to believe that its destiny could be plotted by themselves in any tidy document. They, too, believed in the perfectibility of man and society as an ultimate possibility but not in their own capacity to define its terms. Their hard sense told them that on the basis of our present knowledge no one can possibly conceive the nature and characteristics of that ultimate perfection, or do more than advance the race by degrees in what appears to be its general direction. Ultimates of any kind, in the realm of social as well as scientific truth, were pushed by them far off into a probably unattainable future as goals to be forever approached as they forever recede.

There are dignity and health in this attitude of mind, and a sincere respect for the human race. It is an attitude not possible to damaged egos craving compensation by dominance over the fate of others—which emphasizes the distinction between this type and the genus of Rousseau, Robespierre, Napoleon, Marx, William II, Lenin, Trotzky, Mussolini, Hitler, and others of our contemporaries whose names will come readily to mind.

The leaders of this school could see other men and themselves as the poor sticks they are and yet realize that if given the chance they can do more for their own good than can possibly be done for them by any concentrated direction. These shrewd minds recognized the indisputable fact that the quickest way to develop a man is to make him responsible for his own affairs, and that this is the surest way to give scope to the able—those who have something to contribute to the general good as distinguished from those who have nothing. It appeared clear to them that the worth of individuals makes up the value of the race, and the contributions of individuals make up its progress. Since the worth and contributions of individuals cannot be predicted or scheduled—as an inattentive train boy was to confer incalculable scientific benefits on the world and a lanky country bumpkin was to become perhaps the greatest political leader of his people—the way should be opened for every man to prove his own mettle. Give men freedom of action and equivalent accountability, and you will have innumerable failures and a high percentage of total loss: but you will guarantee that whatever is of value shall have a chance to reveal itself.

To men addicted to fantasy this may seem a wasteful process, but not to creative minds which face the fact that it may be necessary to make 605 tries before the 606th—or any other number—will reveal the truth. A race exploring a hidden universe is fated to do a lot of fumbling. There will be countless weird adventures leading nowhere, and many social misfits in every generation. But it is necessary that everything should be tried, everybody should be free to explore whatever alleys he thinks promising: some of the screw-ball notions will work, some of the alleys won't be blind, and we must know which. We must also accept the unavoidable casualties.

The great inspiration of the Political Revolution within which the Industrial Revolution progressed and achieved its triumphs was the idea that the function of government is to create favorable conditions for exactly this kind of free activity. As an abstract concept this was not wholly new even in the Eighteenth Century, but as the practical objective of government it was a resounding novelty, much more revolutionary in its effects than any mere change of political regimes. After a century and three-quarters of familiarity it is hard for us to realize that it is still the newest and freshest political motivation the world has yet experienced.

2

By one of those circumstances which give a certain plausibility to the idea of Providence, there existed in America in the late Eighteenth Century a newly assembled people ready to be formed into a nation under these intellectual influences. It had been extracted mainly from the democratic background of Britain and set down in a virgin land of immense resources. It was a perfect subject for political innovation, a fair field for a clean job of work such as could not be done among the rubble heaps of tradition that cluttered Europe.

And there flourished in this waiting laboratory a generation of political thinkers whose aggregate acumen and courage have never been surpassed in any other time or place. These men were of the tough-minded school, and what they worked out in America between 1770 and 1790 was an experimental technique of government as non-committal as to its outcome as any other laboratory procedure. The "democracy" they established—and it was not even called *that* until many years after its beginning—did not purport to be a social or economic order, it enforced no pattern on the future, and was directed toward no predetermined ultimate objective. It was a means of guaranteeing the freedom of the individual to work out his own salvation in his own way, but what that salvation might finally prove to be the founders did not presume to define, any more than they would have legislated in advance the outcome of any other experimental approach to truth. They were so non-committal as to end results that they even neglected at first to safeguard the conditions of the experiment, and the individual's life, liberty, and his right to pursue his happiness were protected as an afterthought—in amendments.

The men who devised the Constitution of the United States were themselves individualists who did not see eye to eye on many of its details, and the final document was a collection of compromises completely satisfying none of them. Even the most rational minds in the field of political and social philosophy will assume certain factors to be determined beyond question, certain expedients to be justifiable short cuts. Every one of the founders brought to the job of constitution-making a little herd of these sacred cows, which had to be sacrificed in the interest of common agreement. This may have pained the owners at the time, and armed unfriendly critics since, but actually it gave the Constitution its supreme virtues of indeterminateness and adaptability. It left no obstacles to the processes of change and growth which were implicit in the plan, and those who were first to administer it understood perfectly that they were presiding over the development of an unfinished system.

Under the guidance of Washington, Hamilton, Jay, Adams, Jefferson, Marshall, Madison, our system acquired coherence and effectiveness as an instrument of freedom. It contained many imperfections and offenses against its ideal—even the anomalous institution of human slavery—but these did not make a state of consistent health any the less desirable or less presumably attainable.

The founders could not foresee the immense territorial expansion of the United States or its tremendous industrial development, although Jefferson had an inkling of the former and Hamilton of the latter. They were planning, on a frontier, for an agrarian, mercantile society. But the primary condition of individual freedom which they established for their experiment—the release of the creative energies of multitudinous human units —is precisely the condition most favorable to all industrial and economic progress. The great success of the United States has not been due only to the fact that it started as the frontier of a rich, unexploited land, but to the fact that it could so readily shift its interest from the geographical frontier to frontiers of science and technology. Our wealth today, as the wealthiest nation of the world, is not anything that nature planted in the rocks and soil of this continent: it is the continuous stream of unpredicted and unplanned but closely meshed contributions from countless single human sources.

Throughout the Nineteenth Century, this concept of government enabled human energy and ingenuity to function as it had never done before, with stupendous results, wherever it was determinant. And there were tough-minded men in all nations then, as there are now, with the difference that then they were definitely in the ascendancy. Under Burke's initial leadership they captured Great Britain, and the extraordinary combination of practicality and sentiment characteristic of the British enabled them to work out, slowly and painfully, a system of political liberty without sacrificing the more decorative features of the feudal system. France went through many convulsions but never quite relinquished her dream of *"liberté, egalité, fraternité,"* and made spasmodic efforts to realize it. The principle of constitutional government was accepted without serious question in all civilized nations, even tentatively in Russia, and a strong libertarian movement in Germany rose to a climax—and a fatal set-back—in the disastrous revolutions of 1848. For a hundred years the ideal of personal freedom of thought, speech and action was intellectually dominant not only in the lands where it was given at least partial realization in the political structure but also in those wistful regions where it remained an unattained dream. It was responsible for an era of increasing abundance, rising production, the expansion of trade, the union of peoples, international peace and stability.

For devotion to freedom also paid dividends, over a long time, in serenity and peace. Paradoxically, men grow more dependent on each other as they grow more independent in the ordering of their own lives: a condition of freedom is that a man must share the results of his labor and ingenuity with others who in turn share with him. The division of labor is a requisite to success in our environmental warfare, and division of labor in modern technologies depends on a broad network of trade. Through the Nineteenth Century the Western World grew closer and closer together in larger and larger unions, and trade became freer and more far flung. Between 1815 and 1914 there were no world wars, the habit of peace became deeply ingrained in Western thought and practice, and men came to consider the stability of their world as something they had made reasonably certain forever. Which makes them look pretty silly today.

3

A mere century and three-quarters is a very short time—too short—for the world to evolve into a Utopia, no matter how good a start it makes; and it is a very long time for human beings to hold fast to a clear-cut but rigorous ideal. Liberty is an exacting discipline, one-half the making of difficult decisions and one-half the acceptance of responsibility for those decisions. To be free is not simple, it demands a heroic and steadfast spirit. Peoples and their leaders have never been known to maintain themselves at an exalted spiritual level, with clarity of vision and firmness of purpose, through many successive generations. Aims become blurred as they are partially achieved, principles lose their exigence with use. As Maxwell Anderson makes Washington say at Valley Forge, "This liberty will look easy by and by when nobody dies to get it." *

While the Western world was making immense advances under its Eighteenth Century impetus toward a rational organization of society, the momentum acquired from that impetus was declining. The processes and machinery set going by its initial impact might continue to function even with increasing efficiency, but

* Maxwell Anderson, Valley Forge, Anderson House, Washington, D. C., 1934, p. 166.

the creative intelligence which had given them direction was gradually withdrawn.

The Industrial Revolution and the Political Revolution are simultaneous and interdependent phenomena, but it does not follow that they must progress in perfect synchronism. In a favorable political climate the Industrial Revolution has been self-energizing, advancing like a flood over a flat plain, a flood that continually augments itself by opening up innumerable fresh springs at its perimeter. As each clearly defined objective is attained, others equally concrete are indicated ahead. Thus the mental energy which is the movement's propelling force can be applied with maximum effectiveness and is constantly renewed. Once fertilized it will go on laying multitudinous eggs until free action is denied it; which explains why it has continued to proliferate at an accelerating tempo even as political confusion has increased both domestically and internationally.

As this breath-taking advance has altered, in a mere century and three-quarters, all our ways of working, trading, living, thinking, and co-operating, it has also changed the conditions of political liberty in a way that demanded equally swift adaptation of customs and institutions. Adaptability to changing circumstances may be the essential characteristic of the political experiment in this country, but there can be no guarantee that men competent to do the adapting will always be present as needed. Problems in this amorphous realm are seldom concrete and clearly defined. Successful statecraft in a free society calls for sheer creative intelligence, a combination of insight, wisdom, integrity, imagination, the will to progress, all deliberately exercised. Such gifts have rarely existed in quantity, and as the need for great and original statesmanship grew more acute the supply dwindled. Contrast the quality of political leadership in England and America at the end of the Eighteenth Century with that at the beginning of the Twentieth. When it was most necessary to continue the adaptation of free institutions to changing conditions, the vision of the people and the vision of their leaders were both overcast.

Responsibility for the maintenance of any system rests on those who honestly believe in it. If we here in the United States had made good on the promises made at our founding, and realized

the aims of individual liberty under present-day conditions, our
system would not now be in danger. It would never have been
challenged, because it would have proved itself beyond question.
And its massive success would have gone far toward stabilizing
the world situation, polarizing world trends in a way to avoid the
general chaos of the past thirty years.

4

It is tragic that the United States, leading the world in industrial development, hasn't also led the world in solving a problem
that was sufficiently evident a century ago to inspire Marx's fantastic formulas. Since then we have done a vast deal to correct
its evil effects but the problem itself remains almost precisely as
it was then. It has had an immense volume of intellectual fire
directed around and about it at all its attendant circumstances;
but the bull's-eye itself remains to date untouched.

It is hard to believe that if we had produced a succession of
creative minds as perceptive and daring as those which devised
our political system, this difficulty would not have been taken in
their stride. But we did not, and at the time when the industrial
problem began to be clearly defined, in the middle decades of
the Nineteenth Century, our best minds in the political sphere
were engrossed with other matters. By the time the questions of
slavery and national unity were out of the way and partly as a
result of the division over these questions, the industrial pattern
had crystallized to the point of acceptance. Since then our progress in dealing with its unfortunate basic characteristics has been
microscopic, and the rest of the world has not done anything like
as much even in alleviating its painful consequences.

The unsolved problem is, quite simply, the status within the industrial system of the multitude of workers upon whom it depends.

If we assume that ownership and management are the head of
the industrial system, these workers bear about the same relationship to the system as a whole that a man's body from the chin
down bears to his whole being: their relative weight in the general scheme is similar, their health, vigor and effective co-ordina-

tion are as vital to the system's welfare. Yet, as the industrial system has developed, workers are in the position of alien dependents upon it. The great majority of them are excluded from any possibility of proprietorship in their own means of livelihood, and therefore from the degrees of social dignity and economic independence which the citizens of a free state should enjoy.

A man who is not conscious of social dignity and economic opportunity equal to all others is not in a frame of mind to exercise political rights without bias, so that the political system suffers. And if he feels that his part in the industrial system is a precarious and unprivileged one, that his stake in it is a matter of chance not affected by his own efforts, the industrial system will not have his wholehearted support; so that it too suffers.

Thus we have evolved a civilization which relies and *must* rely on industrial production for its well-being, but has not made its industrial system also serve adequately the ends of individual liberty and human dignity and therefore has not made it function with anything like its possible efficiency; and has suffered social, economic, and political maladjustments as a consequence. The weakness of our position is not in our basic doctrine of individualism, but in the fact that so many of our people have been excluded from its benefits.

This is no denial of the immense improvement that has taken place during the past century in the circumstances of all who derive their livelihood from industry. Here in the United States this improvement has been phenomenal, unprecedented in the history of the world. In fact, the only people here whose condition resembles that of industrial workers in Marx's time are those who have not yet found a place in the industrial system—such as the field hands, sharecroppers, and migrant workers of the south and west. But we have recently shown that, operating at its full capacity, the industrial system is capable of dispensing a prosperity which is not confined to those directly employed in industry but spreads to all other elements of the population as well. If this is true when at least half of the system's output is in goods which cannot be used to better our living conditions, it is easy to see what immense strides in general well-being will result if production of consumer goods can be maintained at the same rate.

Full and uninterrupted functioning of the whole system is best for everybody—the owners of capital, the management-specialist group, the workers are at one on this point; while society as a whole obviously can advance in welfare most swiftly through a continuous flow of the goods and services that come from all its elements at work. This can happen only in a factionless society, one that is united in furthering an identity of interests. Why, knowing this, have we allowed circumstances to exist which prevent any such concentration of loyalties and efforts?

5

The reasons for such a spectacular failure of human intelligence cannot be stated in a few neat phrases. Not all the statesmen of the Nineteenth and Twentieth Centuries have been stupid, by any means, and plenty of people both in and out of statecraft have recognized the gravity of an open cleavage in our industrial civilization. A full explanation of why all the available ability and perception accomplished so little would take volumes, but it is possible to indicate in a little space certain trends of thought which combined to divert constructive effort from the main issue and keep that bull's-eye untouched.

One of the most extraordinary aberrations of the Nineteenth Century was the growth, in the free nations, of the doctrine of *laissez faire*. This was a *reductio ad absurdum* of the concept of personal liberty. The phrase was originated as a political slogan, it is said, by the Lyons silk manufacturers under the *ancien régime*, when they rejected government aid in a time of distress—"Let us attend to it." In the dialectics of Nineteenth Century doctrinaires it became an objection to *any* governmental interference in the private and especially in the business relationships of individuals: since a man is free, he must suffer no restraint in the conduct of his affairs, even when his affairs include doing some other equally free citizen in the eye. It was an argument for a legalized state of dog eat dog. The citizen is to be protected from interference by the policeman in his God-given rights of robbery, assault, and mayhem—so long as these are not crudely personalized and physical. In the last extremity we find Herbert Spencer protesting against a public health service as an infringement of the citizen's sacred privilege of poisoning himself and infecting his neighbors.

Since we have great facility in rationalizing whatever is to our own advantage, this view of the function of the state in a free society came to be sincerely held by many who had the upper hand. In practice its effect was to maintain the *status quo*, whatever that might be at the moment, and effectually retard any adaptation of institutions to changing circumstances. It had especially evil consequences because the State had already created a breed of corporate entity which exercised all these rights and privileges of the individual to do as he pleased in business but was not subject to any of the mortal limitations of a human being. Against such a Frankenstein's monster blessed by *laissez faire*, poor Joe Doakes became a hunted little rabbit indeed.

If *laissez faire* could be restored to its original import as a rejection of government *aid*, much could be said for it in these times. But as a denial of governmental police powers or an objection to change, it has no serious intellectual defenders today, although it may still be lodged as a secret loyalty in a number of hopelessly inflexible minds. It survives principally as one epithet in the vocabulary of statists and collectivists, who hurl it at any effort to subject the expansion of governmental powers to critical scrutiny.* But in its heyday *laissez faire* was a major impediment to the evolutionary extension of individual liberty to those elements of the population who did not already enjoy it.

Another major obstacle, working against *laissez faire* at the other end of the scale of absurdity, was the Marxian elevation of the class cleavage to the level of a "historic necessity," an essential factor in human progress. A tragically divided society isn't helped to unite by giving divine sanction to the division itself as one of those mysterious ways in which God moves, His wonders to perform. There is little immediate relief in assuming that wrongs will be righted at some vague cataclysmic day when one side, its fury carefully husbanded and augmented, will utterly

---

* This book undoubtedly will be called, by statists who notice it, a defense of *laissez faire*.

destroy the other and thereafter have the world to itself. This typically Germanic mental and emotional attitude has infected society far beyond the limits of the Marxian school itself and its offshoots, influencing labor circles even when they accept no other tenets of Marxism.

Working against the downward pressure of *laissez faire*, the idea of inevitable class conflict has been the opposing blade of a very effective pair of shears to nip off any budding spirit of social unity. This mutually stimulative reaction may be understandable, but it is none the less deplorable, and tragic in its results.

Mental petrifaction rather than liberal intelligence may have been the rule for a long time at capitalist levels, but it is equally true that the trade-union movement has been singularly limited in its conception of the best interests of industrial workers. Concentrating principally on wages and hours, it has helped to obtain a much fairer division of the profits of industry, but while most of these gains have been made against the stupid opposition of capital, certain very substantial ones are due to the spreading enlightenment of management. High wages, reasonable hours, propitious working conditions have immense social value, but other trade-union objectives have been far less justifiable.

Too many union policies and practices are dominated by a fixed assumption that the interests of the workers are in conflict with the interests of the system and the society of which they are the major element—a manifest absurdity. Belligerence become a habit entails a number of evils, from which the workers themselves are the chief sufferers: the undemocratic, militaristic type of organization existing in many unions, where a clique of commanders perpetuates itself in power without any adequate control by the membership; the treatment of union funds as private war chests, not subject to ordinary rules of public audit and accountability; the opportunity and incentive thereby offered to unprincipled, racketeering leadership. In recent years, laws passed ostensibly for the workers' benefit have accentuated these evils, until today we find the corporation bugaboos of a generation ago replaced by equally terrifying legal fictions called, for instance, Lewis and Petrillo.

Engrossed in constant tactical skirmishes, trade-unionism has done no more than capital to obtain for the workers a participatory status in the industrial system. It has not even mapped a rational program leading to that end. It is true that real participation would bring grave responsibilities, require the reversal of many characteristic trade-union policies, and call for a new type of leadership—sobering thoughts that may make the prospect less attractive to many who are now in control. These powers have not assisted capital to realize that labor must be taken into partnership for the good of the system as a whole, and the management-specialist class has only lately begun to swing its powerful influence in that direction. But unless labor is willing in all seriousness to undertake responsibilities along with privileges and alter its habits accordingly, and unless capital and management meet labor halfway in working out a practical partnership, the future of all three groups will remain alarmingly precarious and their state of well-being will fall far short of what it might become in a unified, free society.

CHAPTER XVI

WAYS TO UNITY

THE ACHIEVEMENT of a valid social unity in this country is not such a remote, Utopian dream as one might think, now while the noise of bitter industrial conflict fills our ears. Recognition of its urgency is spreading quietly among thoughtful leaders of capital, management, and labor, accelerated by the growing seriousness of the strife itself with all its calamitous implications. And tentative steps toward alliance have been taken in many organizations, with impressive results in every case.

A substantial number of profit-sharing plans have long been in effect. There are several instances of annual wage guarantees maintained for ten to twenty years, by corporations which have minimum fluctuations in volume of business. Numerous corporations have retirement pension systems independent of governmental social security. A great many companies provide medical, dental, and ocular services, hospitalization, sick benefits, paid vacations, educational opportunities, building and loan services, co-operative retail stores, recreational facilities, etc. These are important recognitions of labor's right to share in the benefits of enterprise, and they have been profitable to employees, employers, and society. Wherever practiced, they prove the social advantage of peace and harmony in the industrial system.

But these advanced practices are limited, with a few exceptions, to old, rich and stable businesses. They indicate a receptivity of capital and management to alliance with labor, but none of them amounts to a true partnership in which risks, opportunities, and responsibilities are shared in just proportion by capital, management, and labor alike.

At present, by and large, throughout industry, even in the most progressive sectors, a worker either has a job or he has none. He either receives a wage, usually fixed by his bargaining agency, or he receives none. It makes no real difference to him whether the enterprise in which he participates makes ten million dollars or is in the red, so long as he holds his job. Under this all-or-nothing practice, immensely valuable co-operation is lost to the system through lack of direct interest, while labor is exposed to recurrent calamity. Whenever a company's production is curtailed, so that income lessens to the point where outlay must be reduced, workers are laid off. Otherwise, in most cases, there soon would be no money to pay anyone and the company would cease to be an employer for all time. Economic collapse would become more abrupt and complete.

It goes without saying that dividends to capital and any sort of bonus to management should always and usually do cease automatically with profits; but if further reductions are necessary the adjustment of pay rolls to existing financial resources is unavoidable, and preserves the possibility of recovery. At present there is no other method of making the adjustment than by dropping workers out of the industrial system entirely. But this is only a little less calamitous than an attempt to maintain the *status quo* to the limit of resources would be. Whenever economic factors are out of alignment, these cutbacks and layoffs are never isolated; they become general, the number of unemployed rapidly increases, fear spreads, buying power swiftly contracts when it is most needed, a downward spiral is accelerated and misery is multiplied.

The only practicable alternative to this wholesale amputation with all its evil consequences is a system which adjusts expenses upward or downward with income in a way to keep the labor force intact, reassured, productive, and self-supporting at all times. Such a system would reduce the causes of recessions, put brakes on downward slides and blunt their effects in many ways.

Increased labor income in times of prosperity would allow a greater cushion against adversity. Assurance of constant employment under all conditions, even at a lower rate when conditions are bad, would tranquilize the minds of millions of workers and forestall the panic which now stirs at the first alarm. Mounting fear of unemployment is always one of the great accelerators of depression, hardly second in destructive effects to unemployment itself. With fear allayed, sudden contractions of consumption would be less likely to occur. Wholesale turnover in the labor force, one of the major wastes in the modern economy, would be avoided, the ingenuity and energy of millions would be retained in the fight to stop and reverse any downward movement.

In this way, and in no other so far as most businesses are concerned, the "guaranteed annual wage" becomes practicable. Wages can never be guaranteed, and should not be, at the levels to which labor is entitled to aspire in times of high production, and they certainly should not be frozen at lower levels. Any dead level of prospects is the most stultifying and enervating influence imaginable. It would turn any people in a few generations into a race of ambitionless automatons.

The "security" which has been so much touted in recent years as the major aim of humanity is this minimal, oriental kind of blessing and never can be anything more. There *can* be a floor above disaster, and should be, but this is nothing to satisfy the hopes of men. This country was made great by people who aspired to a great deal more than security, and if it remains great it will be because it is still inhabited by that kind of people. What labor should have, along with all other men, is the assurance of an uninterrupted opportunity to make its own fortunes in a system which scales its rewards to the intelligent, the diligent, the skillful, and the productive. Labor's position will be satisfactory only if it is assured this permanence of opportunity, and not merely if it is guaranteed against starvation.

2

What any sound solution of the industrial problem must accomplish is the making of labor a participant in the system instead of a dependent on it; a participant, that is, in both its successes and its failures, with a fair share of responsibility for each, with rewards and sacrifices proportioned as exactly as possible to the fortunes of its particular section of the production front. Labor must acquire a stake in the system from which it derives its livelihood, a stake with opportunities and risks of the same type that capital has always possessed.

This implies no weakening or abridgement of the capitalist system—quite the reverse. The right to own, use, and enjoy property is essential to any practicable freedom: without it a man becomes a helpless robot in subjection to the State in which all proprietorship is concentrated. And the right to own property implies the existence of surplus values, which Marx denied and the realistic Russian State admits,* with surplus values translating themselves into the tokens of stored-up energy we call capital. Capital unquestionably has been acquired by unfair means in too many cases, and it is often misused: these venalities are proper objects for the exercise of the police power of the state, like any infraction of social morals. It is probable that a developing technique of dealing with the misuse of capital can reduce it at least to the incidence of plain theft and fraud. But it is far better to accept the possibility of evil deeds than to rule that no man shall ever possess the capital means to order his own life, make his own ventures, indulge his private interests and endow enterprises dear to his heart. Without this essential freedom a nation shuts the door on immense unpredictable good.

The inclusion of labor as an active participant in the industrial system is a logical extension and completion of capitalism, as it is a necessary extension and completion of the individualist system of human relationships. It is a straight-line progression which capitalism needs so badly that there is great uncertainty as to how long it can exist without it. By this extension the present representatives of capital will acquire a horde of vitally interested partners, converted from the same number of suspicious antagonists.

Capital will contribute to the conversion its exclusive right to possession and disposal of the profits of industry: it must be prepared to share this right with its new partners. This exclusive right already is under grave attack as a survival of the ancient master-

* See the apologia in *Science and Society*, Spring, 1944, previously cited.

and-serf relationship of the feudal system, carried over into mechanized industry at its early beginnings when labor appeared to be a negligible, expendable commodity. Labor today is not only by far the biggest element in industry, numerically and financially —labor pay rolls consume a major portion of the gross receipts of most producing corporations—but it also is industry's indispensable market. And it is highly organized and vigorously if not always wisely led. A vital right from which this predominant element is excluded is in a very precarious position indeed. A composition had better be made before the system as a whole is wrecked by conflict and society suffers disastrous consequences.

Management will contribute to the conversion its exclusive control of industrial operations and policies. Already it exercises this control under warrant of the representatives of capital: it must be prepared to see this supervisory right extended to include the new partners as well. Here, I think, there will be little obstruction. If labor is at one with capital and management in the support of an enterprise, sharing directly in its fortunes, management will be no more reluctant to justify its procedures to the representatives of labor than to the representatives of capital. The support and aid it will receive from the labor force will amply compensate for any organizational changes. Solidarity of the whole system is the dream of all intelligent management.

Labor on its side must be prepared to accept responsibilities and risks along with privileges. Its partnership must be a real one and not all gravy, with increased opportunity, security, authority, and dignity balancing any hypothetical sacrifices. A union of interests would contribute immensely to the stability and prosperity of each industrial enterprise and of the economy as a whole, and risk would decline proportionately. But risk would still exist and would have to be faced by the new partners just as it has always been faced by the old. Since labor does not have accumulated resources to fall back upon in adversity, as owners of capital are presumed to have, it would be necessary to put a floor under this risk at a practicable level which might entail hardship but would preclude disaster.

This would require a radical change in labor union policies, especially as to wage rates and work standards. Instead of the present fixed, uniform wage rate for each category of labor, regardless of the individual worker's ability or diligence or the profits of the enterprise, a sliding scale would have to be accepted. Instead of the Russian method of payment scaled to speed up performance, with all profits going to the State, a real partnership under our system would mean that pay above a minimum floor would consist of a proportionate share of net profits, with labor itself as an interested party helping to police individual incompetence or shirking. The traditional objections of "sweating" and "speed-up" could not be brought against a system in which labor assisted in setting the standards of work and profit-participation. And since the possibility of loss is accepted by labor there must be a balancing possibility of gain well in excess of existing wage standards. With everyone pulling together this latter possibility should become a strong probability.

The "labor-management" committees already operating in a limited way in many plants, or something similar, would thus acquire genuine responsibility and authority of much broader scope. They would become boards of strategy to assist in attaining production and sales objectives, representative assemblies through which the constructive thinking of labor could be relayed to management and the plans of management justified and approved by the labor staff. Like capital's Boards of Directors, with which they might be merged, they would hold a power of review but would quickly learn to allow management a relatively free hand as to tactics, subject to checking on the score of results.

Any such drastic readjustment would mean that within the industrial system we should have had a reconciliation of differences, an agreement on common objectives, and a voluntary setting up of consultative and executive machinery to attain these ends by orderly processes. This is exactly what we have had, more or less adequately, in the political sphere for a long time. It should not be impossible to transfer the same attitudes and methods to the industrial sphere. And we should not be discouraged by the fact that we cannot, at this moment, foresee just what final detailed forms such a harmoniously operating system will take. It would be disquieting if, at this moment, we thought we could.

3

You might think that this problem of social union would be a topic of universal discussion consuming at least as many lines of print as the problem of international union with which it is so closely meshed, but this is not the case. The establishment of peace between nations engages many able and vocal minds; the problems of peace *within* nations on which the other depends is a quiet preoccupation spreading beneath a less articulate surface. Of course there is the earnest battle between those who would abolish the problem by clamping collectivist irons on us and those who think the peace of the prison is not exactly the kind of peace we want. But even these latter are not being conspicuously active in discovering how to unite the whole population as active participants in the individualist system they support.

The lack of overt discussion is not entirely indicative of the trend of thought. The interdependence of all elements in society is looming larger in the consciousness of the more intelligent leaders of capital, management, and labor, and a great deal of non-publicized thinking is going on as to how it can be recognized by effective measures. It may suddenly break through the surface in the form of practical plans and actual experience. Obviously, forces that have congealed in opposition for so long, fixing many of the conspicuous features of social and economic organization, piling up huge interests on both sides in favor of the *status quo,* are nothing to be shifted easily into a new pattern. It will be found that many vested interests in labor leadership will be as inclined to prejudice against change as any vested interests of capital, and new leadership will have to come from around the ends of the Chinese Walls on both sides. The rallying point may well be the more thoughtful members of the management-specialist group, whose chief interest is in the improvement of the system as a whole and not in the preservation of any of its forms.

It is clear that premature, *ex parte* expedients will do more harm than good. Ill-considered applications of force to specific areas of the field will only serve to deepen animosities and stimulate factional loyalties. Institutions may be defined by legislation, but in a free society this is a formality that waits on agreement. In recent years we have suffered from a tendency to rush to pass a law whenever a difficulty presents itself, to expect every situation needing attention to be dealt with by governmental intervention instead of by common action. This is a reversion from democratic processes under the influence of the world-wide trend toward statism. As a result we have accumulated a tangle of ill-advised legislation which will need painstaking care to straighten out, and we should avoid depositing more on the heap.

The Wagner Labor Act is a fine example of how not to charge into the industrial mine field. Its ostensible objective, the setting up of legal machinery for collective bargaining, has behind it a preponderant weight of considered opinion. All thoughtful people recognize the archaic absurdity of the strike as the sole means of settling disputes, in a society where justice is supposed to be every man's right without resort to private force. But legal machinery in this as in other fields of jurisprudence should operate impartially to promote peace and justice, so that the interests of all participants and society as a whole are served. Instead, the crude devices of this act merely transfer weapons from one camp to the other and encourage the warfare to go merrily on. The Smith-Connally Act, essentially a repartee, was an equally stupid effort to shift the balance the other way. As with any factional legislation, additional obstacles to ultimate harmony are set up by both these acts. Equitable adjustments were offered in the Hatch-Ball-Burton proposals and advances toward a proper balance were made in the Case Act, only to be greeted by loud outcries from labor spokesmen who wrongly believe that their present unfair advantage is beneficial. The catalytic value of these proposals is great and their reception is significant: they emphasize the fact that there must be agreement on even-handed justice and order as objectives before any effective mechanism to attain them can be created.

Of greater import are the advances toward rapprochement between the two national labor unions, the United States Chamber of Commerce, and other employers' organizations. The movement

is tentative, as any first venture among such giant difficulties must
be, and the immediate results may not be exactly millennial. But
the fact that a start has been made, at the point where it must
be made, is immensely heartening. When these chief representatives of the factions at loggerheads accept responsibility for finding a way to harmony and deliberately exclude political action
during the gestation period, we see a revival of the fundamental
democratic process: the molding of institutions by understanding
and agreement in advance of legal codification.

The ground to be covered extends far beyond anything on the
present agenda of these conferees, and their effort may be a trial
balloon fated to drop limply back to earth. It will have plenty of
opposition from those minds, on both sides, where a clot of *laissez
faire* still blocks the coronary arteries. But many people are quick
to recognize horse sense and good will when they see them, and
may roll up a backing of approval to carry this beginning to successes not now foreseen. If, five years from this writing, we see
that the attempt at agreement has progressed substantially, or has
failed and had no successors, we shall have a pretty accurate indication as to what the fate of this country will be.

Meanwhile the ferment proceeds. Symptomatic of a growing
will toward union is a plan which has been carefully worked out
by a New York financier and industrialist, Mr. Henry Keuls, assisted by Mr. Ross Kenyon, and quietly circulated among those
whom the authors think may be interested. It is pregnant with
suggestion—so much so that I have given a more detailed account
of it in an appendix.* Its purpose is "to give workers security in
their jobs when business slumps and to insure distribution to
workers and shareholders of the largest possible proportion of
corporate income." It predicates the establishment of a uniform,
guaranteed, minimum wage, which would be received by everybody in a company's employ from president to office boy. After
necessary reserves are set up, all profits would then be distributed
pro rata to all stockholders and employees, on an agreed basis of
allocation. Then when earnings declined, payments on each share
of stock and to each employee (from president to office boy)

* Page 299.

would contract automatically by a uniform percentage, but in the case of the employees never below the minimum wage. When earnings rose, as they more probably would do with everybody working together for success, payments would rise by the exact percentage of increase and all would share proportionately in the good fortune of the enterprise.

The plan is an effort at absolute fairness. Naturally it raises many questions, a great number of which Mr. Keuls and Mr. Kenyon have anticipated and answered. The greatest question of all is the possibility of achieving, between mutually suspicious factions, the degree of agreement necessary to the launching of such a plan. It is clear that mutual suspicion must be allayed, and mutual confidence in the good will of all factions established before a start can be made. But this state of confidence already exists in certain companies, and could be rapidly extended as the value of co-operation is demonstrated. It must be a psychological renaissance to which legislation can contribute little if anything.

4

In a free system such as ours is meant to be, political action can be highly effective in promoting well-being if it is applied in its legitimate spheres: if it is directed to fostering conditions favorable to the expansion of production-consumption and the efficient policing of the whole society against dishonest and unfair practices and the application of *force majeure*. Government also performs many functions and conducts many projects which cannot properly be undertaken for profit by citizen enterprise, and these activities plus its administrative organization make government a great and legitimate employer and purchaser. This being true, its works can be programed to support sagging curves in the economic graph. But if we resort to political action as a direct short cut to prosperity, the effects will be tragically destructive. By no conceivable system of state unemployment insurance, state guarantees, or state spending can prosperity be permanently sustained. These at times may be necessary recourses for the alleviation of suffering but they themselves introduce further drastically disturbing influences into the economy. The present strong tendency to rely on expedients of this kind is a result of a natural but deplorable oversimplification of our problems.

Less than full use of productive capacity may be a tragic waste, but there are multitudes of men who do not think of it as anything so abstract: it clouts each one of them over the head as a private and personal state of no-job, or the fear of no-job. Under the all-or-nothing system of employment, an average of ten million workers endured a state of joblessness continuously from 1929 to 1940, and for several of these years the number was substantially greater. Several times ten million dependents suffered with the jobless, and millions more lived in a state of fear. Full employment returned only with the war, and now that the war is over it is not surprising that the familiar fear rises again: doubt of the future in the great majority of minds translates itself into forebodings as to the fate of one's personal income.

As a result we have a very widespread, deep, and perfectly understandable concern with the simplified question of whether the supply of jobs in the immediate future will equal the number of people who want them. And since unemployment is the evil we fear, let's find some simple formula to prevent it, let's pass a law against it. This is an impulse not surprising in view of world trends and our own recent practices, but it is neither rational nor realistic. Its danger is that it concentrates on the end result instead of the causes, and the national will to keep everybody at work may defeat itself by applying its pressures at the wrong end of the lever; like a farmer who concentrates on the thought of fine, ripe apples but neglects to nourish and spray the trees on which they grow. Unemployment itself cannot be made the point of attack; to switch the metaphor, you can no more cure it by direct treatment than you can cure smallpox by treating the pustules that form on the skin. The trouble is in the blood stream.

Government in peacetime cannot guarantee "60 million" or X million jobs, or balance an "employment budget" beyond its own legitimate payroll, unless, as Mr. Adolf Berle * told the Temporary National Economic Committee, it enters "activities now supposed to be private" and makes "wealth creation" its function.

* Testimony of May 16, 1939, previously cited (Chapter III).

The State by its nature can tolerate no competition in any field it enters, and if it undertakes to create wealth at all it must be prepared to end by taking over responsibility for the creation of all wealth. Mr. Berle viewed this outcome complacently: "Over a period of years, the government will gradually come to own most of the productive plants of the United States."

Sir William Beveridge maps the same prospect for Britain and details it more fully,* but is not frank enough to call it by its right name. To carry out Sir William's plan, the State would take full responsibility for "total outlay," i.e., for the amount of all national expenditure, public and private (p. 135); for the location and relocation of industry and population (p. 167); for the "organized mobility of labor," i.e., for herding it about as it is needed (p. 174); for the "co-ordination and stabilization" of all investments, public and private, "in accordance with the priorities of a single national plan" (p. 177); for a "price policy," i.e., for the fixing of prices (p. 201); stated very guardedly, for the fixing of wages (pp. 198 and 207); for the "supervision" and "regulation" of all businesses "above a certain size" and all trade associations, and, "in the final stage," for the state ownership of these businesses (p. 204). Sir William sees these policies expanding to complete state domination of "all the main spheres of economic activity," such as utilities, transportation, agriculture, manufacture, and housing (p. 177), but does not stress the fact that this domination would also require strict state regulation, i.e., rationing, of all consumption and a ruthless exercise of state authority to enforce its rules. To call such a directed society "free" is to misuse words to the point of effrontery. It is in fact a sweetly benevolent approach to totalitarianism, and outlines the logical progression of state attempts to manage the economy for full employment, either in what Sir William *calls* a free society but defines as nothing of the kind, or in what we Americans mean by a free society.

The fact that the State can create full employment through production for war has misled many who do not see that it has no relevance to peacetime circumstances. In war, government initiates production for a single consumer, the military machine,

* *Full Employment in a Free Society*, Norton, 1945.

which specifies exactly, in advance, the goods and quantities it requires. This is a simple operation wholly different from normal production to satisfy the innumerable needs *and wants* of multitudinous individuals of varying tastes. Production for war is in no sense the creation of wealth: it is in fact production for total waste.

Even this simplified subjection of so much energy to state direction demands far-reaching controls of wages, prices, materials, and hours, and the rationing of consumer goods. State direction extended over the production of consumer goods demands equivalent extension of direction over its distribution since the State cannot produce for distribution in a free, competitive market: it cannot plan and carry out the production of wealth unless it also plans and controls the disposition of the wealth it produces. This is a truth so obvious that its statement is its demonstration. We are led inevitably to that "strictest accounting and control of the measure of labor and consumption of each member of society." Such control obviously is incompatible with abundance as we conceive it, so that the price of government-sustained full employment is rationed privation. This truth we can see in the process of demonstration over great areas of the world's surface.

It is still seriously advocated, after our own experiments in leaf raking, that the State continue production for waste in peacetime, in the form of "made work," as a simpler and easier expedient than the fantastically intricate processes of wealth creation and wealth allocation. "It is better," says Sir William Beveridge, "to employ people on digging holes and filling them up again, than not to employ them at all." * The Pharaohs of Egypt anticipated Sir William much more constructively: at least the pyramids remained to show for the Egyptian people's time, sweat, and lack of unemployment.

For the State deliberately to set its people at "made work," to direct them into the simplified channel of production for waste, except under the compulsion of unavoidable war, is a crime against the race and its dignity. Also it is futile. "Made work" is a dead-end enterprise, a sterile and enervating process, with none of the

* *Full Employment in a Free Society*, p. 147.

self-reproductive potency of citizen enterprise. It is a kind of economic masturbation in default of lawful wedlock.

If government undertakes a direct obligation to maintain full employment, and does not frankly define and assume responsibility in advance for the sequence of measures which will be necessary to make such a guarantee good, government is simply perpetrating a gigantic and unforgivable fraud on the people.

5

The only work worthy of human beings is the doing of things and making of things, tangible and intangible, that satisfy the worker's own needs and desires and the desires and needs of other people. In a society as complex as ours, work calls for the application of ingenuity and energy by myriads of individuals in response to a crisscross of impulsions, urges, incitements interchanged through complicated media between all the individuals of the multitude. The forces operating are almost infinitely intricate, far too much so to be comprehended in their entirety by any finite mind or group of minds, and impossible to direct from any central source. When we reject direction, bureaucratic controls, a managed economy, "made work," the appalling version of "freedom" offered in Sir William Beveridge's counsels of despair, we are doing two things: we are refusing to let our ingenuity and energy be canalized and metered, we are refusing to let our wants and desires be interpreted and satisfied according to a ration book.

In this country, wants have been so eager and the means to satisfy them so ready that there has been plenty of the right kind of work and plenty of confidence in the future to keep us all busy throughout most of our history in spite of imperfect co-operation by the various elements of society. Almost certainly, we now have what it takes to maintain, after a brief period of adjustment to peace, a level of production for civilian use much higher than ever before in our peacetime past. The needs, opportunities and resources listed earlier in this book * are the grounds for this confi-

* See Chapter III.

dence, and the Department of Commerce has given it statistical confirmation in evidence that the total national production is reaching a level of 160 billion dollars during 1946.

The take-off is not our problem: it has been prepared for us and while it may be delayed or even thwarted by industrial strife it has immense propulsive forces behind it. The national problem is not even that of sustaining the starting level of production-consumption, since it dare not remain static at *any* level. The critical thing we have to do is to see that production-consumption, whatever its starting level may be, acquires and maintains a normal, healthy rate of acceleration.

At present, about 700,000 new workers join the labor force every year, and jobs must be ready for them. As it takes an average of $5,000 or $6,000 worth of plant and equipment to give one man a job—in some industries much more—the total industrial plant must expand each year by 3.5 to 4 billion dollars' worth of additions. Productivity per man-hour is being boosted constantly by improved technologies and work methods—it has more than doubled since the turn of the century—and each worker must earn more in real wages so that he will have enough to buy at least the equivalent of his own contribution.

Work hours should not decrease beyond the optimum point for maximum welfare and productivity of the worker, since the national supply of goods and services is proportionate to the input of energy. Instead of decreasing in amount, as a penalty to be escaped if possible, work should and can grow more absorbing, satisfying, and fruitful: this happens as merely muscular and repetitious activity is progressively replaced by automatic machinery and the proportion of work calling for intelligence, knowledge, and skill increases. Contrary to the impression of many amateurs, this actually is the present trend in industry: don't forget that many men are engaged in designing, building, and maintaining a machine, and keeping it supplied with work, to one who operates it.

Thus the necessity for a cyclic movement is indicated: the industrial plant expands to absorb the annual increment of new workers, output per capita rises, wages rise proportionately so that consumption per capita can keep pace with output, people are enabled to live fuller, freer, better furnished lives to make the whole process worth while.

We as a people have huge unsatisfied needs, and as far as we can see these needs are infinitely expansible. Also as far as we can see we have the means—material, scientific, and technological—to satisfy these needs. From all past and present evidence, resources in all three categories will continue to expand as rapidly as we can make use of them. Thus it would appear that we have all that is required to keep in motion the compensatory cycles of an expanding economy. But there is another factor also essential, and this one is psychological: we must be animated by a belief that the advance can and will continue. Confidence, and the daring it breeds, are the forces needed to activate the whole cyclic process of wealth creation.

6

Marshal Foch long ago said and then proved that an army is defeated when it believes itself to be defeated, and not until then. In peace as in war, fear induces its own fulfillment. When fear of the future spreads among a people, economic disaster is thereby made inevitable: the caution, retrenchment, contraction dictated by ordinary prudence accelerate the trends that incite them. During the dozen years before the war we proved that even the most powerful nation in the world cannot exert its strength for its own good on a diet of defeatism and consolation: no man is made daring by the comforting assurance that the State is busily making crutches for him in the macabre certainty that he will break his legs. What army could ever win a battle if its generals concentrated solely on the evacuation of the wounded? The wounded must be cared for, yes, but no amount of preparation for adversity will take the place of a dynamic spirit. But more lately we have proved, too, the heartening truth that even the most thoroughly bandaged pseudo-invalid will respond to a challenge to his strength and dignity: arouse him sufficiently, and pills and nurses go out the window and the red blood starts racing again.

Confidence and the courage and daring it breeds are inspired by consciousness of the adequacy of one's own strength and resources. In facing events we need not be guaranteed success, or even that political consolation prize, "security"; but we do need to feel that the cards aren't stacked against us and that the issue will depend to a decisive extent on our own acts and efforts. In that belief we can act vigorously and creatively, exert ourselves, take risks, make the kind of ventures of which many fail but some, now and again, prove to be the immensely fertile seeds of future expansion.

This is the mood of growth, and it is a mood characteristic of the American people throughout our history except for the recent atypical interlude. Prior to 1929 it enabled us, in spite of periodical setbacks, to double our output every twenty years and, in so doing, expand the work force, increase earnings and raise the standard of living with similar consistency.* It is the only mood in which we can hope to continue the necessary expansion of employment, the multiplication of opportunities, the exploitation of the immense possibilities presented by science and technology, the consequent progressive enrichment of living.

Bringing it down to individual cases, a man must regard the future with considered optimism if he is to stake his efforts and money on coming events, start the new little enterprises that he hopes will grow into bigger ones, and live as well as his situation justifies—consume up to his capacity. He must believe that the economy is sound, the State his competent and disciplined servant and protector, and the continuity of peace assured. In each instance, high consumption and the prompt putting to work of savings through investment are predicated on faith in the future. Multiply this sanguinity by millions and you have the greatest propulsive force and the only really effective propulsive force a nation can possess.

It therefore becomes the first duty of a people and its agent, the State, to establish sound grounds for a mood of confidence.

* The neat charts in Mr. Wallace's amorphous little siren song, *Sixty Million Jobs*, Simon and Schuster and Reynal and Hitchcock, 1945, present these facts graphically while they undermine his arguments for the vaguely statist techniques he proposes.

CHAPTER XVII

TO CLEAR THE PATH

THE REDUCTION of our most pressing problem to a state of mind does not make it easy to solve. Stable confidence shared by millions can be no jerry-built improvisation, run up by busy propaganda agencies. It will have to be constructed of hard facts, clearly seen, weighed and found adequate—a solid confidence built of many solid confidences, bound together by a basic faith in the continuance of a free system with all the stimulus to creative energy a free system alone can provide.

It is true that this faith cannot be complete unless it includes a conviction that the internal breach threatening the future of society is on the way to being healed before it ruins us. Such an assurance may be, at present, a mere glimmer in a murky scene, but it has the vitality of all great concepts and if it is given any factual impetus at all it will grow and spread from troubled mind to troubled mind like the light of dawn. There will be irresistible force in a realization that social unity is not only a possibility, but that the movement toward it is in progress and will persist until all groups stand together in equality of opportunity and responsibility, and in harmony of aims.

Government cannot accomplish social unity by direct action, or guarantee an adequate level of prosperity while a practicable union is being worked out; but it can provide leadership toward the one objective and a factual basis for confidence that the other is attainable. It may very well do so. In these times a great many men should be inspired to a superior type of leadership—there are so many empty chairs waiting invitingly among the immortals. If we should turn up a crop of leaders at all comparable to those who guided this country through its early decades, the response from the people will amount to a transfiguration. They yearn desperately for wise, unselfish, vigorous, devoted guidance. Trust in the quality and intentions of official leadership will be a second major factor in the whole structure of confidence on which our future fortunes will rest.

Intentions are as important as ability: they need reassuring and unequivocal demonstration. Leadership, no matter what its caliber, will be ineffective unless it convinces the people that it understands, believes in and is working within the organizational pattern of a free society. For sixteen years that pattern has been stretched into odd shapes, until there is widespread befuddlement as to what government is trying to do to and for us, a state of uncertainty breeding doubt and fear. Somehow our basic principles seem to have been mislaid in the confusion—but they are still ours, we haven't adopted any others. Nothing will lift our spirits higher than to be convinced that, at such controls as a free people entrusts to its government, we have men who understand the kind of engine they are running and will operate it skillfully in accordance with its functional design. Trust in the driver is the first requisite of a comfortable journey, trust inspired by unquestionable competence at the controls.

We are fully aware, of course, that our government is very different from the simple machine it was in its early federal days. A great deal of its present complexity is not only unnecessary but obstructive, and it needs to be stripped of many superfluous parts and motions; but it will still be an intricate mechanism performing an immense range of essential works. It would be hopelessly baffling if its design, like that of any engine no matter how complicated, were not controlled by certain simple fundamental principles which provide a plane of reference for every action and every part. In our government, this plane of reference is the freedom of the individual citizen. We must realize that not even the citizen's immediate, private welfare takes precedence over this: a welfare society inevitably becomes a controlled society. The basic difference between a free society and a controlled society is that in a free society the State's gravest responsibilities, no matter how many other functions it may perform, are always those that have to do with keeping it free. Every issue must be tested against, and no measure is right unless it accords with, this fundamental responsibility.

At the back of the American mind there is still a deep-seated conviction, now stirring to full consciousness again, that it is the mission of a State organized and dedicated as ours has been to see that the fewest possible obstacles are allowed to block the paths of its citizens; that the way is cleared for the fullest development and freest exercise of its citizens' creative abilities and energies; that citizens have the widest practicable range of choice in arranging their lives and applying their efforts; that opportunities and rewards are apportioned with absolute external impartiality, the only differentiation being that made automatically by each individual's own inherent energy, capabilities, character, and predilections.

This is no anarchic doctrine, and it is no invitation to a rat race. We see the State's responsibilities as both positive and negative: to provide the means and opportunity for the full development of the individual, amid conditions that inspire it, as well as to eradicate whatever threatens to interfere with it; while the individual himself, whose State serves him to these ends, carries a heavier burden of responsibility than a member of a controlled society can possibly know. A free man is not only responsible to himself and society for what he does with his own life and affairs —he cannot shift the burden to any higher authority—but he is in duty bound to see that no act or practice of his own infringes on the equal rights of any other man. He bears the maximum obligation to self-discipline and restraint. And we are prepared to insist that it is the function of the State not only to guard his rights but to see that he lives up to his obligations.

This of course is a counsel of perfection, an ideal statement of the ethics of a free society, much more pure than ever has been observed in practice either in this country or elsewhere. But no standard is worthy of allegiance unless it is as perfect and constant as it can be made—whether it measures inches or human conduct. And a people loses confidence not because its standards are set too high, but only when it senses that its standards are not being respected and observed with the fidelity to which even frail human beings can attain if they try; while nothing inspires a people more than a consciousness that its leaders are sincerely devoted to the maintenance of its purest ideals, and are equal to their responsibilities.

2

In spite of what is happening in the rest of the world, or perhaps because of it, conditions are ripe here for the full revival of a vigorous national mood. Our principles are beginning to shine with a renewed radiance, all the brighter by contrast, and profound loyalties are stirring. We are all set for a resurgence of commonsense realism, the restoration of a sense of technical competence in social organization, a growing solidarity in support of certain very direct and practical programs. In this mood we shall be amazed at how easily we shall see our way through any number of thickets that in the recent past have seemed hopelessly · impenetrable.

We shall see that, if we create the material and psychological conditions in which job givers need all available workers, we shall have no unemployment problem; if we maintain an immense volume of production-consumption, the fiscal dangers that threaten us will diminish accordingly; if our people are steadily improving their lot in expanding freedom, the enemies of freedom will be discomfited; if we elevate and adhere to our standards of individual liberty, the menace of state tyranny which has drawn too close for comfort in recent years will recede; if we lead the world toward universal well-being, world peace will cease to be an elusive dream.

A very elementary statement of causes and consequences, yes— it may seem surprising that they need to be restated. But it is just now that their validity is reasserting itself through the stupendous cloudy efforts that have been made here—and are still being made throughout much of the world—to substitute some kind of black magic. It is dawning on powerful elements of a great people that unemployment, depressions, and want can be exorcised, not by any abracadabra pronounced in Washington, but only by maintaining the chain action which works from confidence to initiative and on through expanded production to more abundant jobs, a more stable economy, and more generally diffused well-being. And with this comes a realization that only an America greatly prospering in freedom can lead the rest of the world to the inseparable goals of prosperity, freedom, and peace.

If this rational clarity prevails in our counsels, we may expect to see significant changes in governmental technique, redirecting pressures toward creating conditions in which many men are encouraged to take the risk of starting new undertakings which create more wealth—well-being—and new and precious kinds of wealth; and in so doing create more and better jobs until labor is offered in a seller's market to employers who compete for it. So long as there is a sound basis for belief that the policies and skill of government are adequate to maintain these conditions requisite to expansion, we shall not be harried by long or serious depressions. And we shall see want diminish as, and only as, the creation of wealth accelerates and more ample supplies of goods and services flow outward through all sectors of society.

When we know where we want to go, obstacles in the path clearly identify themselves; and the first step toward their removal —recognition of their existence—has been taken. All the usurpations of government, all its dictatorial powers, extravagances and inefficiencies here or abroad; all the social fissions and inequalities of economic privilege and opportunity in this country; all the international tensions and selfish conflict of nationalistic interests throughout the world—are seen to be unsettling to confidence and therefore psychological hindrances to advancement even before they oppose physical barriers. We need a world in which all men move freely, in equal dignity, without fear; in which knowledge and thought are exchanged and discussion flows without any kind of hindrance; and a world in which all the material things that make for good living move freely from the sources that can produce them to the needs they can fulfill. We need, in short, Utopia.

But no matter how definitely our course may be set, the long road in the general direction of Utopia will twist and turn and be blocked by forces we here in America can only influence, if at all, by logic and example. We cannot even do that—our logic and example will have no weight—unless our own house is in order and our fires burning brightly on well-swept hearths. We first must get through a sizable job of renovation on our own premises.

There is a strong temptation always to keep our eyes on the faraway, glittering objectives, and forget the rubbish accumulated at our feet. It is a wrench to turn from the great problems that flatter our dignity by their mere contemplation to give our attention to the relatively insignificant but very effective thongs that bind our ankles at this moment. But unless we can do that, and rid ourselves of immediate impediments, we shall stay planted exactly in one spot. It is not merely that we won't be able to advance toward all-important, distant goals; we may be overwhelmed where we stand by tides of disaster we are unable either to turn back or escape.

Peoples, like individual people, advance one step at a time, in a sequence that cannot admit a hiatus. Seven league boots for men or nations are an escapist dream. If we want to arrive at the far more enthralling tasks of establishing world government, world-wide liberty, social unity, peace and universal prosperity, we must first do away with such immediate, home-grown hindrances as an overblown bureaucracy, a debilitory tax system, an inadequate policing against unfair practices. When we have cleared up these obstacles, and by the act of doing so, we shall be prepared to move on to the more spacious levels of our great social problems and the problems of a world at loggerheads. If we can't do man-size jobs we certainly won't have a chance at giant tasks.

3

First on a domestic clearance program is the excess of government accumulated for several years prior to the war and necessarily multiplied during it. Until government powers, properties, and personnel are demobilized, fined down to athletic, rational proportions, confidence in the future will be tinged with uneasiness while healthy citizen activity is inhibited.

At one time there was reason to fear that reduction of State obesity would be powerfully resisted, but in changed circumstances the will has been right even though the practical difficulties of the task have exceeded the talents brought to bear on them. Government-owned productive plants are being transferred to citizen control; there is even some reluctant dispersal of government personnel. It was not feasible to drop all economic controls the instant our enemies surrendered, and turn loose a pent-up buying power on the meager supplies of goods then available; but there has been a dim realization that when government action, even though forced by total war, has led us right up to the brink of inflation, then government must retrace its steps rapidly but warily until we are no longer in the presence of this particular calamity. This is a precarious task: it is much harder to relax controls of materials, prices, and wages than to acquire them.

There is still grave danger that, if government is too hesitant or clumsy about getting out of the danger zone, we may find ourselves overwhelmed by the most common of postwar catastrophes. The only sure safeguard against inflation is a supply of goods approximating the demand, and whatever retards production is as positively inflationary as an expansion of currency, credit, and income not balanced by goods produced. Arbitrary controls of prices, wages, materials, and profits are inevitably retardants, and in a peacetime economy it doesn't take long to build up irresistible inflationary forces behind these feeble dams. The only safe way to relieve them is to encourage the current of production to flow normally and to swell as rapidly as possible.

This is merely a specific demonstration of the basic truth that, in a free society, the exchange of goods and services should be free of all restraints except those outlawing fraud, deceit, misrepresentation, harmful wares, monopoly, unfair practices of all kinds, and the exploitation of weakness and ignorance. These are very broad exceptions and no State has ever done an adequate job of policing against them. But given a strict maintenance of these ethical standards, the free interplay of forces in a competitive market is the only means capable of regulating so complex a mechanism as the modern economy. Our national experience, augmenting the experience of ages, proves that there is nothing else one-half so effective in stimulating initiative, expanding the creation of wealth, and advancing the general well-being.

Admittedly there is waste in this method. It is the factor of error unavoidable in any human undertaking, but in a free market waste is not deliberately planned and frozen as in a directed economy and there are innumerable corrective forces exerted against it. Also it is far better for people to make a percentage of mistakes than never to be able to exercise their own discrimination. Those who assume that they know what is best for us have every right to try to persuade us to their way of thinking but no right to substitute their will for our education.

Besides, who is capable of knowing surely what is best for us? Waste in a free market is exceedingly hard to identify with any certainty. People's mere wants are as legitimate as their material needs, and there may be substantial values in sheer frivolity. And there is always the possibility that the trivial gadget of today may become a mighty tool of civilization tomorrow, as has happened many times in the past century.

When a few assume responsibility for all, they are barred by their stewardship from taking chances. They can be wise only after the event and it is their duty to keep unplanned events from happening. Only free people can indulge in wide untrammeled experiment, this being the essence of freedom and the method of all progress; and only free people have enough resources to afford the risks of experiment. In this type of cultivation, the weeds considerately die, the useful plants survive; the one chance we can't afford to take is that of rooting out both before we know which is which.

4

Since the State has a prime responsibility to maintain its own credit, it has no alternative to ruthless taxation during total war, and for as long afterwards as fiscal prudence requires. But a free economy cannot expand unless the people retain an ample portion of their income for the cultivation of their own gardens instead of pouring it into the desert of the public treasury. Therefore tax rates should be reduced as rapidly as a proper funding of the public debt plus the greatest practicable economy in public expenditures will permit.

But we need tax reform that will extend far beyond mere reduction in rates: we need a careful and exact redefinition of the State's
very dangerous right to tax, and a system of taxation in conformity
with this definition. By statist logic it is quite justifiable to use
taxation as a punitive weapon; or as a means of regulating citizen
enterprise, restricting the accumulation of capital values, and "re-
distributing" those already in existence; or for whatever other purpose the State chooses. But these practices are contrary not only
to the logic but to the ethics of a system dedicated to the preservation of individual freedom. They are aberrations arising from
two erroneous assumptions: that wealth consists of money rather
than the dynamic process of production; and that it is the State's
business to say how much money a citizen shall have rather than
to police his methods of getting and using it. The paternalistic
idea that the State can "redistribute" the capital values represented by money is an utter fallacy: it can only absorb them,
destroying their potency for self-reproduction.

Far from being an evil, the accumulation of capital values
under citizen control is absolutely essential to the operation of a
free economy; and fresh accumulations, continually being formed,
are absolutely essential to the expansion of a free economy. Any
malpractice in the aggrandizement of capital values, or any mal-
feasance in their administration, should be rigorously suppressed
under the police powers of the State. But it is necessary that capital values exist in volume and be constantly at work augmenting
the flow of goods and services if the general well-being is to be
advanced. For the State to absorb these values into its own sterile
system, instead of encouraging them to refertilize the productive
process, is worse than a political crime: it is a surgical blunder.
It is a process of attrition, a form of execution by inches.

We can see a case of sterilization of the economy by taxation
at an advanced stage in Britain, where it has been practiced for
a quarter of a century longer than here. So long as there were
big accumulations from a rich past to be broken down, Britain
could prosper by devouring her own substance. But she emerges
from the war not only with her hump of fat a mere memory, but
with her competitive position hopelessly prejudiced by a generation of retarded industrial development; and unable to stage a

recovery without what amounts to a charitable replenishment of her capital values. Having proved that partial statism and a free economy are incompatible, Britain now plunks for a statism which must become complete in the effort to attain its objective of an even distribution of values; at which point, inevitably, the values left to be distributed will be exactly zero.

If a society is to advance under its own steam it is fatal to remove, by taxation or otherwise, the incentives which lead men, in the hope of adequate rewards, to take the risks of embarking on untried ventures or deny them the means to do so. The rulers of Russia quickly discovered that they could not make even their completely regulated economy work without graduated rewards, and now dole them out in a widely varying scale through the narrow funnel of the State. We require a broader access. When all men are saints they may be willing to work without incentives, take risks without hope of commensurate rewards, and strive for nothing more personal than the common good. Some men do this now; but many of the politicians who would use the States' tax powers to compel this kind of self-abnegation are themselves convincing evidence that disinterestedness is still far from universal.

The base of taxation should be as broad as the population itself. Rates of course should be scaled to ability to pay—who profits more should pay accordingly; but everyone who earns anything at all should contribute something, no matter how little, to the support of his government. He should feel a direct proprietary as well as patriotic interest in his government and the way it is run. And there should be no such thing as tax-exempt income from any source or for any purpose whatever, and no discrimination for or against any type of legitimate income.

Federal, state, and municipal taxation should be co-ordinated, and the whole complicated structure simplified and stabilized. Instead of constantly changing and unpredictable tax legislation, shaped by hasty improvisation with no reasoned consideration of its effects on the economy as a whole, we should be able to work out a permanent program that will be just and adequate within the limits of the State's legitimate right to tax. It should service and reduce the public debt during the period of high national income that is certainly ahead, so that if increased public expenditure is called for in any kind of later emergency the national credit will be equal to the strain. It should not so much assist expansion positively as refrain from placing any obstacles in its path. It should restore the citizen's confidence that the taxing power will not be used to impede or wreck his undertakings and that the State, although a rigorous policeman, is a friendly protector and not a conniving enemy.* Scarcely anything could be more stimulating to the expanding production and new job creation we must have.

5

As the productive processes of a people are freed from direct meddling and control by the State, a thorough and efficient exercise of the State's police powers becomes increasingly imperative. The citizen not only expects the State to refrain from infringing his rights by its own mistaken or unwarranted acts, he also expects it to guard him against the cupidity, deceit, malevolence, and bullying of all other citizens, groups, organizations, minorities, or majorities. Interference from citizen sources never can be as evil as interference by the State, because it never can be as inclusive or as irresistible. But it can do tragic damage, especially if the State condones and therefore in effect sponsors it.

In the Twentieth Century we have had to find ways of dealing with antisocial forces peculiar to these times. As the Industrial Revolution has extended the possible range of anyone's influence, and produced bigger and bigger concentrations of economic power —units employing more men, serving wider markets, influencing more lives—it has become possible to do both good and evil on a scale undreamed of by finite human beings of the past. Men are enabled to take advantages and exert pressures that are strange, subtle, and immensely forceful, and society is compelled to guard its collective and personal interests against the encroachments of ingenious, tireless, selfish agencies armed with novel powers. It

---

* The most comprehensive, liberal plan for tax reform I have seen is to be found in the thoughtful document prepared for the Committee for Economic Development by Beardsley Ruml and H. C. Sonne.

has been necessary for public opinion to recognize and brand anti-social behavior, the infringement of other men's rights, as it appears in these innumerable unfamiliar guises and circumstances. This is a spotting process which will have to be continued as long as our institutions undergo evolutionary changes, and as long as scientific and technological advances place new powers in the hands of individuals, groups, and associations.

To the activities of corporate bodies chartered by the State, the past two generations have applied a progressively clarified ethical code. In accepted theory and under the law, the same honesty and accountability are now demanded of corporations as of individuals, while corporations are quite properly denied many rights of privacy and independent action which the individual enjoys. It is no longer lawful for individual or corporation to take unfair advantage of others through the overpowering of competition, combination in restraint of trade, conspiracy to control prices, wages, or supplies, the monopolization of materials or markets, or any other of the many devices that once were freely employed.

It may never be possible to eliminate evil business practices entirely—there will always be devious men who will find new ways of evading ethical standards, or new disguises for the old ways. There are still many dangers to be dealt with. Society and the State will need to revise the code continually, and can never relax their vigilance in enforcing it. But it is a major social triumph that the principle of corporate responsibility to society has been firmly established. Extension of the code to close all loopholes depends on our alertness, and its enforcement depends on the efficiency and diligence of the policing authority. The direction we should take has been clearly defined and it has the complete approval of public opinion.

While we have made substantial progress in this phase of human relationships, we have left an ethical vacuum in other quarters so serious that it is now the most urgent problem we have to deal with. The rampant irresponsibility of corporations fifty years ago is matched today by the conduct of certain elements controlling organized labor; because of the great voting power wielded by these forces, which corporations never possessed, the public has been distracted by political influences from defining a code of union responsibility to match the codes of individual and corporate responsibility. Injustices from which workers so long suffered provided a plausible excuse for allowing their leadership to acquire powers and immunities equally magnified, by way of redress, and unfortunately there have been and still are political leaders who see that organized labor can be used politically more easily under dictatorial control than if it were democratically administered.

Labor organization for the defense of labor's rights is absolutely essential at this stage of our social development, and it has accomplished vitally necessary improvements in labor's status, just as the corporations of a half-century ago had greatly improved the common lot through expanded production in spite of their all-too-frequent robber-baron leadership. Also, there are unions which are honestly and ably administered and democratically organized, but these are so merely because men of exceptional probity are at their heads and not because any such ethical standards are imposed on them by public authority. Many other unions, and among them some of the most influential, are absolute dictatorships, with "constitutions" which can be suspended at the leaders' will, without regular elections of officers by secret ballot, without proper accounting of funds, without responsibility for the observance of contracts, without the privilege of protest or even free discussion by the membership. These conditions invite and encourage racketeering and reckless leadership, place the members in a state of subjugation no citizens of a democracy should be forced to endure, and jeopardize the future expansion of the national economy.

But labor unions are not private clubs, any more than the corporations that employ their members. Unions are the necessary instruments of collective bargaining, representative of labor's rights in a society which does not yet fully protect these rights through civil institutions, as the rights of property ownership, for instance, are protected. As such, unions perform more than a quasi-public function, and since their standards, policies, and acts affect the interests of society as a whole they are matters of profound public concern. As essential factors in the democratic process they cannot be allowed to stand outside it.

We cannot expect reform to come from within, any more than we could expect stockholders to reform the state of irresponsibility in which corporations once operated. Reform will come from an awakened public conscience inspiring political leaders who have the acumen to appeal to the ranks of labor over the heads of their administrations. Workers will be immensely benefited by obtaining actual control of their own unions, under covenants whereby the State, representing all the people, will assume the guardianship of labor's rights and the orderly adjudication of labor's suits, as it is expected to act for all other groups and individuals. And society as a whole will benefit enormously if the great and vitally important labor group is inducted into the democratic system as one of society's integral elements and not left outside as its detached antagonist. This is a first essential step toward the ultimate amalgamation of all social groups.

At this critical transition we cannot afford to enter the future with an elliptical moral code or fractional police surveillance—the public conscience and its constable, the State, must insist on a fair field and no favors for all elements that may contribute to the general well-being. The immense crop of new wealth-creating activities now ready to spring from the scientific and technological developments of these times need their fair share of room and air and sun: our hope of the future lies in their high birth rate and healthy growth. It is the duty of the State to guard the competitive position of every one of these activities against unfair encroachment by selfish forces, whether these serve special interests in capital, labor, agriculture, religion, or politics. Antisocial powers are equally evil in the hands of the Duke of Westminster, the Chairman of the Labor Relations Board, the Directors of the United States Steel Corporation, or the President of the United Mine Workers' Union. There is no excuse for special privileges in any hands whatever, and in a free society no just cause or authentic right should require the support of any force not freely available to all.

To state this unassailable truth is to indicate how much we still have to do in the development of free institutions.

6

If government discharges its most basic obligation to preserve
and protect the individual liberties of its citizens; and if the fiscal
policies and practices of the State are redirected to encourage the
greater flow of goods and services by which alone the welfare of
the whole people is advanced; and if the State efficiently and impartially polices the entire society against unfair acts, restrictive
influences, and irresponsible exercises of power from any source
whatsoever—we shall have created the conditions in which popular confidence can grow to decisive strength. The floodgates of
dammed-up energy will be opened, the mighty concatenation of
circumstances favorable to advancement can attain its maximum
effectiveness, billions of wheels will turn productively, a hundred
and forty million lives will be offered the opportunity of enrichment.

It is very true that we do not live alone, that our fate is linked
with many others. We dare not forget for a single moment that
the world is split by a bitter ideological war, that many nations
are desperately unhappy, and that no nation no matter how rich
and powerful is safe from destruction so long as there is a possibility that atomic explosives may become available to even a
small group of sufficiently desperate or sufficiently ruthless men.
We are entering the most perilous course mankind has ever traveled from its birth.

But in this situation, too, our greatest and only trustworthy
safeguard is our sound and internally impregnable well-being. The
happiness and peace of the world must be mothered somewhere,
at a point from which it can grow and spread—it will not be deposited evenly over the face of the earth like a dew from heaven.
The world needs more than anything else at least one happy,
flourishing nation, a great and powerful nation and a peace-loving
nation. We are the only people who conceivably can attain that
plane in time to lead the world away from the irretrievable disaster with which it is flirting recklessly today.

We *are* peace loving, I think, with utter sincerity and practical unanimity. We haven't a spotless record and we have just proven that we are in no sense soft; but the number of people among us at this stage of our history who glorify war in their hearts or who want to see this nation ever at war again could be rounded up in almost any county jail without overcrowding. We want no colonial expansion anywhere, we want no hegemonies or special privileges abroad, we are perfectly contented with the *Lebensraum* we now enjoy. Nor does it appear that we have any territorial possessions coveted by other nations, for which we have our anti-imperialist disposition to thank.

We are also a tolerant people. There are many of us, a great majority I am sure, who will resist an invasion by alien ideologies as bitterly as we would resist an invasion by alien armies, and for exactly the same reasons. But we are perfectly willing to see these ideologies adopted for experimental tryout within the boundaries of any other nation, so long as that nation minds its own business as consistently as we mind ours. We recognize that statist regimes must ultimately resort to force rather than conviction for their self-preservation, and this is repugnant to our sense of decency. And we realize that when statist regimes undertake to extend their dominion by force, we are faced with a threat to ourselves: if unchecked it is only a question of time until they will deem their force adequate for the job of taking us over too. But a statist nation which convinces us that it is satisfied to work out its theories at home, without external propagation by force, as Russia did before Mr. Stalin's alliance with Hitler in 1939, will be regarded with benevolent neutrality. We are quite sure we know how the experiment will resolve itself in time, and although we regret the attendant suffering we also admit every people's right to find salvation by its own route. We are quite prepared to restrict our ideological defense to the intellectual plane and live at peace with any self-restrained nation no matter what course it may take in pursuit of what it considers its own felicity.

The thing we have to do is to carry through our own experiment to its ultimate, unquestionable success. If our nation, after its recent surpassing demonstration of reserve strength, makes itself a center of impregnable prosperity, as it can so easily do, the home of a people steadily advancing to hitherto unattained levels of well-being, animated by a spirit of fairness and good will, we shall have given this distracted world the thing it needs most— a demonstration of the practical value of respect for the dignity and freedom of the individual human being, and the superior effectiveness of peaceful arts as a means to human happiness.

In that event we can give the world the leadership it craves, and which it will accept from us far more readily than from any other source. We cannot guarantee the world against lethal acts by paranoid types, but we can make it much less easy for such types to obtain the mastery of great nations as Hitler and Mussolini proved was possible in the turbulent, leaderless past. We need not fear reactionary ideologies, since our principles of individual liberty will have proved spectacularly their rightness. And if we can foster the spread of these principles throughout the world, not by force or even argument but by the formidable power of example, the world will move toward the union of all sovereignties in one sovereignty of the human being.

The world has no other acceptable destiny, and we have no other means of furthering it.

APPENDIX

THE KEULS-KENYON PLAN TO
STABILIZE EMPLOYMENT

MR. KEULS and Mr. Kenyon preface their explanation of their plan with an able analysis of the problem of full production and full employment which this country must solve, and find that our most urgent need is "to find ways and means to distribute, as widely as possible throughout the population, the entire volume of goods and services produced." They describe their plan as "essentially profit-sharing, intended for adoption by business corporations, to provide for the automatic distribution to employees and stockholders of all earnings above amounts required as reserves for expansion and to stabilize employment by the automatic adjustment of wages with fluctuations of corporate earnings. A job even at greatly reduced pay is better than no job at all."

The authors avoid any doctrinaire tendency to assume that they have evolved an ultimate formula. Very reassuringly, they qualify their suggestions as directional rather than final: their statement has none of the "Eureka!" assurance that characterizes many less carefully considered plans for economic improvement promoted by incautious theorists in these unsettled times.

"Developed slowly over a period of years, the plan is put forward now as one of the many partial answers necessary in solving the fundamental problem. There is no thought that any company can adopt the plan precisely as presented. The intention is to outline a set-up which for any individual corporation can be appropriately modified, while keeping the advantages of the scheme proposed."

Fundamental Purpose

"The purpose underlying the plan is twofold: to give workers security in their jobs when business slumps, and to insure distribution, to workers and stockholders, of the largest possible proportion of corporate income.

"Instead of laying off workers when there is less work to do, a company operating under the plan will spread what work is available among the entire force, working at lower wages. And until wages get down to the basic minimum, something will continue to be paid by way of dividends on the common stock. The thought is to put into operation automatically a force which, when business declines, will tend to retard the drop in consumer purchasing power, and which therefore will operate to oppose the recession in business and reduce its severity."

The Basic Idea

"The basic idea of the plan is that after necessary reserves for expansion have been set aside, the entire balance of corporate income shall be distributed in wages and in dividends; the distribution being on the basis of a yardstick period established and agreed upon at the time the plan is put into operation. With the exception of a small uniform base wage which remains fixed, the compensation of all who work for the corporation, officers and employees alike, and the dividend rate on the common stock of the corporation shall move up and down together in the same ratio as compared with rates prevailing in the yardstick period. . . .

"An obvious advantage of the plan is that every employee will have a financial interest in the earnings of the corporation as direct and immediate as though he were a holder of its common stock. Equally fundamental is the advantage that all earnings above necessary reserves will be distributed."

Reserves for Expansion

"Reserves for expansion are of the utmost importance. Already the fact has been mentioned [in the introduction] that about four billion dollars must be invested each year in additions to plant and equipment in order to provide jobs for the 700,000 new workers in the labor market. While some of the necessary capital will come from the savings of individuals much must be provided by plowing back of corporate earnings for purposes of expansion.

"Under the workings of the plan, the amounts set aside as

reserves for expansion directly affect and in fact determine the compensation of all employees. After the decision has been made with regard to the reserves to be set aside, the adjustment of wage and dividend rates will be automatic; a matter of computation only.

"It is therefore an essential element of the plan that the decision with regard to amounts necessary as reserves for expansion shall be made by some group which includes representatives of all employees of the corporation. The stockholders, the amount of whose dividends will be determined by the decision, will presumably be represented by the officers and directors of the corporation. A corollary will be that those representing the employees must be informed with regard to and consulted on all plans for company expansion. Employees, through their representatives, will be called on to aid in the solution of company problems at the planning level. This step toward democracy in industry should result in the development of a new and more technically trained type of labor leadership and bring to industry the benefit of reservoirs of imagination and brain power now only partially made use of. . . ."

Wage Adjustments

"For a forty-hour week every employee of the corporation from president to office boy will receive, in good times and bad, a basic wage of $20.00. [Obviously a tentative figure, subject to change.] Payments above that amount, hereafter referred to as profit-sharing payments, will depend on and fluctuate with the earnings of the corporation. Dividends on the common stock will depend on the same earnings and will fluctuate along with profit-sharing payments, the two moving up and down together by similar percentages.

"Under the plan, wages and dividends will be adjusted quarterly. It would, of course, be impossible to set the wage scale in any quarter on the basis of the earnings of the preceding quarter, in view of the time required for necessary accounting processes. The plan therefore contemplates that wages and dividends for any quarter shall be based on earnings for the second preceding quarter; for instance for the first quarter of any year on the basis of earnings for the third quarter of the previous year."

Profit-Sharing Basis

"To each employee of a company adopting the plan, from president to office boy, there will be issued a certain number of profit-sharing certificates, the number depending on the compensation received during a certain quarter accepted as the yardstick period. Each certificate will entitle the employee to receive in each quarter, as profit-sharing compensation, the same compensation, the same number of dollars paid by the corporation in that quarter as dividends on one share of its common stock. The number of certificates issued to each employee will be just sufficient to give him, together with his basic wage of $20.00 per week, the same total compensation which he received in the yardstick quarter.

"For instance, if the common stock paid $1.00 per share in the yardstick quarter, an employee who earned $50.00 per week in such quarter will receive 390 certificates. His pay for the first quarter under the plan will then be:

Basic wage, 13 weeks at $20.00	$260.00
Profit sharing, $1.00 on each of 390 certificates	390.00
	$650.00

"The total will be precisely as before and will be paid to him as before, $50.00 per week. The certificates determine the amount but do not affect the method of payment."

"This explanation relates, of course, to the case of a corporation all employees of which are paid fixed salaries. Application of the plan to employees paid on the basis of hourly rates, with overtime, and to employees paid at piece work rates or on other wage incentive plans, are covered in subsequent sections.

"When an employee is promoted from one position to another or when he is given an increase in compensation by reason of increased efficiency in the same position, the method will be to issue to him additional profit-sharing certificates. The basic rate of $20.00 per week will remain unchanged.

"Continuity of service with the corporation will be recognized by issuing to each employee at the end of each of his first twenty full calendar years of service, additional profit-sharing certificates to the amount of 3% of those then held by him."

The Yardstick Period

"The first step in putting the plan in operation for any particular company must be to select a certain quarter in the financial history of the company which can fairly be used as a standard; a yardstick against which to measure future results, and from which to make adjustments of compensation and dividends to conform to fluctuations in company earnings. Most desirable, of course, as a yardstick, will be the most recent quarter for which figures are available, unless to use it will involve obvious inequalities.

"In the selection of the yardstick quarter it will of course be necessary to consult with and have the agreement of representatives of all employees. Their future compensation will be based upon the quarter selected. They must understand the plan and approve of it and cooperate in it from its inception. Otherwise the plan will be doomed to failure.

"When the yardstick quarter has been chosen, certain individual adjustments will be necessary. Employees who by reason of sickness or other causes have been unable to make normal earnings must be given special consideration in the issuance of profit-sharing certificates. Matters of this kind should be decided by some group including representatives of both management and employees."

Operation of the Plan

"Assume that in the first quarter of a certain year a corporation decides to put the plan in operation as of the start of that quarter; and that the fourth quarter of the previous year is accepted as the yardstick period. Profit-sharing certificates will be issued to all employees on a basis of compensation in the yardstick quarter. Compensation and dividends on common stock will continue during the first and second quarters of the year at the rates prevailing in the yardstick quarter.

"For the third quarter, however, both wages and dividends will be adjusted on the basis of first quarter results. And for each succeeding quarter, adjustments will be made on the basis of results of the second preceding quarter.

"To establish wage and dividend rates for the third quarter, a profit-sharing fund will be determined from the known results of the first quarter. The amount, in dollars and cents, attributable to each profit-sharing certificate and share of common stock will then be ascertained by dividing the fund by the aggregate of the profit-sharing certificates and shares of common stock outstanding at the end of the first quarter. Such amount per share or profit-sharing certificate will automatically become the third quarter dividend rate on the common stock and, equally automatically, will determine and establish the third quarter profit-sharing compensation of every employee of the company, from president to office boy. Each employee paid on the basis of a weekly salary will be entitled to receive in the third quarter a profit-sharing compensation [paid in 13 weekly installments] equal to the number of profit-sharing certificates held by him multiplied by the dividend rate established for the common stock. . . .

"The amount of the fund will be arrived at by making two adjustments to first quarter earnings (net earnings after deduction of estimated income and excess profits taxes).

"First, there will be added to such net earnings the aggregate amount of all profit-sharing compensation paid to employees during the quarter; all compensation above the basic wage of $20.00 per week.

"Second, something will be set aside as an addition to reserves for expansion. The decision with regard to the amount to be set aside will, as already explained, be made by some group consisting of representatives of both management and employees. The amount decided on will then be deducted from the aggregate of net earnings and profit-sharing compensation. The balance will constitute the fund. Calculated from the figures of the first quarter, it determines dividends and profit-sharing compensation for the third quarter.

"Note that the establishment of compensation and dividend rates for the third quarter from first quarter results is automatic, a mere matter of computation, with the exception of the decision concerning the amount to be set aside as reserve for expansion, a decision the responsibility for which is shared jointly by management and employees."

The quarterly adjustment is illustrated by the example of the employee holding 390 profit-sharing certificates: a 10% rise in the quarterly earnings to be distributed would increase his weekly wage to $53.00, at the same time that the stock dividend is increased from $1.00 to $1.10 per share.

Hourly Wages and Overtime Pay

For simplicity in illustrating the application of the plan to hourly rates and overtime, an employee is assumed to have received $1.25 an hour for a 40 hour week during the yardstick period, or a weekly pay envelope of $50.00. Like the salaried employee receiving the same wage, he will be issued 390 profit-sharing certificates which entitle him to $.75 an hour for 13 weeks of 40 hours each, or $390.00. This $.75 an hour plus his base wage of $.50 an hour ($20.00 a week) will equal his yardstick pay of $1.25 an hour. Thus during the first two quarters of the plan his pay envelope will contain the same as during the yardstick period. In the third quarter, with a 10% rise in the common dividend rate, the certificates would entitle him to $.825 an hour and his weekly envelope would contain $53.00. "He would be paid for overtime on the basis of the adjusted hourly rate."

Examples are given of the adaptation of the plan to piece work and wage incentive plans. The authors believe "that the present plan can be applied to and superimposed upon almost any wage incentive plan."

Permanent Employment

"Implicit in the plan is the idea that no worker regularly employed shall be discharged or laid off, except for cause and after a hearing before some group in which the employees are represented. If the workers can feel secure that they will not be laid off when bad times come and that they will continue to receive at least the base wage of $20.00 per week, they will not complain about automatic reductions in compensation during periods of business decline. Reduced business and lower corporate earnings will mean decreasing pay for all who work for the corporation, with the larger cuts falling on those in the higher salary brackets. Percentage-wise, the decrease will be smaller the nearer an employee is to the unchanging cushion of $20.00 per week.

"There should, of course, be a certain trial period, during which a new employee would not be regarded as a regular member of the organization but could be dismissed without cause and without consulting employee representatives. Once an employee is accepted as a regular worker, he then from that time on shares with all other employees and with the stockholders the varying fortunes, good and bad, of the corporation. Secure in the knowledge that his job will not go out from under him, his high morale resulting from peace of mind will enable him to turn out the best work of which he is capable."

Employee Participation in Management

"Obviously the plan can be successful only with full approval and cooperation of the majority of the employees. Right at its inception they must understand it fully, approve it and be willing to have it put into effect. They must be convinced of its soundness and that it will operate to their advantage, particularly in the matter of security in their jobs. For this and the assurance of higher pay, possibly much higher, when times are good, they must be willing to make the sacrifice involved in agreeing to accept wages automatically reduced when earnings decline. . . .

"By making employees of all ranks participate in decisions heretofore the sole function of management and at the same time giving them a direct financial stake in corporate earnings, they will be made to feel that the enterprise in a very real sense belongs to them, and will at every level of employment be using their imaginations for the benefit of the business as a whole, feeling entitled to come forward with ideas of all kinds. The success of war industry in using various systems of rewards for helpful suggestions has given some idea of what may be accomplished by directing the entire mental power of the employees on the problems of the organization."

Advantages of the Plan

The authors point out that the community will benefit through the stabilization of employment, retardation of declines and wide distribution of corporate earnings. The employees will obtain security in their jobs, and the possibility in good times of wages "much higher than any on record."

"A further benefit to workers will be psychological, harder to define than job security and higher wages, but almost equally important. This is the satisfaction that will come from making full use of mental abilities. Because participating in management at various levels, even up to the planning of expansion, the workers will be thinking of and for the corporation. They will have the satisfaction of seeing sound suggestions acted on. And they will share in any increased earnings which result."

Stockholders will benefit by the distribution of some dividends so long as there are funds to pay any employee (including the president) more than $20.00 a week; the plan will exert a powerful influence toward stabilization of earnings, will reduce labor turn-over, increase efficiency. "Earnings relatively stable but with an underlying trend upward are advantageous to everyone: management, employees and stockholders."

Management will benefit by the improved morale and interest of the labor staff, stability of the labor force, reduced financial difficulties. It will also make new capital easier to obtain.

"The assurance of distributions to stockholders at all times except when wages are at the minimum level will attract to industry the risk capital which for the last ten years has been in hiding, thereby helping to provide the four billion dollars needed annually to create additional jobs for new workers. . . ."

The authors, in conclusion, recommend that the basic wage be continued for the lifetime of an employee after retirement, possibly exempting the corporation and its employees from Social Security taxes.

"The final thought is that if the plan were generally adopted, payments to employees and stockholders might increase to an extent such that income and profits taxes on corporations could be abolished. The funds which the government requires might be collected through taxes on the incomes of individuals, the persons who would otherwise be spending the money as ultimate consumers. Such a change in our system of taxation would afford to the business of the country a stimulant beyond all calculation. With corporations operating under a plan providing for the distribution of substantially all earnings, no sound objection could be raised."

Open Shelf Department

INDEX